A Computational Logic Handbook

Editors:

Werner Rheinboldt
University of Pittsburgh
Pittsburgh, Pennsylvania

Daniel Siewiorek
Carnegie-Mellon University
Pittsburgh, Pennsylvania

Editorial Advisory Board:

Kazuhiro Fuchi, Director
Institute for New Generation Computer Technology (ICOT)
Tokyo, Japan

Makoto Nagao
Kyoto University
Kyoto, Japan

PERSPECTIVES IN COMPUTING, Vol. 23
(Formerly "Notes and Reports in Computer Science and Applied Mathematics")

A Computational Logic Handbook

Robert S. Boyer
J Strother Moore

Department of Computer Science
University of Texas at Austin
Austin, Texas

and

Computational Logic Incorporated
Austin, Texas

ACADEMIC PRESS, INC.
Harcourt Brace Jovanovich, Publishers
Boston San Diego New York
Berkeley London Sydney
Tokyo Toronto

ACADEMIC PRESS, INC.
1250 Sixth Avenue, San Diego, CA 92101

United Kingdom Edition published by
ACADEMIC PRESS INC. (LONDON) LTD.
24-28 Oval Road, London NW1 7DX

Symbolics, Symbolics 3640, and Zetalisp® are trademarks
of Symbolics, Inc.
Sun, Sun 3/280, and Sun 3/60 are trademarks of Sun Microsystems, Inc.
Lucid and Lucid Common Lisp are trademarks of Lucid, Inc.
Unix® is a trademark of AT&T Information Systems, Inc.

Library of Congress Cataloging-in-Publication Data
Boyer, Robert S.
    A computational logic handbook / Robert S. Boyer, J Strother
  Moore.
      p.   cm.
      Bibliography: p.
      Includes index.
      ISBN 0-12-122952-1
      1. Automatic theorem proving.   2. Logic, Symbolic and
  mathematical.   I. Moore, J Strother, Date.   II. Title.
  QA76.9.A96B684 1988
  511.3--dc19   88-22175
                                                            CIP

Printed in the United States of America
88 89 90 91   9 8 7 6 5 4 3 2 1

Contents

13. Hints on Using the Theorem Prover   315

14. Installation Guide   335

Preface

This book is a user's guide to a computational logic. A "computational logic" is a mathematical logic that is both oriented towards discussion of computation and mechanized so that proofs can be checked by computation. The computational logic discussed in this handbook is that developed by Boyer and Moore.

This handbook contains a precise and complete description of our logic and a detailed reference guide to the associated mechanical theorem proving system. In addition, the handbook includes a primer for the logic as a functional programming language, an introduction to proofs in the logic, a primer for the mechanical theorem prover, stylistic advice on how to use the logic and theorem prover effectively, and many examples.

The logic was last described completely in our book *A Computational Logic*, [4], published in 1979. The main purpose of the book was to describe in detail how the theorem prover worked, its organization, proof techniques, heuristics, etc. One measure of the success of the book is that we know of three independent successful efforts to construct the theorem prover from the book.

In the eight years since *A Computational Logic* was published, the logic and the theorem prover have changed. On two occasions we changed the logic, both times concerned with the problem of axiomatizing an interpreter for the logic as a function in the logic but motivated by different applications. The first attempt was motivated by the desire to permit metatheoretic extensibility: the efficient use of functions in the logic as new proof procedures once they have been proved sound. This work was completely described in [5] and resulted in minor changes to the formalization of literal atoms, the introduction of **QUOTE** notation, and axioms defining a weak interpreter for a fragment of the logic. The second attempt was motivated by the desire to permit bounded quantification and the introduction of partial recursive functions. This work was described in [11]. It scrapped the previously added axioms for an interpreter and added axioms defining a more powerful one.

In both [5] and [11] we described accompanying changes in the theorem prover itself, most notably in the heuristics for expanding recursive functions (where we no longer always expand a function when its controlling arguments are explicit constants) and new heuristics for simplifying calls of the interpreter on constants representing terms.

There have been two truly important changes to the theorem prover since 1979, neither of which has had to do with additions to the logic. One was the integration of a linear arithmetic decision procedure. The other was the addition of a rather primitive facility permitting the user to give hints to the theorem prover.

During the period 1980-1984 we integrated into the rewrite-driven simplifier a linear arithmetic decision procedure. The goal—which was not entirely achieved—was to free the heuristic component of the simplifier from having to deduce the consequences of a decidable fragment of its theory, permitting the axioms for that fragment to be ignored. In the case of linear arithmetic this meant we could eliminate from the simplifier's view such troublesome facts as the transitivity of less than and the monotonicity of the Peano addition function. However, to achieve the intended goal it was necessary to make the decision procedure serve the simplifier in all the roles that the omitted axioms had previously. This was very difficult because of the complexity of the simplifier. We eventually adopted a decision procedure for the rationals which gave good performance and coverage in the integer case but which is not complete for the integer case. The resulting "linear arithmetic package" has proved to be very robust and useful. The entire history of our experiment and the final arrangement of heuristics and the decision procedure is completely described in [12].

The second important change was the addition of a primitive hint facility. The two most commonly used hints can be paraphrased as "consider the following instance of the previously proved theorem **n**" and "do not consider using the previously proved theorem **m**." Prior to the implementation of the hint facility, the user could guide the system to a proof—as we did for the prime factorization theorem in [4]—by the proper statement of lemmas to be proved before the main theorem. The hint facility just made it less difficult to lead the theorem prover when that was necessary. Because our hint facility contributed no new ideas to the literature of automatic theorem proving we have not documented it previously.

The most important changes have occurred not in the logic or the code but in our understanding and use of them. The past eight years have seen the heavy use of the logic and theorem prover. They have been pushed into successful applications far beyond those we reported in *A Computational Logic*. The most impressive number theoretic result proved in 1979 was the existence and uniqueness of prime factorizations; it is now Gauss's law of quadratic reciprocity. The most impressive metamathematical result was the soundness and completeness of a propositional calculus decision procedure; it is now Gödel's incompleteness theorem. These results are not isolated peaks on a plain but just the highest ones in ranges explored with the system. Among others are Fermat's theorem and Wilson's theorem, the unsolvability of the halting problem, the tautology theorem, and the Church-Rosser theorem. In program verification it is now hardly meaningful to choose a single peak. In 1979 it was the correctness of the Boyer-Moore fast string searching algorithm; among the many we are now proud of are the invertibility of the RSA public key encryption algorithm, the equivalence of sequential and parallel executions of a bitonic sort algorithm, the correctness of a gate-level design of a microprocessor, the correctness of a simple multitasking operating system, and the correctness of a compiler and link-assembler for a nontrivial programming langugage. An annotated list of references to the important results proved by the system is given on page 5.

The improvements to the logic and theorem prover, especially linear arithmetic and the hint facility, have certainly helped make these conquests possible. But perhaps the most important change since the publication of *A Computational Logic* was that in 1981 we moved from SRI International, where we were involved exclusively in research, to the University of Texas at Austin. Our research home at the University of Texas was the Institute for Computing Science. However, as professors in the Department of Computer Sciences, we teach. In 1981 we began teaching a graduate course, now called *Recursion and Induction*, on how to prove theorems in our logic, and we initiated a weekly logic seminar attended by graduate students, other faculty members, and logicians from local research organizations. These efforts dramatically increased the number of people familiar with our work. In addition, we began using the theorem prover to check the proofs of theorems we wanted to present in class (e.g., the unsolvability of the halting problem).

Almost all of the results we are now most proud of were carried out under the direction of former students who saw our mechanically checked proofs of the simpler theorems (unsolvability or RSA) and came to us believing they could lead the expeditions to the harder theorems. Almost invariably we thought they were wrong—they simply didn't understand how obstinate the theorem prover is, how weak the logic is, how many hacks and kludges there are inside. And almost invariably we were right about their naivete but wrong about their talent and persistence. Time and time again our students came forth with impressive results. We haven't revised our opinion of our system—it is obstinate, the logic is weak, and there are many hacks. But we have nothing but praise for the graduate students who have used our system with such success: David Russinoff, Warren Hunt, Natarajan Shankar, C.-H. Huang, Bill Bevier, Bill Young, David Goldschlag, Jimi Crawford, and Michael Vose.

In summary, there have been comparatively minor changes to the logic and theorem prover since the publication of *A Computational Logic*, but there have been dramatic increases in both the difficulty of the problems to which the system has been applied and the number of people who use the system. We believe that the theorem prover as it stands today (except for the provisions for hints) is adequately described by the combination of [4, 5, 12, 11]. We describe the hint facility here and do not otherwise attempt the thorough documentation of our techniques. What was lacking, in our view, was a thorough treatment of how to use the logic and the theorem prover. That is the main objective of the current work.

To make this volume self-contained we present a complete description of the current logic and as much information about how the system works as is necessary to describe how to use it. That said, however, we think of this book as a continuation of *A Computational Logic* rather than a replacement for it.

The decision to document the logic and system now should not be taken as a declaration that it is "fixed." In particular, we still have serious misgivings about the pragmatics of our new interpreter for the logic, **V&C$**, and the bounded quantifier, **FOR**. We will, undoubtedly, either improve the system's handling of these functions or we will replace them entirely with new and hopefully better formal constructs. Our decision to document the current system stems in part from our perceived scientific duty to tell the community exactly what we are doing and in part from the realization that the user community has grown sufficiently large that written documentation will save us the time we otherwise spend telling people how to use the system.

As previously noted, it is to our user community that we owe our biggest debt. The contributions of the graduate students of the University of Texas, especially those that we supervised, cannot be overemphasized. In particular, we acknowledge the contributions of Bill Bevier, S.C. Chou, Ernie Cohen, Jimi Crawford, David Goldschlag, C.H. Huang, Warren Hunt, Myung Kim, David Russinoff, Natarajan Shankar, and Bill Young. In addition, we have profited enormously from our association with Hans Kamp, Chris Lengauer, Norman Martin, John Nagle, Carl Pixley, and Bill Schelter. Topher Cooper has the distinction of being the only person to have ever found an unsoundness in a released version of our system.

Many people have contributed to this handbook, including all of the users named above. We would like to especially thank Natarajan Shankar, who helped write part of Chapter 4 and some of the proofs in Chapter 5. In addition, many errors in the handbook were found by students who took our courses. We especially thank Tom Verhoeff and Sam Dooley, who read the handbook very carefully.

Finally, special note must be made of the contributions of Matt Kaufmann. Matt has used the theorem prover to do several interesting proofs, including the correctness of a unification algorithm and the correctness of a Towers of Hanoi solution. In addition, Matt undertook the careful scrutiny of the preliminary version of the code implementing bounded quantification and partial functions. His months of study uncovered several subtle bugs and led to many clarifying comments and helpful suggestions. In addition, he went over the handbook with a fine-tooth comb.

We also most gratefully acknowledge the support of our colleagues at the Institute for Computing Science, especially Don Good and Sandy Olmstead who created and maintained at the Institute a creative and relaxed research atmosphere with excellent computing facilities. In 1986 we moved our entire verification research group off campus and established Computational Logic, Inc.

Notwithstanding the contributions of all our friends and supporters, we would like to make clear that ours is a very large and complicated system that was written entirely by the two of us. Not a single line of Lisp in our system was written by a third party. Consequently, every bug in it is ours alone. Soundness is the most important property of a theorem prover, and we urge any user who finds such a bug to report it to us at once.

The development of our logic and theorem prover has been an ongoing effort for the last 15 years. During that period we have received financial support from many sources. Our work has been supported for over a decade by the National Science Foundation and the Office of Naval Research. Of the many different grants and contracts involved we list only the latest: NSF Grant DCR-8202943, NSF Grant DCR81-22039, and ONR Contract N00014-81-K-0634. We are especially grateful to NSF, ONR, and our technical monitors there, Tom Keenan, Bob Grafton, and Ralph Wachter, for years of steady support and encouragement.

We have received additional support over the years from the following sources, listed chronologically: Science Research Council (now the Science and Engineering Research Council) of the United Kingdom, Xerox, SRI International, NASA, Air Force Office of Scientific Research, Digital Equipment Corporation, the University of Texas at Austin, the Venture Research Unit of British Petroleum, Ltd., IBM, National Computer Security Center, and Space and Naval Warfare Systems Command.

Since 1984 the major part of our funding has come from the Defense Advanced Research Projects Agency. At UT we were supported by ARPA Order Number 5246. At Computational Logic, Inc., we are supported by ARPA Order Numbers 9151 and 6082. The research described here was supported in part by the U.S. Government. The views and conclusions contained in this book are those of the authors and should not be interpreted as representing the official policies, either expressed or implied, of the Defense Advanced Research Projects Agency or the U.S. Government.

The first draft of this handbook was written entirely by Moore and required slightly over a year to write. During that time his wife, Miren, and their children, Lisa, Nicolas, Jonathan, and Natalie, made many sacrifices so that he could work with few interruptions. We are especially grateful to them for their understanding and patience.

Part I

The Logic

1 Introduction

By a "computational logic," we mean a logic that is both oriented towards discussion of computation and mechanized so that proofs can be checked by computation. We are the authors of one such logic and its associated mechanical theorem prover. This book explains how to use the logic and the theorem prover.

The book is divided into two parts. In Part I we discuss the logic, without regard for its mechanization. In Part II we discuss its mechanization. Part I answers the questions "what are the axioms and rules of inference?" and "how does one use the logic to state and prove theorems?" Part II answers the question "how does one use the Boyer-Moore theorem prover to prove theorems?"

Do not be put off by the size of the documentation. Much of the verbiage here is devoted to spoon-fed introductions and primers, examples, and stylistic advice on how to use the logic and its implementation effectively.

Two chapters have been designed as reference guides.

- Chapter 4 is the technical heart of Part I and is a detailed description of the syntax, axioms, and rules of inference of the logic. In addition to defining the logic, we carefully define many metalinguistic and metatheoretical notions used in the description of the logic.

- Chapter 12 is the technical heart of Part II and is a reference guide to the theorem prover. It is organized so that you can read only the parts relevant to a given command or concept and cross-referenced so that you can track down unfamiliar notions.

Having tried to allay your fears of the book itself, we now give a brief overview of the logic and the theorem prover and what has been done with them. Then we give an overview of this book.

1.1. A Summary of the Logic and Theorem Prover

Technically the logic is a quantifier-free, first-order logic resembling Pure Lisp [24, 25]. Its axioms and rules of inference are obtained from the propositional calculus with equality and function symbols by adding (a) axioms characterizing certain basic function symbols, (b) two "extension principles," with which one can add new axioms to the logic to introduce "new" inductively defined "data types" and recursive functions, and (c) mathematical induction on the ordinals up to ε_0 as a rule of inference. However, among the "certain basic functions" axiomatized is an interpreter for the partial recursive functions which then permits the introduction of concepts with the same essential properties as bounded quantifiers and such higher-order features as schemators and functional objects.

The logic is mechanized by a collection of Lisp programs that permit the user to axiomatize inductively constructed data types, define recursive functions, and prove theorems about them. This collection of programs is frequently referred to as "the Boyer-Moore theorem prover," although the program that implements the theorem prover itself is only one—albeit the largest—of many programs provided in the system.

The theorem prover's behavior on a given problem is determined by a data base of rules. The rules are derived by the system from the axioms, definitions, and theorems submitted by the user. In particular, each time a new theorem is proved it is converted into rule form and stored in the data base. When new theorems are submitted the currently "enabled" rules determine how certain parts of the theorem prover behave. In this way the user can lead the machine to the proofs of exceedingly deep theorems by presenting it with an appropriate graduated sequence of lemmas. In such applications the theorem prover resembles a sophisticated proof checker more than an automatic theorem prover.

While the user's participation in the proof discovery process is crucial to the construction of deep proofs, the user assumes no responsibility for the correctness of the proofs constructed. That is the burden of the theorem prover—or, more accurately, the burden of its authors. However, to use the system effectively it is necessary to understand the kinds of rules used by the system, how each class of rule affects the system's behavior, and how rules are generated from formulas.

The logic may be viewed as an applicative programming language. It is possible to define functions in the logic and execute them with reasonable efficiency on concrete data, without ever *proving* anything about them. A simple execution environment is provided as part of the system.

The logic and theorem prover have been used to formalize and prove many interesting theorems in mathematics, metamathematics, theory of computation, and computer science. We give an annotated list of selected applications in the next section.

The theorem prover is written in Common Lisp in accordance with *Common Lisp The Language* [34]. The source code is more than 900,000 bytes long.

1.2. Some Interesting Applications

First-time users of the logic and theorem prover are frequently frustrated by the weakness of the language and the inability of the theorem prover to see the obvious. A commonly expressed thought is ''You can't do anything with this system!''

Below is an annotated list of selected references to theorems proved by the system. We include it for two reasons. First, just knowing that some people—and not merely the authors—have used the logic and theorem prover to do interesting things is often enough encouragement to get you started. Second, if you are stuck and cannot see how to proceed, perhaps the way will be clearer if you obtain and read the relevant-sounding work mentioned below. In fact, as noted in Chapter 14, the standard distribution of the system comes with three files of examples, **basic.events**, **fm8501.events**, and **goedel.events**. Many of the results cited below are contained in those files, and we indicate which examples are in which files.

You should understand, in view of the foregoing remarks on the role of the user, that—for the deep theorems at least—the theorem prover did not so much *discover* proofs as *check* proofs sketched by the user.

- **Elementary List Processing**: Many elementary theorems about list processing are discussed among the examples in [4]. The appendix includes theorems proved about such concepts as concatenation, membership, permuting (including reversing and sorting), and tree exploration. See the **"proveall"** section of **basic.events**.

- **Elementary Number Theory**: Euclid's theorem and the existence and uniqueness of prime factorizations are proved in [4] (see **EUCLID, PRIME-FACTORIZATION-EXISTENCE**, and **PRIME-FACTORIZATION-UNIQUENESS** in the **"proveall"** section of **basic.events**). A version of the pigeon hole principle, Fermat's theorem, and the invertibility of the RSA public key encryption algorithm (see [28]) are proved in [9] (see the **"rsa"** section of **basic.events**). Wilson's theorem is proved in [29] (see the **"wilson"** section of **basic.events**). Finally, Gauss's law of quadratic reciprocity has been checked; the theorem, its definitions, and the lemmas suggested by Russinoff are in the **"gauss"** section of **basic.events**.[1]

- **Metamathematics**: The soundness and completeness of a decision procedure for propositional calculus, similar to the Wang algorithm (see [36]), is proved in [4] (see **TAUTOLOGY-CHECKER-IS-SOUND** and **TAUTOLOGY-CHECKER-IS-COMPLETE** in the **"proveall"** section of **basic.events**). The soundness of an arithmetic simplifier for the logic is proved in [5] (see **CORRECTNESS-OF-CANCEL** in the **"proveall"** section of **basic.events**). The Turing completeness of Pure Lisp is proved in [13] (see the **"tmi"** section of **basic.events**). The recursive unsolvability of the halting problem for Pure Lisp is proved in [10] (see the **"unsolv"** section of **basic.events**). The tautology theorem, i.e., that every tautology has a proof in Shoenfield's formal system, is proved in [30] (see the **"tautology"** section of **basic.events**). The Church-Rosser theorem is proved in [31] (see the **"church-rosser"** section of **basic.events**). Gödel's incompleteness theorem is proved in [32][2] (see **goedel.events**).

- **Partial Functions**: The mechanically checked proofs of the termination properties of several partial functions are given or sketched in [11] (see the **"quant"** section of **basic.events**). In particular, we discuss the nontermination of the recurrence **(RUS X)** $\Leftarrow$ **(ADD1 (RUS X))**, the fact that a certain recurrence terminates iff the argument is a "proper" list ending in **NIL**, the totality of the 91-function, the totality of the function defined by

```
(RV X)
   ⇐
(IF (AND (LISTP X) (LISTP (CDR X)))
    (CONS (CAR (RV (CDR X)))
          (RV (CONS
               (CAR X)
               (RV (CDR (RV (CDR X)))))))
    X)
```

and the fact that **RV** reverses its argument. In [26] we prove that the Takeuchi function terminates (see the **"ztak"** section of **basic.events**).

---

[1]Both Wilson's theorem and Gauss's law were proved under the direction of David Russinoff.

[2]The tautology theorem, the Church-Rosser theorem, and Gödel's incompleteness theorem were proved under the direction of Natarajan Shankar.

- **Bounded Quantifiers and Higher-Order Functions**: Many theorems have been proved about the "higher-order" function **FOR** which takes expressions among its arguments and provides a form of bounded quantification. Among these theorems are classic "schematic" quantifier manipulation theorems such as

$$\sum_{i=0}^{n} g(i) + h(i) \;=\; \sum_{i=0}^{n} g(i) \;+\; \sum_{i=0}^{n} h(i) \, ;$$

- In addition, these schematic theorems have been used in the proofs of other theorems requiring quantifiers to state, such as the binomial theorem:

$$(a+b)^n \;=\; \sum_{i=0}^{n} \binom{n}{i} a^i b^{n-i} \, ;$$

- The proofs of many of these theorems and the techniques used are explained in [11] (see the **"quant"** and **"binomial"** sections of **basic.events**).

- **Communication Protocols**: Safety properties of two transport protocols, the Stenning protocol and the "NanoTCP" protocol, are proved in [16].[3]

- **Concurrent Algorithms**: A mechanized theory of "simple" sorting networks and a proof of the equivalence of sequential and parallel executions of an insertion sort program are described in [22]. A more general treatment of sorting networks and an equivalence proof for a bitonic sort are given in [18]. A proof of the optimality of a given transformation for introducing concurrency into sorting networks is described in [23].[4]

- **Fortran Programs**: A verification condition generator for a subset of ANSI Fortran 66 and 77 is presented in [6]. The same paper describes the correctness proof of a Fortran implementation of the Boyer-Moore fast string searching algorithm. A correctness proof for a Fortran implementation of an integer square root algorithm based on Newton's method is described in [7]. The proof of a linear time majority vote algorithm in Fortran is given in [8].

- **Real Time Control**: A simple real time control problem is considered in [14]. The paper presents a recursive definition of a "simulator" for a simple physical system—a vehicle attempting to navigate a straight-line course in a varying crosswind. Two theorems are proved about the simulated vehicle: the vehicle does

---

[3]These theorems were proved under the direction of Ben DiVito.
[4]These theorems were proved under the direction of Chris Lengauer and C.-H. Huang.

not wander outside of a certain corridor if the wind changes "smoothly," and the vehicle homes to the proper course if the wind stays steady for a certain amount of time[5] (see the **"controller"** section of **basic.events**).

- **Assembly Language**: A simple assembly language for a stack machine is formalized in [4]. The book also gives a correctness proof for a function that compiles expressions into that assembly language (see **CORRECTNESS-OF-OPTIMIZING-COMPILER** in the **"proveall"** section of **basic.events**). In our standard benchmark of definitions and theorems is a collection that defines another simple assembly language, including "jump" and "move to memory" instructions, and proves the correctness of a program that iteratively computes the sum of the integers from 0 to n. The correctness proof is complicated by the fact that the program instructions are fetched from the same memory being modified by the execution of the program (see **CORRECTNESS-OF-INTERPRETED-SIGMA** in the **"proveall"** section of **basic.events**).

- **Operating System**: A small multitasking operating system kernel written in the machine language of a uni-processor von Neumann computer is developed and proved correct in [1]. The kernel is proved to implement a fixed number of conceptually distributed communicating processes. In addition to implementing processes, the kernel provides the following verified services: process scheduling, error handling, message passing, and an interface to asynchronous devices. The operating system consists of about 300 executable machine instructions. The listing of the system requires 620 lines, including assembler directives. The system, including its tables and save areas, occupies about 3K words on the host machine. A complete listing of the system and the proof is given in [1].[6]

- **Language Implementation**: The correctness of the implementation of a nontrivial programming language on a microprocessor is described in [27]. The language, called Piton, is a stack-based assembly level language providing seven abstract data types, execute-only programs, global arrays, and many other high-level features. Piton is defined via an interpreter written as a function in the logic. It is implemented on the FM8502 microprocessor, a modification of the FM8501 discussed below. The implementation is via a compiler and link-assembler written as functions in the logic. The com-

---

[5]This proof was carried out with the assistance of Mike Green.
[6]This work was carried out by Bill Bevier.

piler produces symbolic FM8502 assembly code from given Piton program and data descriptions. The link-assembler transforms the output of the compiler into a binary core image for FM8502. The theorem proved establishes that the semantics of non-erroneous Piton computations are preserved by the FM8502 execution of the core image produced by the compiler and link-assembler.

• **Hardware Verification:** The correctness of a ripple carry adder is given in [20]. The adder is a recursively defined function which maps a pair of bit vectors and an input carry bit to a bit vector and an output carry bit. The theorem establishes that the natural number interpretation of the output is the Peano sum of the natural number interpretations of the inputs, with appropriate consideration of tl :e carry flags. An analogous result is proved for twos-complement integer arithmetic. The recursive description of the circuit can be used to generate an adder of arbitrary width. A 16-bit wide version is shown. Propagate-generate and conditional-sum adders have also been proved correct. Also in [20] is the correctness proof of the combinational logic for a 16-bit wide arithmetic logical unit providing the standard operations on bit vectors, natural numbers, and integers. The dissertation then presents a recursively described, microcoded cpu, called the FM8501, and proves that the device correctly implements an instruction set defined by a high-level interpreter[7] (see **fm8501.events**).

In Appendix III we present a brief comparison of the complexities of several of these theorems and proofs.

1.3. The Organization of this Handbook

Chapter 1 is this introduction.

The logic is presented twice, once in Chapter 2 in tutorial form and again in Chapter 4 in the precise, legalistic English of the logician. This is our attempt to overcome a well-known problem in the presentation of technical material: should the presentation be oriented toward the novice—who wishes to understand the subject but is also desperate for examples, motivation, and explanation of the implications of the various "design decisions"—or should it be oriented toward the knowledgeable reader—who understands the main ideas but wants a succinct and precise presentation to use as a reference guide?

In Chapter 2 we provide an introduction to the logic as a programming lan-

---

[7]These proofs were carried out under the direction of Warren Hunt.

guage. We familiarize you with our syntax for terms, such as the variable symbol **X** and the function application **(PLUS X Y)**, and for constants, such as the "literal atom" constant **'ABC** and the list constant **'((A . 7)(B . 1))**. We describe the behavior of the primitive functions and data types. We illustrate the use of the primitive data types to represent conventional data structures such as lists, tables, trees, and terms. We explain how to add new data types to the logic. We explain the principle of recursive definition and why we have imposed the various restrictions on it. We illustrate some simple recursive definitions and then show the results they produce when evaluated on constants. We illustrate the representation of the ordinals up to ε_0. We discuss the general purpose interpreter for the logic, and we discuss the provisions for bounded quantification. Because we do not exhibit the axioms or rules of inference actually defining the logic in this chapter, we do not deal with the notion of proof here.

In Chapter 3 we discuss the problem of using the logic to formalize problems. This is always a major stumbling block in the path of new users: how to convert the question "is this program (algorithm, function, system, idea) correct?" into the question "is this formula a theorem of the logic?" There are really two problems here: how to use mathematics to formalize everyday concepts in computer science and how to use this logic in particular. The first problem is hard because there is a major philosophical gap between the user's personal intentions and desires and any formal rendering of them. But many users of the logic wade into this "specification problem" without fully understanding how treacherous it is. We try in this chapter simply to illustrate several specification problems by formalizing some informal specifications for stacks, queues, and a sort function. Then we turn to the specific formalization problems raised by our logic. For example, we discuss the absence of quantification and infinite objects, and we discuss various techniques for formalizing nondeterminism and language semantics.

In Chapter 4 we describe the syntax, axioms, and rules of inference precisely. To be sufficiently precise when explaining our abbreviation conventions and the terms used to describe axiom schemas and rules of inference, we also define in this chapter a host of metalinguistic and metatheoretical notions, e.g., what we mean by the "explosion" of an ASCII character sequence, what we mean by a "type restriction" in the declaration of a new data type, and what we mean by the "governing" terms in a definition. We might have segregated these metanotions into a preliminary chapter, thus drastically reducing the size of the precise description of the logic, but we have decided to define our technical terms as close as possible to their first use in the hopes that by seeing them used immediately the reader will better grasp the concepts. We have carefully labelled each paragraph of the chapter as to whether it concerns terminology, abbreviation conventions, axioms, etc.

Most readers will find Chapter 4 hard going unless they have already read the primer or are already familiar with our logic. Nevertheless, Chapter 4 is one of the two main parts of this handbook. It is absolutely essential that you master the material here if you wish to use the logic correctly. How can the logic be used incorrectly if the machine takes responsibility for the soundness of the proofs? The answer is simple: the machine guarantees that the formulas it pronounces "theorems" in fact follow from the axioms and definitions. But we offer no assurance that those formulas *mean* what you want them to mean (that's the formalization problem). Unless you really understand the formal logic you will not be able to capture, with definitions and theorems, the concepts and relationships you will be grappling with when you apply the logic.

In Chapter 5 we illustrate how theorems are proved in the logic by carefully explaining many hand constructed proofs, starting at the level of propositional calculus and quickly ascending to inductive proofs about simple recursive functions. Several new rules of inference are derived, including so-called "structural induction." Essentially this chapter bridges the gap between the sense of "proof" defined by the logic and the sense of "proof" supported by the mechanical theorem prover. The theorem prover's style of proof is more closely "proof" in the mathematician's sense than the formal logician's sense. In particular, the machine does not print out a sequence of formulas, each of which is either an axiom or follows from previous ones by a named rule of inference. The machine takes much larger steps and uses many derived rules of inference (such as decision procedures). The foundation of our trust in the theorem prover is the privately held conviction that every "proof" it produces can, in principle, be converted into a formal proof. It is not necessary that you read Chapter 5 if you accept the theoretical equivalence of these two senses of proof.

Chapter 6 briefly explains the basic proof techniques implemented in our theorem prover and how they are organized. We explain the details of the proof techniques later. Most of this chapter is devoted to a mechanically produced proof of a simple arithmetic theorem and then a move-by-move analysis of it to acquaint you with the style of the theorem prover's techniques and output.

The theorem prover, *per se*, is just a part of the mechanization of the logic. In addition to proving theorems, the user must be able to carry out other logical acts, such as defining functions and adding new data types. Moreover, there is the key problem of the system's data base of facts which largely determines how well the system performs on problems of practical interest. Finally, there are the mundane but essential features of any computing system: how to get it started, how to stop it, how to save your work, how to find out what is happening. These issues are discussed in Chapter 7. We also summarize the commonly used commands, discuss error handling and typein, and conclude with a few cautionary words about possible confusions arising from the similarity of the logic to Lisp.

Chapter 8 is just a demonstration of the theorem prover. We show it proving several theorems about the simple list processing function **REVERSE**. These proofs show the theorem prover at its best and may leave the impression that it is an automatic theorem prover.

Chapter 9 is called **How to Use the Theorem Prover** but might also be titled **How To Use the Theorem Prover to Discover Proofs** or **How to Interact with the Theorem Prover** or **How to Read Theorem Prover Output**. The chapter discusses how experienced users interact with the system. We start by revisiting the demonstration theorems in Chapter 8. However, this time, instead of letting the theorem prover show off, we use it as we would to explore new ground. Producing a proof in this style is really a more interactive, cooperative endeavor in which the theorem prover helps the user find a proof. Or is it the other way around? The chapter also describes how the experienced user tends to use a text editor as a key component in his hierarchical development of a complex proof. Despite its brevity and lack of precision—much of its advice is given by example only—this chapter may be the most valuable one in the handbook because it encourages you to think about the theorem prover in a different way than you might otherwise.

Chapter 10 is a description of how the theorem prover works, with particular attention on those aspects of its behavior under the control of the user through previously proved theorems. We also discuss the use of clausal form in the internal representation of formulas and the notion of the "type" of a term in the logic. This chapter is an important prerequisite for the next one.

Chapter 11 describes the various kinds of rules used by the system, how each kind of rule affects the behavior of the system, and how rules are generated from formulas. Understanding this material is a key to the effective use of the theorem prover.

Chapter 12 is the reference guide to the theorem prover. It is organized as a long series of sections, each section titled by and devoted to a single command or concept. The sections are listed alphabetically. You should probably read the reference guide once straight through. Thereafter, you will probably access it randomly via the table of contents or the index of this handbook.

Chapter 13 is just a long collection of hints on how to use the system. We explain the kinds of definitions the system "likes" and those that it is "biased against." We give some guidelines on the effective use of the various kinds of rules. In general, the chapter is a random collection of vague, airy-fairy, and contradictory remarks. If we could make it precise and accurate we would simply mechanize all this advice and omit the chapter. As things stand, we leave to you the problem of sorting it all out.

Chapter 14 is a description of how to create an executable version of the theorem prover at your local site from the sources we provide.

The handbook has three appendices.

The first, Appendix I, illustrates the use of the logic as a programming language by defining a function that parses strings of ASCII characters into the formulas of the logic. The appendix serves the additional purpose of formalizing the syntactic conventions of the logic.

The second, Appendix II, lists the axioms for our primitive data types, namely the natural numbers, ordered pairs, literal atoms, and the negatives. These axioms are generated from the shell axiom schemas given in Chapter 4 and are included for two reasons. First, since they illustrate the axiom schemas they might help readers understand the schemas better. Second, the reader who wishes to ignore the provision for user-defined types could substitute these axioms for the "shell principle" and simplify the formal logic.

The third, Appendix III, gives some statistics on the relative complexities of the theorems and proofs explored with the theorem prover during its 15 year history.

2   A Primer for the Logic

Formally, a logic consists of three parts: (a) a language in which formulas are written, (b) a set of distinguished formulas called *axioms*, and (c) a set of transformations, called *rules of inference*, with which one can derive new formulas from old. A *theorem* is any formula that is either an axiom or can be derived from theorems using the rules of inference.

The notions mentioned above are entirely *syntactic*. It is possible to discuss the logic from a *semantic* point of view. This involves attaching a *function* to each *function symbol*. Then, given an assignment of values to the *variable symbols* of a term or formula, it is possible to determine the *value* of the expression by evaluation. Given an interpretation of the function symbols, a formula is said to be *valid* if its value is "true" under all possible assignments of values to its variable symbols. A *model* of a logic is an interpretation under which all of the axioms are valid. Note that if all axioms are valid and the rules of inference are validity preserving, then every theorem is valid. Informally, if a formula is a theorem then it is "always true." There is a model for the logic presented here.

The logic presented here contains two "extension" principles under which the user can add new axioms to the system with the guarantee that the model for logic can be extended to accommodate the new axioms. The principles permit the axiomatization of "new" data types and the definition of "new" recursive functions.

Because of these extension principles it is not meaningful to speak of *the* logic in the traditional sense that implies the choice of some fixed set of axioms. We more often speak of the *primitive* or *Ground Zero* logic and of various extensions obtained by adding new data types and definitions.

Almost all of the functions axiomatized in the logic are *total recursive*. That is, given an application of a function to explicit values, we can determine algorithmically the explicit value which is provably equal, under the axioms, to the given application. The exceptions to the totality claim all have to do with the provision in the logic of an interpreter for the partial recursive functions.

The mechanization of the logic includes commands for evaluating functions on explicit values. Thus, the logic and its mechanization provide an *applicative programming language* and *execution environment*. On applications of partial functions, the execution environment may "run forever" (until one of the finite system resources is exhausted), but if an answer is returned it will be correct under the axioms. Furthermore, using the theorem prover it is often possible to *prove* that such an application "runs forever."

In this chapter we informally present the Ground Zero logic as a programming language. We describe the formal language in which formulas are written and give the most common of our abbreviation conventions. We describe the "input/output behavior" of each of the functions in the Ground Zero logic, and we describe the two extension principles. The formally inclined reader can think of this chapter as an informal description of the semantics of the logic and a semantic justification of the extension principles.

In Chapter 4 we give a complete and precise description of the language, the axioms, the rules of inference, and the extension principles. That chapter is completely self-contained. We believe that the experienced user of the system will find questions about the logic answered far more quickly and clearly in that chapter than in this primer. However, we believe the new user will find the primer a better introduction to the logic.

2.1. Syntax

Statements in the logic are called "terms." A term is either a variable symbol or else is the application of a function symbol of n arguments to n terms.

The variable and function symbols are strings of uppercase alphanumeric characters and certain signs, namely

$$ \$ \ \hat{} \ \& \ * \ \_ \ - \ + \ = \ \sim \ \{ \ \} \ ? \ < \ > $$

Variable and function symbols must start with an alphabetic character. Thus, **X**, **PLUS**, **ADD1**, and **PRIME-FACTORS** are symbols, and **Prime-factors**, **A[X]** and **1E3** are not.

We use the prefix syntax of Church to write down terms. For example, we write **(PLUS I J)** where others might write **PLUS(I,J)** or **I+J**. We permit "white space"—spaces, tabs, and carriage returns—to occur arbitrarily between symbols and parentheses.

Here is a term, displayed in three different arrangements.

```
(EQUAL N (PLUS (REMAINDER N K)
               (TIMES K (QUOTIENT N K)))))

(EQUAL N
       (PLUS (REMAINDER N K)
             (TIMES K (QUOTIENT N K))))


( EQUAL N ( PLUS ( REMAINDER N K
) ( TIMES K ( QUOTIENT N K ) ) ) )
```

In the definition of a term, we required that functions be applied to the correct number of argument terms. The claim that the expression above is a term implicitly informs the reader that **EQUAL**, **PLUS**, **REMAINDER**, **TIMES**, and **QUOTIENT** are all function symbols of two arguments. The following expressions are not terms:

(EQUAL X)

(EQUAL X Y Z)

Technically, **(PLUS X Y Z)** is not a term because **PLUS** takes two arguments.

Comments can be written in a term, by preceding them with a semicolon. All text from the semicolon up to but not including the next end-of-line is ignored. Thus, here is a term:

```
(IF (ZEROP N)        ;If N is 0
    N                ;return N
    (ADD1 N))        ;otherwise, return N+1
```

As new functions and objects are introduced into the logic, we introduce abbreviation conventions to permit their succinct expression.

2.2. Boolean Operators

(TRUE)   A constant we abbreviate with **T**. **T** is used as the "true" truth value in the functional analogues of the Boolean operators.

(FALSE)   A constant we abbreviate with **F**. **F** is the "false" truth value in the functional analogues of the Boolean operators. **T** and **F** are distinct.

(IF X Y Z)   If **X** is **F**, return **Z**; otherwise return **Y**. We call the first argument of an **IF**-expression the *test*, and we call the second and third arguments the *true* and *false branches* of the **IF**, respectively. Note well that the test is compared to **F** and if different from **F** the true branch is taken. Thus, since (as we shall see later) **0** is different from **F**, **(IF 0 Y Z)** is **Y**.

(EQUAL X Y)	Return **T** if **X=Y** and **F** otherwise.
(TRUEP X)	Return **T** if **X=T** and **F** otherwise.
(FALSEP X)	Return **T** if **X=F** and **F** otherwise.
(AND P Q)	Return **T** if both **P** and **Q** are non-**F**; otherwise return **F**. Note: the "truth table" for **AND** is:

AND	F	non-F
F	**F**	**F**
non-**F**	**F**	**T**

Because **AND** is defined with **IF**, any non-**F** input produces the same output as **T**. Thus, **(AND 3 0) = T**.

(OR P Q)	Return **T** if either **P** or **Q** is non-**F**; otherwise return **F**.
(NOT P)	Return **F** if **P** is non-**F**; otherwise return **T**.
(IMPLIES P Q)	Return **T** if either **P** is **F** or **Q** is non-**F**; otherwise return **F**.

2.3. Data Types

One of the ways the user of the logic can extend it is by the addition of axioms to define a "new" class of inductively constructed objects. The *shell principle* provides this facility. From the perspective of the logic as a programming language, the shell principle is a mechanism by which the user can create new data types. But the principle is also used in the initial creation of the Ground Zero logic to axiomatize the natural numbers, ordered pairs, literal atoms, and the negatives. We discuss these "primitive" data types as examples of the use of the shell principle after we have described the general principle.

The principle permits the axiomatization of typed **n**-tuples with type restrictions on each of the **n** components. The axioms necessary to characterize the new type are generated from axiom schemas by instantiating them with names provided by the user.

Below we show the general form of an invocation of the shell principle. The lower case words in typewriter font used below, namely, **const**, **n**, **base**, **r**, $\mathtt{ac_i}$, $\mathtt{tr_i}$, and $\mathtt{dv_i}$, would, in an actual invocation, be filled in by the user with particular function names, numbers, etc.

Shell Definition.
Add the shell **const** *of* **n** *arguments*
with (optionally, base function **base**)
recognizer function **r**,
accessor functions $\mathtt{ac_1}$, ..., $\mathtt{ac_n}$,
type restrictions $\mathtt{tr_1}$, ..., $\mathtt{tr_n}$, *and*
default functions $\mathtt{dv_1}$, ..., $\mathtt{dv_n}$.

The above incantation adds axioms to the logic to define a new "data type." Objects of the new type are "recognized" by the newly axiomatized function **r**, which returns **T** or **F** according to whether its argument is of the new type. The "base function," **base**, takes no arguments and returns an object of the new type. The "constructor function," **const**, takes **n** arguments and returns an **n**-tuple of the new type. The **n** functions $\mathtt{ac_1}$, ..., $\mathtt{ac_n}$ "access" the respective components of constructed **n**-tuples of the new type. The **n** "type restrictions," $\mathtt{tr_1}$, ..., $\mathtt{tr_n}$, describe what types of objects are in the components of each constructed **n**-tuple. The **n** "default functions," $\mathtt{dv_1}$, ..., $\mathtt{dv_n}$, are constant functions that specify the values to be used when the supplied argument fails to satisfy its type restriction. Every object of the new type is either the base object, **(base)**, or else is constructed by **const** from smaller objects satisfying the type restrictions.

Here is a sample shell definition:

Shell Definition.
Add the shell **ADD1** of one argument
with base function **ZERO**,
recognizer function **NUMBERP**,
accessor function **SUB1**,
type restriction **(ONE-OF NUMBERP)**,
default function **ZERO**.

By this invocation of the shell principle the function **NUMBERP** is axiomatized to recognize "new" objects constructed from the base object **(ZERO)** by the function **ADD1**. Given a non-**(ZERO) NUMBERP**, **(ADD1 n)**, the function **SUB1** returns the single constituent, **n**. **ADD1** "expects" its argument to be a **NUMBERP** and coerces it to **(ZERO)** if it is not. The **NUMBERP**s are our formalization of the natural numbers constructed from 0 (**(ZERO)**) by the "successor function" **ADD1**. **SUB1** is the "predecessor function."

There are restrictions on how the shell principle can be invoked. These restrictions ensure that the axioms consistently extend the logic and describe a nonempty set of "new" objects.

When the shell principle is invoked, **const**, **base**, **r** and each of the ac_i must be new function symbols, i.e., never before used. The shell principle effectively defines these symbols.

The default functions must either be **TRUE**, **FALSE**, previously introduced base function symbols, or the new base function.

The language for describing the "type restriction" on the components is very primitive. Each type restriction requires of its respective component either that it be of a type among an explicitly given set of types or that it be of a type not among an explicitly given set of types. In particular, each type restriction is a sequence of the form $(flg \ r_1 \ \dots \ r_m)$ where **flg** is either **ONE-OF** or **NONE-OF** and each r_i is either a previously introduced recognizer, **TRUEP**, **FALSEP**, or the new recognizer.

For example, if **NUMBERP** and **LISTP** are among the "current types," then the type restriction **(ONE-OF NUMBERP LISTP)** is satisfied only by objects of type **NUMBERP** or **LISTP**, while the type restriction **(NONE-OF NUMBERP)** is satisfied by objects of any type but **NUMBERP**. Note that **(NONE-OF)** is satisfied by objects of any type. If no type restrictions are provided in the invocation, we use **(NONE-OF)**.

After the shell principle has been properly invoked, **const**, **base**, **r**, and each of the ac_i may be described as follows—following our already established convention for documenting the "behavior" of functions in the logic:

(const x_1 ... x_n)

If x_i satisfies type restriction tr_i, for each $1 \leq i \leq n$, then return an n-tuple of the new type, **r**, with the x_i as the respective components. If any x_i fails to satisfy its type restriction, the corresponding component in the constructed n-tuple is (dv_i). We call **const** the *constructor* function of the new type.

(base)

Return the "base object" of the new type, **r**. That is, **(base)** is an object of the new type but not one constructed by the constructor. If no base object is provided in the invocation, every object of type **r** is constructed by the constructor.

(r x)

If **x** is of the new type, **r**, return **T**; otherwise return **F**.

(ac_i x)

If **x** is an n-tuple of the new type, **r**, constructed by the constructor, **const**, return its **i**th component; otherwise, return (dv_i).

Each shell class is disjoint from all others. In addition, **T** and **F** are different from all shell objects.

It is convenient, in fact, to think of **T** and **F** merely as the base objects of two shell classes recognized by **TRUEP** and **FALSEP** respectively. These two shell classes have no constructors. The user of the logic cannot use the shell principle to axiomatize a class with no constructor.

The Ground Zero theory includes four shells axiomatized with the shell principle:

- **NUMBERP** - the natural numbers

- **LISTP** - the ordered pairs

- **LITATOM** - the words

- **NEGATIVEP** - the negative integers

In the following four subsections we show the invocation of the shell principle used for each of these types and describe the functions axiomatized.

2.3.1. Natural Numbers

With the invocation

Shell Definition.
Add the shell **ADD1** of one argument
with base function **ZERO**,
recognizer function **NUMBERP**,
accessor function **SUB1**,
type restriction **(ONE-OF NUMBERP)**,
default function **ZERO**.

we define the following functions:

(ZERO)	A constant, abbreviated **0**. This is the ''base object'' of the natural number shell.
(ADD1 I)	Return the next natural number after **I**. This is the ''constructor'' of the natural number shell. If **I** is not a natural, **0** is used in its place.
(NUMBERP X)	Return **T** or **F** according to whether **X** is a natural number. This is the ''recognizer'' of the natural number shell.
(SUB1 I)	Return the predecessor of the natural number **I**. If **I** is **0** or is not a natural number, return **0**. This is the ''accessor'' of the natural number shell.

2.3.2. *Ordered Pairs*

With the invocation

Shell Definition.
Add the shell **CONS** of two arguments
with recognizer function **LISTP**,
accessor functions **CAR** and **CDR**,
default functions **ZERO** and **ZERO**.

we define the following functions:

(CONS X Y)	Return the ordered pair whose first component is **X** and whose second is **Y**.
(LISTP X)	Return **T** or **F** according to whether **X** is an ordered pair constructed by **CONS**.
(CAR X)	If **X** is an ordered pair, return the first component; otherwise, return **0**.
(CDR X)	If **X** is an ordered pair, return the second component; otherwise, return **0**.

   Nests of ordered pairs are used to represent finite sequences, binary trees, tables, etc. We will later explain abbreviation conventions for nests of ordered pairs. When we do that we will illustrate the use of such pairs.

2.3.3. *Literal Atoms*

Literal atoms are used to represent symbolic data such as words. We will later introduce an abbreviation for writing literal atoms that makes their use obvious. For the moment, we will simply describe the primitives for constructing, recognizing, and accessing literal atoms.

With the invocation

Shell Definition.
Add the shell **PACK** of one argument
recognizer function **LITATOM**,
accessor function **UNPACK**,
default function **ZERO**.

we define the following functions:

(PACK L)   Construct and return the literal atom with **L** as its "print name." Generally, **L** is a list of ASCII character codes, but it may be any object.

(LITATOM X)   Return **T** or **F** according to whether **X** is a literal atom.

(UNPACK X)   If **X** is a literal atom obtained by **PACK**ing **L**, return **L**; otherwise return **0**.

After explaining the extended syntax, we illustrate how **LITATOM**s are used to represent words.

2.3.4. Negative Integers

With the invocation

Shell Definition.
Add the shell **MINUS** of one argument
with recognizer function **NEGATIVEP**,
accessor function **NEGATIVE-GUTS**,
type restriction **(ONE-OF NUMBERP)**,
default function **ZERO**.

we define the following functions:

(MINUS I)   If **I** is a natural number, return the negative of **I**.

(NEGATIVEP X) Return **T** or **F** according to whether **X** is a negative integer.

(NEGATIVE-GUTS X)
                      If **X** is a negative integer, return the absolute value of **X**; otherwise, return **0**.

The function **MINUS**, when given **0**, creates an unusual "negative" number whose "absolute value" is **0**. That is to say, **(NEGATIVEP (MINUS 0)) = T**. Thus, **(EQUAL (MINUS 0) 0) = F**.

2.3.5. Some Intuitive Remarks about Shells

A very concrete model for shells can be described as follows. Each shell class has a color assigned to it: true is black, say, false is white, natural numbers are red, lists are blue, literal atoms are yellow, and negatives are green. The recognizers are filters that accept only a given color: **TRUEP** returns **T** when presented a black object and **F** otherwise; **FALSEP** returns **T** when presented a white object and **F** otherwise; **NUMBERP** returns **T** when given a red object and

F otherwise, etc. The base objects of each class are marbles of the appropriate color: **T** is a black marble, **F** is a white one, and **0** is a red one. The constructor functions build colored, compartmentalized boxes, with as many compartments as the constructors take arguments: **ADD1** builds red boxes with one compartment, **CONS** builds blue boxes with two compartments, **PACK** builds yellow boxes with one compartment, and **MINUS** builds green boxes with one compartment. Roughly speaking, a constructor function puts each of its arguments into the corresponding compartments of the constructed box. But first it asks whether the presented argument is of the right color: **ADD1** expects its argument to be red, **CONS** and **PACK** don't care, and **MINUS** expects its argument to be red. When a constructor is given the wrong color argument it puts the corresponding default object into the compartment instead. (Each default object is a marble of the expected color.) Finally, the accessors are functions that expect to be given boxes of the appropriate color and, when they are, they merely extract the contents of the corresponding compartment. When an accessor is given an object that is either not a box or is of the wrong color, it returns the corresponding default value.

Thus, the number **2** in this model, **(ADD1 (ADD1 (ZERO)))**, is a red box containing a red box containing a red marble. The ordered pair **(CONS 2 (CONS 0 0))** is a blue box containing two compartments; in the first is a 2 (i.e., a red box containing...); in the second is a blue box containing two compartments; in each is a red marble. What is **(ADD1 T)**? According to the model, **ADD1** builds a red box containing a red... oops! The argument provided, **T**, is black. **ADD1** expects a red argument. So it uses a red marble instead. Thus, **(ADD1 T)** is a red box containing a red marble—the same thing constructed by **(ADD1 0)** or **1**. What is **(SUB1 (ADD1 T))**? Again, **(ADD1 T)** constructs a box containing a red marble. **SUB1** extracts the contents of the compartment, the red marble, and returns it. **(SUB1 (ADD1 T))** is a red marble, i.e., **0**, not **T**.

These intuitive remarks can be formalized to provide a model for the shell axioms, but we do not go into that in this handbook. The name "shell" came from the idea of constructor functions building colored containers, or shells, around their arguments.

Any extension of the theory will contain only a finite number of explicitly declared shells. In Ground Zero we have six shells, counting **T** and **F** among them. One might therefore ask "is every object in the model of one of the given shells?" Put more informally, "are the only colors black, white, red, blue, yellow, and green?" The answer is "no." If the answer were "yes, there are only six colors," then the theory would be inconsistent as soon as we invoked the shell principle again to axiomatize purple triples.

Finally, new users of the logic are often surprised and baffled to see the natural numbers axiomatized in a way analogous to ordered pairs. But **SUB1** is to **ADD1** exactly what **CAR** is to **CONS**. Table 2.1 illustrates the correspondences. That is, **ADD1** constructs a 1-tuple recognized by **NUMBERP** and ac-

Table 2.1

const	(base)	r	accessors	
–	(TRUE)	TRUEP	–	
–	(FALSE)	FALSEP	–	
ADD1	(ZERO)	NUMBERP	SUB1	
CONS	–	LISTP	CAR,	CDR
PACK	–	LITATOM	UNPACK	
MINUS	–	NEGATIVEP	NEGATIVE-GUTS	

cessed by **SUB1**. **CONS** constructs a 2-tuple, recognized by **LISTP** and accessed by **CAR** and **CDR**. **28** is a red box containing **27**. **(CONS T 0)** is a blue box containing **T** and **0**. **27** is the first component of **28** in exactly the same sense that **T** is the first component of **(CONS T 0)**. However, red boxes have only one compartment while blue ones have two.

We now return to the mainstream of our presentation of the logic by continuing the documentation of the primitive functions.

2.3.6. COUNT

The function **COUNT** determines the ''size'' of a shell object. In particular, given an object (actually, an explicit value) constructed entirely by applications of shell constructor and base functions, **COUNT** returns the number of constructor function applications.

(COUNT X)　　　　If **X** is **T** or **F**, return **0**; if **X** is the base object of some shell, return **0**; if **X** is a constructed n-tuple, return **1** plus the sum of the **COUNT**'s of the n components.

For example, let **x** be the constant

```
(CONS (ADD1 (ADD1 (ZERO)))
      (CONS (PACK (CONS (ZERO) (ZERO)))
            (ZERO)))
```

Then, **(COUNT x)** is **6**. Put in the metaphorical terms of the previous subsection, when **COUNT** is presented with an object composed entirely of boxes and marbles, **COUNT** returns the number of boxes.

COUNT is unusual in that its definition ''grows'' as new shells are defined. The user of the theory cannot define a function like this. The reason is that in order to permit ''data abstraction,'' the only way to obtain the n components of a shell object is to apply the n accessor functions. Thus, the user who tries to define a function like **COUNT** will find himself enumerating each of the known shells. Such a definition would be incomplete when a new shell is added.

2.4. Extending the Syntax

We adopt several conventions to permit the succinct expression of shell constants.

0 is an abbreviation of **(ZERO)**; the positive integer **n** is an abbreviation of the nest of **n** **ADD1**'s around a **0**; the negative integer **−n** is an abbreviation of **(MINUS n)**. Thus 2 abbreviates **(ADD1 (ADD1 (ZERO)))** and **−4** abbreviates **(MINUS 4)**.

We permit certain function symbols to be applied to "too many" arguments by right associating the function. The function symbols in question are **AND**, **OR**, **PLUS**, and **TIMES**. For example **(AND P Q R)** is an abbreviation for **(AND P (AND Q R))**.

Nests of **CAR**s and **CDR**s are abbreviated with function symbols of the form **C...A...D...R**, e.g., **(CADAAR X)** is an abbreviation of **(CAR (CDR (CAR (CAR X))))**.

During the remainder of this section we describe the **QUOTE** notation, with which list and atomic constants are written down. In this notation, the symbol **QUOTE** is used in a way that makes it appear as though it were a function of one argument; typical expressions include **(QUOTE ABC)** and **(QUOTE (1 2 3))**. However, the "argument" expression is not necessarily a term. While the word "**QUOTE**" is a legal symbol and hence, technically, a legal function symbol, we *never* use **QUOTE** as a function symbol. The entire **QUOTE** expression—the string of characters in the "argument" position, the word **QUOTE**, and the enclosing parentheses—is an abbreviation for a term.

We now ask the reader to adopt an abbreviation convention that has nothing whatsoever to do with terms. Henceforth, whenever you see the single quote mark, (′) immediately preceding a symbol or well-balanced parenthesized string, **s**, pretend you saw **(QUOTE s)** in place of the single quote mark and **s**. Thus, **′ABC** should be read as **(QUOTE ABC)**, **′(1 B 3)** should be read as **(QUOTE (1 B 3))**, and **′(A ′B ′′C)** should be read as

$$\text{(QUOTE (A (QUOTE B) (QUOTE (QUOTE C)))).}$$

We now proceed to explain what these strings mean.

If **wrd** is a sequence of ASCII characters satisfying the syntactic rules for a symbol in our logic and the ASCII codes for the successive characters in **wrd** are $c_1, ..., c_n$, then **(QUOTE wrd)**, i.e., **′wrd**, is an abbreviation for

$$(\textbf{PACK} \ (\textbf{CONS} \ c_1 \ \ldots \ (\textbf{CONS} \ c_n \ 0) \ldots)) \, .$$

Thus, **'ABC** is an abbreviation of **(PACK (CONS 65 (CONS 66 (CONS 67 0))))**.

'NIL, which is an abbreviation for

$$(\textbf{PACK} \ (\textbf{CONS} \ 78 \ (\textbf{CONS} \ 73 \ (\textbf{CONS} \ 76 \ 0)))) \, ,$$

is further abbreviated **NIL**. Recall that the symbol **NIL** is not a variable symbol. Note that the object **NIL** is a **LITATOM** and, hence, is not **F**. Thus, to the surprise of many Lisp programmers, **(IF NIL Y Z) = Y**.

(LIST x_1 x_2**...** x_n**)** is an abbreviation for

$$(\textbf{CONS} \ x_1 \ (\textbf{LIST} \ x_2 \ \ldots \ x_n)) \, .$$

(LIST) is an abbreviation for **NIL**.

Finally, we provide a convention for abbreviating certain **LISTP** constants. The convention is similar to the "dot" notation of Lisp. The notation is extremely succinct but frequently causes trouble for newcomers. Table 2.2 illustrates our conventions. We so abbreviate any term built entirely with **CONS**es from numbers (i.e., terms built with **ADD1**s, **ZERO**s, and **MINUS**es) and those **LITATOM**s (i.e., terms built with **PACK**s) admitting the abbreviation convention noted above. If **x** is such a term, we abbreviate **x** by a single quote mark (**'**) followed by the "explicit value descriptor" of **x** as defined below. If **x** is a **NUMBERP** or **NEGATIVEP** abbreviated by **n**, its explicit value descriptor is **n**. If **x** is a **LITATOM** abbreviated by **'wrd**, its explicit value descriptor is **wrd**. Otherwise, **x** is a **LISTP** and of the form **(CONS** x_1 **(CONS** x_2 **... (CONS** x_n **fin)...))** where **fin** is the first non-**CONS** expression in the **CDR** chain of **x**. If **fin** is **NIL**, then the explicit value descriptor of **x** is an open parenthesis followed by the explicit value descriptor of x_1, a space (or arbitrary amount of white space), the explicit value descriptor of x_2, a space, ... the explicit value descriptor of x_n, and a close parenthesis. If **fin** is non-**NIL**, then the explicit value descriptor of **x** is as it would be had **fin** been **NIL** except that immediately before the close parenthesis there should be inserted some space, a dot, some space, and the explicit value descriptor of **fin**.

The reader unfamiliar with dot notation is urged to inspect Table 2.2 in light of the above definition.

Actually, our notation is somewhat more elaborate than indicated above because it is possible to include **T**, **F**, and new shell constants inside quoted objects. However, we do not give the details here.

The last example in Table 2.2 hints at one of the most important uses of quoted constants in the logic: the representation of terms in the logic. By so embedding the terms of the language into the logic we can define an interpreter for the logic as a function in the logic and provide many features that otherwise

Table 2.2

x	abbreviation of x
(CONS 1 (CONS 2 NIL))	'(1 2)
(CONS 1 (CONS 2 'ABC))	'(1 2 . ABC)

(CONS (CONS 'A 1)
 (CONS (CONS 'B 2)
  (CONS (CONS 'C 3)
     NIL)))
	'((A . 1)
	 (B . 2)
	 (C . 3))

(CONS (CONS 'A 'B) (CONS 'C 'D))	'((A . B) C . D)

(CONS 'EQUAL
 (CONS 'X
  (CONS ''ABC
    NIL)))
	'(EQUAL X (QUOTE ABC))

would be considered "higher order."

2.5. Conventional Data Structures

Ordered pairs are used to construct lists or finite sequences, tables, binary trees, and many other data structures. Literal atoms are typically used to represent such symbolic constants as words. In this section we illustrate typical uses of these data structures.

The literal atom **NIL** is conventionally used to represent the empty list. This sometimes causes confusion since **NIL** is not a **LISTP**. Perhaps "**CONSP**" would have been a better name for **LISTP**.

Given the representation of some list **s**, the ordered pair **(CONS x s)** is the conventional representation of the list obtained by adding the new element **x** to the front of **s**. Thus, the list of the first five positive numbers is conventionally represented by

    (CONS 1 (CONS 2 (CONS 3 (CONS 4 (CONS 5 NIL)))))

which may be abbreviated as

    (LIST 1 2 3 4 5)

or

'(1 2 3 4 5).

If **1st** is a nonempty list, then **(CAR 1st)** is the first element in the list, and **(CDR 1st)** is the list of the remaining elements. Thus,

```
(CAR '(1 2 3 4 5))           = 1
(CDR '(1 2 3 4 5))           = '(2 3 4 5)

(CADR '(1 2 3 4 5))
=
(CAR (CDR '(1 2 3 4 5)))
=
(CAR '(2 3 4 5))             = 2


(CADDR '(1 2 3 4 5))         = 3
(CADDDR '(1 2 3 4 5))        = 4
(CADDDDR '(1 2 3 4 5))       = 5

(CDDDDDR '(1 2 3 4 5))       = NIL
```

"Head" and "Tail" might be more memorable names for **CAR** and **CDR**, when they are used to access the components of ordered pairs representing lists in the conventional way. It should be stressed that there is nothing inherent in **NIL**, **CAR**, **CDR**, and **CONS** that dictates the choice of **NIL** as the empty list, the choice of **CAR** for the storage of the first element, or **CDR** for the storage of the remaining elements. It is merely a matter of convention. We could as well use the atom '**ABC** to denote the empty list and reverse the roles of **CAR** and **CDR**. In that representation, the list of the first five positives would be written

(CONS (CONS (CONS (CONS (CONS 'ABC 5) 4) 3) 2) 1)

or

'((((((ABC . 5) . 4) . 3) . 2) . 1).

From this example it should be clear that the **QUOTE** notation *does* encourage the use of the traditional convention for representing lists!

Literal atoms are commonly used to represent symbolic data such as names, operators, and attributes. For example, in an application in which the days of the week are relevant, one might choose to denote each day with a number. But it might be more perspicuous to use literal atoms, e.g., '**MONDAY** for the first work day, '**TUESDAY** for the second, etc.

'**MONDAY** is, of course,

```
(PACK ' (77 79 78 68 65 89 . 0)) .
```

It is the **QUOTE** notation, rather than **PACK**, which suggests a connection between **'MONDAY** and the word "monday".

Here are some examples illustrating how **PACK** and **UNPACK** work, in **QUOTE** notation:

```
(UNPACK 'MONDAY) = ' (77 79 78 68 65 89 . 0)

(PACK (CONS 77 (CDR (UNPACK 'RAN)))) = 'MAN
```

Of course, it is frequently the case that literal atoms are used inside list structures. For example, the work days are

' (MONDAY TUESDAY WEDNESDAY THURSDAY FRIDAY) .

Lists are frequently used to represent tables. A very common form of list is an "association list" which represents a two column table such as that displayed in Table 2.3. The association list representing Table 2.3 is the list of successive

Table 2.3

key	value
ADD1	1
DIFFERENCE	2
PLUS	2
SUB1	1
TIMES	2
ZERO	0

key-value pairs:

```
' ((ADD1 . 1)
  (DIFFERENCE . 2)
  (PLUS . 2)
  (SUB1 . 1)
  (TIMES . 2)
  (ZERO . 0))
```

Finally, ordered pairs are commonly used to represent trees. The simplest form of tree is the binary tree. Thus, the tree

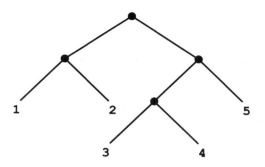

might be represented by

> **(CONS (CONS 1 2) (CONS (CONS 3 4) 5))**

which may be written

> **′((1 . 2) (3 . 4) . 5)**

However, with lists one can conveniently represent trees with branching rates other than two. For example, a common representation of the tree shown below, which has ''operators'' of varying arity stored at the nodes

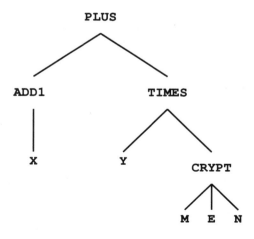

is the list

> **′(PLUS (ADD1 X) (TIMES Y (CRYPT M E N)))**

In this representation, each node of the tree is represented by a pair whose **CAR** holds the information for the node and whose **CDR** is a list of the subtrees. Observe the close similarity between such trees and the terms of our logic. In fact, the **QUOTE** notation makes this similarity strikingly obvious. We call **' (PLUS X Y)** the "quotation" of the term **(PLUS X Y)** and will eventually define a function, called **EVAL$**, with the property that the **EVAL$** of **' (PLUS X Y)**, in a suitable environment, is equal to **(PLUS X Y)**.

We will illustrate functions for manipulating these conventional data structures after we have discussed the definitional principle.

2.6. Defining Functions

The user can define new functions by adding equations that permit calls of the new functions to be reduced to calls of old ones. We illustrate the principle of definition many times in this section. However, the functions defined in this section are not part of the Ground Zero theory and are presented for illustrative purposes only.

The equation

Definition.
(STEP X) = (ADD1 (ADD1 X))

defines the new function **STEP**, which takes one argument, **X**, and returns the successor of its successor. Thus,

$$(\text{STEP } 5) = (\text{ADD1 } (\text{ADD1 } 5))$$
$$= (\text{ADD1 } 6)$$
$$= 7$$

A typical invocation of the definitional principle is

Definition.
(fn x$_1$ ... x$_n$) = term

We say that the *formals* of **fn** are **x$_1$**, ..., **x$_n$**, and the *body* of **fn** is the term **term**.

When the principle of definition is invoked, **fn**, the formals, and the body must satisfy four restrictions.

1. **fn** must not be already defined or even mentioned in any axiom of the logic.

2. Each of the formals must be a variable, and they must all be distinct.

3. The body must be a term and may contain no variables other than
the formals. That is the body may contain no "global" variables.

We explain the fourth restriction later.

In general the restrictions on definitional equations are present to insure that
there exists one and only one function satisfying the equation.

Violating restriction 1 may lead to unsatisfiable constraints on the function
"defined." For example, defining a function named **CAR** will almost certainly
lead to inconsistent statements about its properties. One subtle consequence of
this restriction is that it prohibits mutually recursive definitions: if **F1** is defined
in terms of **F1** and **F2**, then a subsequent attempt to define **F2** will fail because
F2 is already mentioned in an axiom. We show how we get around this prohibition
in the next section.

Violating restriction 2, as in the following example

"Definition."
(FN X X) = 2

yields "definitions" that fail to specify the value of the function on all combinations of arguments. For example, what is **(FN 1 2)**?

Violating restriction 3, as in

"Definition."
(FN X) = Y

may yield "definitions" of "functions" that seem to return many different
values for the same input. For example, if the equation above were admitted as
an axiom then, by instantiation, we could prove **(FN 1) = T**. But we could
also prove **(FN 1) = F**. Thus, we could prove **T=F**, which is not true.

Here are some examples of simple function definitions:

Definitions.
(NLISTP X) = (NOT (LISTP X))

(FIRST X) = (CAR X)

(REST X)   = (CDR X)

(NULL X)   = (EQUAL X NIL)

(SECOND X) = (FIRST (REST X))

(THIRD X) = (FIRST (REST (REST X)))

These definitions illustrate one reason to define a function: to package, under a
memorable name, a commonly used nest of function applications. Such defini-

tions do not really add anything to our expressive power since we could always say the same thing by using the old nest of functions. But they make it easier to build complex systems.

The power of function definitions is most apparent when one starts to write *recursive* definitions, i.e., definitions in which the newly defined function symbol is used inside the body of its own definition.

For example, here is an equation that permits us to determine the number of elements in a list:

```
(LEN L)
   =
(IF  (NULL L)
     0
     (ADD1  (LEN  (REST L)))))
```

Observe that from this equation we can derive

```
(LEN ' (A B C))  =  (ADD1  (LEN  ' (B C)))
                 =  (ADD1  (ADD1  (LEN  ' (C))))
                 =  (ADD1  (ADD1  (ADD1  (LEN NIL))))
                 =  (ADD1  (ADD1  (ADD1 0)))
                 =  3
```

Thus, we actually have introduced a new concept. No nest of "old" functions would yield the same result as **(LEN L)** on every possible **L**. Without an equation such as this we could not talk formally about the "length of a list."

We generally say a function is *recursive* if it is called inside the body of its own definition; a function is said to be *nonrecursive* otherwise. Thus, in this usage, **LEN** above is recursive and **SECOND** is nonrecursive. This terminology is at odds with the standard mathematical terminology where "recursive" is equivalent to "computable." **SECOND**, while nonrecursive in our sense, is certainly computable! Our usage of the terms is entirely consistent with everyday practice in programming—not a very strong recommendation of a convention at odds with mathematics...

The power of recursive definitions comes at a price. Consider the following derivation from the equation "defining" **LEN** above:

```
(LEN 0)  =  (ADD1  (LEN  (REST 0)))   ;  (NULL 0)  = F
         =  (ADD1  (LEN  (CDR 0)))    ;  REST  is CDR
         =  (ADD1  (LEN 0))           ;  (CDR 0)  = 0
```

If the equation "defining" **LEN** is available as an axiom, we can show that **(LEN 0)** is one greater than itself!

```
(LEN 0)  =  (ADD1  (LEN 0))
```

But from the definition of **ADD1** and the natural numbers we can show that for all **X**, **X** $\neq$ **(ADD1 X)**! Hence, by instantiating **X** to be **(LEN 0)** we can get

$$\text{(LEN 0)} \neq \text{(ADD1 (LEN 0))}.$$

We can thus prove that **(LEN 0)** both is and is not **(ADD1 (LEN 0))**. This is an intolerable state of affairs for a logic: adding a "definition" rendered the logic inconsistent. The problem arose because there is no function satisfying the alleged definition.

The fourth restriction on definitional equations prevents this problem. Ideally we would like an easily enforced syntactic requirement that admitted every equation that defines a function and prohibited any equation that does not. Unfortunately, no such requirement can exist. Our fourth restriction is, however, sufficient and does not often prohibit useful definitions: the recursion in the definition must be proved to terminate. It can be shown that if the recursion terminates, then there exists a function satisfying the equation—namely, the function computed by an ideal computing machine which follows the recipe laid out in the definition.

To formalize restriction 4, we formalize the notion of the ordinals up to ε_0 and the well-founded relation **ORD-LESSP** on those ordinals. We then require

4. There must exist an ordinal measure of the arguments of **fn** that can be proved to decrease according to **ORD-LESSP** in each recursive call of **fn**.

We discuss the ordinals later. However, the natural numbers constitute the initial ordinals and, on two natural numbers, **ORD-LESSP** is equivalent to the familiar "less than" relation.

Violating restriction 4, as in the "definition" of **LEN** above, often (but not always) produces inconsistent axiomatizations. Here is an acceptable definition of a similar concept:

Definition.
```
(LENGTH L)
   =
(IF (LISTP L)
    (ADD1 (LENGTH (CDR L)))
    0).
```

A measure satisfying restriction 4 in this case is **(COUNT L)**. The recursive branch is taken only if **L** is a **LISTP** and it can be shown that if **(LISTP L)** then **(COUNT (CDR L))** is strictly smaller than **(COUNT L)**. More formally, we have

Theorems.
```
(ORDINALP (COUNT L))
```

and

```
(IMPLIES (LISTP L)
         (ORD-LESSP (COUNT (CDR L))
                    (COUNT L)))
```

Note that **(LENGTH 0)** = 0 since 0 is not a **LISTP**.

It is very common for a single argument of a recursive function to get smaller in each recursion; **COUNT** is the most commonly used measure function. Note carefully, however, that the measure justifying a definition is an arbitrary term which can take into account all of the arguments, not just a single one. While some measure of the arguments must decrease, it may be that no single argument gets smaller.

Below we illustrate the point just made. Consider the function that returns a list of the natural numbers from **I** to **J**. We call the function **FROM-TO**

Definition.
```
(FROM-TO I J)
  =
(IF (LESSP J I)
    NIL
    (CONS I (FROM-TO (ADD1 I) J))).
```

If **J** is **LESSP** ("less than") **I**, the answer is the empty list. Otherwise, the answer is obtained by "consing" **I** onto the naturals from **I+1** to **J**. That is, we collect the naturals from **I+1** to **J** and then add **I** to the front. Observe that one argument increases in each recursion while the other stays constant. What is getting smaller?

This definition is acceptable because the **DIFFERENCE** between **(ADD1 J)** and **I** decreases in each recursion. That is

Theorem.
```
(IMPLIES (NOT (LESSP J I))
         (ORD-LESSP (DIFFERENCE (ADD1 J)
                                (ADD1 I))
                    (DIFFERENCE (ADD1 J)
                                I)))
```

2.7. Recursive Functions on Conventional Data Structures

Because of the need to prove termination, recursive functions on lists generally terminate on an **NLISTP** check ("not **LISTP**") rather than the **NULL** check conventionally used in Lisp.   It is convenient to think of **(NLISTP X)** meaning "**X** is empty."

Let's define now another common operation on lists, namely, concatenation.

Definition.
```
(APPEND L1 L2)
   =
(IF (NLISTP L1)
    L2
    (CONS (CAR L1)
          (APPEND (CDR L1) L2)))
```

That is, to **APPEND** two lists, **L1** and **L2**, consider whether **L1** is empty or not. If it is empty, the answer is **L2**. Otherwise, **(CAR L1)** is the first element of **L1**, and **(CDR L1)** is the rest. The concatenation of **L1** and **L2** in this case is the list whose first element is **(CAR L1)** and whose remaining elements are obtained by recursively concatenating **(CDR L1)** to **L2**. This definition is admissible because **(COUNT (CDR L1))** is smaller than **(COUNT L1)** if **L1** is a **LISTP**.

Here are some examples of **APPEND**:

```
(APPEND NIL '(1 2 3)) = '(1 2 3)

(APPEND '(1 2 3) '(4 5 6)) = '(1 2 3 4 5 6)

(APPEND '(1 2 3 . ABC) '(4 5 6)) = '(1 2 3 4 5 6)
```

Recall the "association list" concept, as illustrated by

```
'((ADD1 . 1)
  (DIFFERENCE . 2)
  (PLUS . 2)
  (SUB1 . 1)
  (TIMES . 2)
  (ZERO . 0))
```

Here is the function that retrieves the first key-value pair with a given key:

Definition.
```
(ASSOC KEY ALIST)
   =
(IF (NLISTP ALIST)
    F
    (IF (EQUAL KEY (CAAR ALIST))
        (CAR ALIST)
        (ASSOC KEY (CDR ALIST)))))
```

The termination argument is the same as that above.

Letting **alist** be the association list shown above, here are some examples of **ASSOC**:

```
(ASSOC 'PLUS alist) = '(PLUS . 2)

(ASSOC 'ZERO alist) = '(ZERO . 0)

(ASSOC 'CUBE alist) = F
```

The following function flattens a binary tree

Definition.
```
(FLATTEN X)
   =
(IF (NLISTP X)
    (LIST X)
    (APPEND (FLATTEN (CAR X))
            (FLATTEN (CDR X)))))
```

Note that **COUNT** decreases in both recursive calls.

Here are some examples of **FLATTEN**:

```
(FLATTEN 2) = '(2)

(FLATTEN '((1 . 2) (3 . 4) . 5)) = '(1 2 3 4 5)
```

Finally, let us illustrate how we deal with the prohibition of mutual recursion. First, what is mutual recursion? We say **f** and **g** are defined *mutually recursively* if the definition of **f** involves calls of **f** and **g**, and the definition of **g** involves calls of **f** and **g**. This might be written

Definitions.
```
(f x) = φ((f (a x)), (g (b x)))

(g x) = γ((f (c x)), (g (d x))) .
```

Observe that if we define **f** first and then **g**, then by the time the definition of **g** is presented, **g** is no longer "new;" it is involved in the axiom for **f**. Thus, restriction (1) of the definitional principle is violated, and **g** cannot be defined. The problem is not merely syntactic: the admission of **f** must necessarily involve the admission of **g** and *vice versa*. How then do we make mutually recursive definitions?

The problem can be overcome by a well-known technical trick: define a function **fg** which computes either **f** or **g** according to an auxiliary argument, **flg** (pronounced "flag"):

Definition.
```
(fg flg x)
   =
(IF (EQUAL flg 'f)
    φ((fg 'f (a x)), (fg 'g (b x)))
    γ((fg 'f (c x)), (fg 'g (d x)))).
```

Note that **(fg 'f x)** is **(f x)** and **(fg 'g x)** is **(g x)**. The admission of **fg** will require justifying the intertwined recursion of **f** and **g**.[8]

To illustrate the removal of mutual recursion in a concrete example, let us consider the function that substitutes a value for a variable into an expression. We want a function, **SUBSTITUTE**, that when called upon to substitute, say, **'(CAR L)** for **'X** in **'(PLUS X (ADD1 Y))**, will produce **'(PLUS (CAR L) (ADD1 Y))**.

Suppose we are substituting some new expression, **new**, for some variable, **var**, into some term **x**. If **x** is a variable, then the answer is **new** if **x** is **var** and is **x** otherwise. If **x** is not a variable it is a list whose **CAR** is the "function symbol" and whose **CDR** is a list of argument terms. We wish to leave the function symbol alone and substitute **new** for **var** into each of the elements of the argument list. But the argument list is arbitrarily long, so we must use recursion to describe the process: if the argument list is empty, return the empty list; otherwise, **SUBSTITUTE new** for **var** into the first argument and cons that onto the result of recursively substituting **new** for **var** into the rest of the argument list. Let us call **SUBSTITUTE-LIST** the function that **SUBSTITUTE**s into each term in the argument list. Then we have a mutually recursive pair of functions, **SUBSTITUTE** calls **SUBSTITUTE-LIST** and

---

[8]This may look like an unattractive solution that could be cured by some syntactic sugar that hides **fg** from the user. We have found such sugar to be unhealthy. When theorems about **f** are proved by induction, the induction hypotheses often involve **g** and *vice versa*. But how can an inductive instance of a theorem about **f** give a hypothesis about **g**? It can't, unless the "theorem about **f**" is actually a general theorem about **fg**. That is, the formal statement of sufficiently general inductively provable conjectures about mutually recursive functions frequently involve explicit mention of the intertwined function.

SUBSTITUTE-LIST calls **SUBSTITUTE** and **SUBSTITUTE-LIST**.[9]

Following the paradigm in which we introduced **f** and **g** by defining **fg**, we now introduce **SUBSTITUTE** and **SUBSTITUTE-LIST** by defining the single function **SUBST**. **SUBST** takes a "flag" argument, **FLG**, which is equal to **'LIST** if it is playing the role of **SUBSTITUTE-LIST** and **T** if it is playing the role of **SUBSTITUTE**:

Definition.
```
(SUBST FLG NEW VAR X)        ;Substitute NEW for VAR in X.
  =
(IF (EQUAL FLG 'LIST)
```
; If **FLG** is **'LIST**, **X** is a list of terms and we substitute
; **NEW** for **VAR** in each element of **X** and return the resulting
; list of terms.
```
    (IF (NLISTP X)
        NIL
        (CONS (SUBST T NEW VAR (CAR X))
              (SUBST 'LIST NEW VAR (CDR X))))
```
; Otherwise, **X** is a term.
```
    (IF (NLISTP X)
```
; If **X** is not a list, it is a variable symbol. Is it **VAR**?
```
        (IF (EQUAL X VAR)      ; If so,
            NEW               ; return NEW;
            X)                ; otherwise, return X.
```
; Otherwise, **X** is the application of its **CAR** to the list
; of terms in its **CDR**. Substitute into each of the argument
; terms with **SUBST 'LIST** and put the function symbol on
; the front.
```
        (CONS (CAR X)
              (SUBST 'LIST NEW VAR (CDR X)))))
```
The function is admitted because the **COUNT** of **X** decreases in each recursive

---

[9]Actually, since **SUBSTITUTE** does not call itself directly, we could unfold the definition of **SUBSTITUTE** in the body of **SUBSTITUTE-LIST** and obtain a recursion entirely in terms of **SUBSTITUTE-LIST**. But we prefer the solution described here.

call.

Here are some examples of **SUBST**:

```
(SUBST T     'A 'V 'V)           = 'A

(SUBST T     'A 'V 'X)           = 'X

(SUBST 'LIST 'A 'V '(V X))       = '(A X)

(SUBST T     'A 'V '(PLUS V X))  = '(PLUS A X)
```

2.8. Ordinals

Using natural numbers and lists we represent the ordinals up to ε_0. ε_0 is the smallest "epsilon number," i.e., the least ordinal o such that ω^o is o.

Table 2.4 illustrates our representation.

Table 2.4

ordinal	representation
0	0
1	1
2	2
3	3
. . .	. . .
ω	'(1 . 0)
$\omega+1$	'(1 . 1)
$\omega+2$	'(1 . 2)
. . .	. . .
2ω	'(1 1 . 0)
$2\omega+1$	'(1 1 . 1)
. . .	. . .
ω^2	'(2 . 0)
. . .	. . .
$\omega^2+\omega+3$	'(2 1 . 3)
. . .	. . .
ω^3	'(3 . 0)
. . .	. . .
. . .	. . .
ω^ω	'((1 . 0) . 0)
. . .	. . .

Let $\mu(\mathbf{x})$ denote the ordinal represented by $\mathbf{x}$. If $\mathbf{x}$ is a natural number, $\mu(\mathbf{x})$ is $\mathbf{x}$. Suppose $\mathbf{x}$ is of the form $'(\mathbf{x_1} \ldots \mathbf{x_n} . \mathbf{k})$ and represents an ordinal. Then $\mu(\mathbf{x})$ is

$$[\sum_{1 \le i \le n} \omega^{\mu(\mathbf{x_i})}] + \mathbf{k}.$$

For $\mathbf{x}$ to represent an ordinal, either $\mathbf{x}$ is a natural number, or $\mathbf{x}$ is of the form $'(\mathbf{x_1} \ldots \mathbf{x_n} . \mathbf{k})$, none of the $\mathbf{x_i}$s are $\mathbf{0}$, each represents an ordinal, and $\mu(x_1) \ge \mu(x_2) \ge \ldots \ge \mu(x_n)$.

A constructive development of the ordinals up to ε_0 very close to ours may be found in "New Version of the Consistency Proof for Elementary Number Theory" in *The Collected Papers of Gerhard Gentzen* [17]. Gentzen's proof of the consistency of elementary number theory uses induction up to ε_0. Thus, by Gödel's incompleteness theorem, we know that induction up to ε_0 cannot be justified in elementary number theory.

The following functions are defined to compare and recognize ordinals:

(LESSP I J)   If **I** and **J** are both natural numbers, return **T** or **F** according to whether **I** < **J**.

(ORDINALP X)   Return **T** or **F** according to whether **X** is the representation of an ordinal less than ε_0.

(ORD-LESSP X Y)
                   If **X** and **Y** are ordinals then return **T** if **X** is smaller than **Y** and **F** otherwise.

Our principles of induction and recursive definition explicitly require certain theorems to be proved about **ORD-LESSP**, establishing that certain quantities decrease in the induction or recursion. In a suitable theory of sets, the soundness of our induction and definition principles can be proved from the assumption that on the **ORDINALP**s **ORD-LESSP** is well-founded, i.e., there is no infinite sequence $\mathbf{o_0}$, $\mathbf{o_1}$, $\mathbf{o_2}$, ... with the property that for each natural number $\mathbf{i}$, **(ORDINALP $\mathbf{o_i}$)** and **(ORD-LESSP $\mathbf{o_{i+1}}$ $\mathbf{o_i}$)**.

The well-founded lexicographic relation on n-tuples of natural numbers induced by **LESSP** can be obtained by an appropriate use of **ORD-LESSP**. For example, suppose that $\mathbf{i_1}$, $\mathbf{j_1}$, $\mathbf{i_2}$, and $\mathbf{j_2}$ are all **NUMBERP**s. Then the pair $\langle \mathbf{i_1}, \mathbf{j_1} \rangle$ is lexicographically smaller than $\langle \mathbf{i_2}, \mathbf{j_2} \rangle$ precisely when

```
(ORD-LESSP (CONS (CONS (ADD1 i₁) 0) j₁)
           (CONS (CONS (ADD1 i₂) 0) j₂)).
```

(The **ADD1**'s above are present to ensure that the **CONS**es produce ordinals.)

2.9. Useful Functions

We now introduce a variety of useful functions. These functions are part of the basic theory either because (a) they are used in our implementation of the interpreter (e.g., **ASSOC**), (b) we have found it necessary, from a practical point of view, to build knowledge of them into the theorem prover (e.g., **DIFFERENCE** is used in the linear arithmetic decision procedure), or (c) the von Neumann machine on which the theorem prover runs provides means of computing the functions that are significantly faster than merely compiling the recursive definitions (e.g., **QUOTIENT**). Our interest in computational efficiency stems from our desire that the logic be a useful functional programming language rather than from theorem proving considerations alone.

2.9.1. *Boolean Equivalence*

(IFF P Q)   If **P** and **Q** are propositionally equivalent, (i.e., both are **F** or both are non-**F**) return **T**; otherwise, return **F**.

2.9.2. *Natural Number Arithmetic*

(FIX X)   If **X** is a natural number, return **X**; otherwise return **0**.

Functions which "expect" their arguments to be natural numbers usually use **FIX** to "coerce" them.

In all of the function descriptions below, all arguments are coerced with **FIX**.

(ZEROP I)   Return **T** if **I** is **0**; otherwise return **F**. Note: Since the argument is coerced with **FIX**, this function returns **T** on non-**NUMBERP**s, e.g., **(ZEROP NIL)** = **T**.

(LESSP I J)   Return **T** if $I < J$; else return **F**. Note: **(LESSP T 4)** = **T**.

(GREATERP I J)
   Return **T** if $I > J$; else return **F**.

(LEQ I J)   Return **T** if $I \leq J$; else return **F**.

(GEQ I J)   Return **T** if $I \geq J$; else return **F**.

(MAX I J)   Return the larger of **I** and **J**.

(PLUS I J)   Return **I+J**. Note: **(PLUS T F)** = **0**.

(DIFFERENCE I J)
   If $I \geq J$, return **I−J**; else return **0**. In number theory this

function is sometimes called "monus" or "nonnegative difference."

(TIMES I J)   Return **I*J**.

(QUOTIENT I J)
Return the integer quotient of **I** divided by **J**. For example, **(QUOTIENT 9 4)** = 2. If **J** is 0, return 0.

(REMAINDER I J)
Return **I** mod **J**. For example, **(REMAINDER 9 2)** = 1. If **J** is 0, return **I**.

2.9.3. List Processing

(NLISTP X)   Return **T** if **X** is not a **LISTP**; otherwise return **F**.

(APPEND L1 L2)
Concatenate the lists **L1** and **L2**. For example,

(APPEND '(A B C) '(1 2 3))
=
'(A B C 1 2 3).

(MEMBER X L)   Return **T** if **X** is an element of **L**; otherwise return **F**.

(UNION L1 L2) Concatenate onto the front of **L2** those elements of **L1** not in **L2** and return the result. For example

(UNION '(A B C D) '(A C E F))
=
'(B D A C E F)

(ADD-TO-SET X L)
If **X** is in **L**, return **L**; otherwise return **(CONS X L)**.

(ASSOC X ALIST)
Return the first element of **ALIST** whose **CAR** is **X**, or return **F** if no such pair exists.

(PAIRLIST L1 L2)
Pair successive elements of **L1** with those of **L2** and return the list of such pairs.

2.10. The Interpreter

Among the functions in the logic is an interpreter capable of determining the value of terms in the logic. Of course, the interpreter does not really operate on terms but rather on constants in the logic that represent terms. We encode variable and function symbols with the corresponding literal atoms. We encode function applications with lists. For example, the encoding of the term **(PLUS X Y)** is the constant **' (PLUS X Y)**. Constants can be written either as function applications or in the **QUOTE** notation. Thus, the term **(CONS 0 1)** may be encoded as **' (CONS (ZERO) (ADD1 (ZERO)))** and as **' (QUOTE (0 . 1))**. We call an encoding of a term a "quotation" of the term.

The interpreter takes as its arguments a (quoted) term and an "environment" which assigns values to (quoted) variable symbols. The environment is an association list. The interpreter determines the value of the term in the environment. Variable symbols are merely looked up in the environment. Numbers and other non-**LITATOM**, non-**LISTP**s evaluate to themselves. Lists whose **CAR** is **QUOTE** evaluate to the **CADR**. All other lists represent function calls of the function symbol in the **CAR** on the arguments in the **CDR**. To evaluate a call of **fn** on some arguments, the interpreter first determines the values of the arguments and then either applies the function named by **fn** (if **fn** is a primitive) or evaluates the body of **fn** in an environment associating the formal parameters with the corresponding argument values (if **fn** is defined). Arguments of **IF**-expressions are handled "lazily."

The function **SUBRP** answers the question "is **fn** a primitive?" If so, we say **fn** "is a **SUBRP**." The name **SUBRP** comes from the tradition in Lisp, where the functions defined with assembly language were called "subroutines." If **fn** is a primitive, the function **APPLY-SUBR** applies it to arguments. Thus,

        (APPLY-SUBR 'ADD1 (LIST 5)) = 6

        (APPLY-SUBR 'CONS (LIST 1 2)) = '(1 . 2)

If a symbol is not a **SUBRP** we call it a "non-**SUBRP**." Non-**SUBRP**s are functions defined by the user with the definitional principle. For such a function name, the functions **FORMALS** and **BODY** return the formal parameters and the body expression of the definition.

For example, let **FINAL-CDR** be the function that returns the "final **CDR**" of a list, i.e., the non-**LISTP** in the rightmost branch of the binary tree:

Definition .
(FINAL-CDR X)
    =

```
(IF (LISTP X)
    (FINAL-CDR (CDR X))
    X).
```

Then

```
    (SUBRP 'FINAL-CDR) = F

    (FORMALS 'FINAL-CDR) = '(X)
```

and

```
    (BODY 'FINAL-CDR) = '(IF (LISTP X)
                             (FINAL-CDR (CDR X))
                             X).
```

The four functions **SUBRP**, **APPLY-SUBR**, **FORMALS**, and **BODY** are undefined on function symbols that have not yet been introduced into the logic. We explain this remark by considering **SUBRP** alone. Logically speaking, there are no axioms characterizing **(SUBRP 'FOO)** if the user has not introduced the function symbol **FOO**. The expression can be proved neither **T** nor **F**. If one tries to evaluate the expression in the execution environment the attempt fails, as would an attempt to evaluate an expression using **FOO** as a function symbol. Should the user invoke the shell principle to introduce **FOO** as a function symbol, an "extra" axiom is added stating that **(SUBRP 'FOO)** is **T**. On the other hand, should the user invoke the definitional principle to define **FOO**, the "extra" axiom states that **(SUBRP 'FOO)** is **F**. In either case, evaluating the expression in the execution environment will then return **T** or **F** as appropriate. The other three functions, **APPLY-SUBR**, **FORMALS**, and **BODY**, are extended similarly when new functions are introduced.

We now consider formalizing the interpreter for the logic. The task is a subtle one if the consistency of the logic is to be maintained. Just as a naive formalization of recursive definition leads to inconsistency, so too does a naive formalization of functional arguments and embedded interpreters. By creatively instantiating functional arguments, one can lead simply defined interpreters down circular paths that require objects satisfying such inconsistent statements as **X=(ADD1 X)**.

For example, suppose the interpreter is called **EVAL** and that it takes two arguments. Consider the function **RUS**, named in honor of Bertrand Russell, defined as

Definition.
(RUS) = (EVAL '(ADD1 (RUS)) NIL)

This definition is admissible under our current restrictions, since **RUS** is not even recursive. (Readers troubled by the fact that the function **RUS** knows about the literal atom **(PACK ′ (82 85 83 . 0))**, otherwise written **′ RUS**, should consider deriving similar problems without using that atom explicitly.)

Under very plausible assumptions about **EVAL** it is possible to derive such contradictions as

$$(EVAL \ ′(RUS) \ NIL) = (ADD1 \ (EVAL \ ′(RUS) \ NIL)) .$$

To avoid inconsistency, we axiomatize the interpreter to return either **F** or a pair consisting of the value **v** of the given expression, **x**, and the cost, **c**, of obtaining it. The cost is the number of function applications involved in the evaluation of **x**. More precisely, the cost of evaluating a variable or **QUOTE**d form is **0**, the cost of evaluating an **IF** expression is one plus the cost of the test plus the cost of the appropriate branch, the cost of evaluating a call of a **SUBRP** is one plus the cost of evaluating the arguments, and the cost of evaluating a non-**SUBRP** is one plus the cost of evaluating the arguments plus the cost of evaluating the body. The interpreter returns **F** if the cost of evaluating the expression is "infinite."

Suppose that we have a computer program that evaluates a term in the logic but which operates under a specified bound on the number of function applications permitted in any attempted evaluation. Suppose the program causes an error and halts if the bound is exceeded and otherwise returns the value of the term. Then our interpreter has the following property: if our interpreter returns the pair <v, c> on some term **x**, then the computer program for evaluating terms would return **v** provided the bound is **c** or greater; if our interpreter returns **F** on **x** then there is no bound that suffices for the computer program to compute **x**.

Our interpreter is not a total recursive function. However, the logic contains an axiom that characterizes it and which is satisfied by exactly one function, namely the one described above. In addition, the interpreter is partially implemented in the execution environment of the system. It is possible to apply the interpreter to **QUOTE**d terms and, sometimes, get back the value and cost pair. Sometimes however the implemented interpreter runs forever. Nevertheless, it is generally possible to *prove* in those cases that the value of the interpreter is **F**. (We say "generally" only because sufficiently rich formal systems contain truths which cannot be proved.)

The name of our interpreter is **V&C$**. "**V&C**" stands for "**V**alue and **C**ost." The dollar sign is affixed to make it easy to find references to the symbol in our theorem prover's source code. We will give the function a more permanent name when we are convinced it is a practical way to proceed.

Recall that when we defined the illustrative function **SUBST** we saw the need for two mutually recursive functions: one to process a single term and another to process a list of terms. The first uses the second to process the list of argument terms in a function application, and the second uses the first to process the individual terms in the list. Since **V&C$** also explores terms, it too is most naturally defined with mutual recursion. We avoid explicit mutual recursion the same way we did with **SUBST**, namely by adding an additional argument which specifies whether the function is processing a single term or a list of terms.

We now illustrate **V&C$**. In the examples we use the notation **vc⊕n** to denote the operation that increments the cost of a value-cost pair, **vc**, by **n** and returns **F** if **vc** is **F**.

Suppose **FINAL-CDR** is defined as shown above.

```
(V&C$ T ' (FINAL-CDR 'ABC) NIL)
=
(V&C$ T (BODY 'FINAL-CDR) ' ((X . ABC)))⊕1
=
(V&C$ T ' (IF (LISTP X)
              (FINAL-CDR (CDR X))
              X)
      ' ((X . ABC)))⊕1
=
(V&C$ T 'X ' ((X . ABC)))⊕3
=
' (ABC . 3)
```

That is, **(FINAL-CDR 'ABC)** evaluates to **'ABC** and requires **3** function calls, one to expand **FINAL-CDR** into its body, one to evaluate the **IF**, and one to evaluate the **LISTP** test in the **IF**.

Here are some other examples of **V&C$**:

```
(V&C$ T ' (FINAL-CDR ' (1 . ABC)) NIL)
=
' (ABC . 7)

(V&C$ T ' (FINAL-CDR ' (1 2 . ABC)) NIL)
=
' (ABC . 11)
```

Note that each time **FINAL-CDR** recurses, the cost is incremented by **4**: one to evaluate the **IF**, one to evaluate the **LISTP** test, one to evaluate the **CDR** in the recursive call, and one to enter the body of **FINAL-CDR** again.

Now suppose for the sake of illustration, that we arranged for **RUS** to be defined so that

```
(FORMALS 'RUS) = NIL

(BODY 'RUS) = ' (ADD1 (RUS)) .
```

Then if we tried to execute

```
(V&C$ T ' (RUS) NIL)
```

the computation would "run forever"—actually, it would abort after exhausting the available stack space on the host machine. No value would be delivered. However, it is possible to *prove*

$$\mathtt{(V\&C\$\ T\ '(RUS)\ NIL)\ =\ F}.$$

The proof follows quickly from the observation that if **V&C$** returns a pair, <**v**, **c**>, then **c**, the cost of evaluating **'(RUS)**, is two greater than **c**, the cost of evaluating **'(RUS)**. (The cost goes up by **2** in each recursion, one for entering the definition of **RUS** again and one for the **ADD1**.)

Here then are the functions that are involved in the definition of the interpreter:

(SUBRP X)   Return **T** or **F** according to whether **X** is the name of a **SUBRP**.

(APPLY-SUBR FN ARGS)
If **FN** is the name of a **SUBRP** that takes n arguments, apply that function to the first n elements of **ARGS** and return the result. If **ARGS** does not have n elements, extend it on the right with **0**'s.

(FORMALS FN)   If **FN** is the name of a non-**SUBRP**, return the list of formal parameters from the definition.

(BODY FN)   If **FN** is the name of a non-**SUBRP**, return the s-expression that is the body of the definition.

(V&C-APPLY$ FN ARGS)
FN is assumed to be the name of a function (a **SUBRP** or non-**SUBRP**) of arity n and **ARGS** is assumed to be a list of n "value-cost pairs." Some "pairs" may be **F**. Apply **FN** to the value components of the pairs and return the corresponding value-cost pair or **F** if either some "pair" was **F** or **FN** fails to terminate. However, a special case is made if **FN** is **IF**: the answer is **F** only if the test or the appropriate branch "pair" is **F**; the termination of the branch not selected by the test is irrelevant.

(V&C$ FLG X ALIST)
If **FLG** is **T** (or any value other than **'LIST**), **X** is treated as a term and evaluated in the environment **ALIST**. If it can be evaluated with a finite cost, the answer returned is the pair containing the value of **X** and the cost. If it cannot be evaluated with a finite cost, the answer returned is **F**. (The implemented version of **V&C$** never returns **F** but runs forever instead.) If **FLG** is **'LIST**, **X** is treated as a list of terms, each is evaluated in the environment **ALIST**, and the list of results is returned.

It is convenient to have a version of the interpreter that deals just with values and not value-cost pairs. We define the following two functions which are analogous to **V&C-APPLY$** and **V&C$**:

(APPLY$ FN ARGS)

> **FN** is assumed to be a function name (a **SUBRP** or non-**SUBRP**), and **ARGS** is a list of values. Apply **FN** to **ARGS** and return the result. **APPLY$** is defined to be just the **CAR** of the corresponding **V&C-APPLY$**.

(EVAL$ FLG X ALIST)

> Return the value of **X** in the environment **ALIST**, treating **X** either as a single term or a list of terms, depending on **FLG** as in **V&C$**. **EVAL$** computes its answer by **APPLY$**ing each function symbol in the term to the recursively obtained values of the argument terms.

Since **APPLY$** is defined to be the **CAR** of **V&C-APPLY$**, it can be shown that **APPLY$** returns 0 when **V&C-APPLY$** returns **F**. That is, if the application of **FN** to **ARGS** provably fails to terminate, **APPLY$** provably returns 0. Of course, **APPLY$**, like **V&C-APPLY$**, will run forever on some executions.

EVAL$ is *not* defined to be the **CAR** of the corresponding **V&C$** but instead uses **APPLY$** to apply each function symbol in the term to the recursively obtained values of the arguments. For example, using **V&C$** to evaluate ′ **(PLUS (RUS) 4)** produces **F**, since ′ **(RUS)** does not terminate. But

```
(EVAL$ T ′(PLUS (RUS) 4) NIL)
    =
(PLUS (EVAL$ T ′(RUS) NIL)
      (EVAL$ T ′4 NIL))
    =
(PLUS (APPLY$ ′RUS NIL) 4)
    =
(PLUS 0 4)
    =
4.
```

EVAL$ on ′ **(PLUS (RUS) 4)** will not evaluate to **4**—it runs forever. However, it can be proved that the **EVAL$** expression is equal to **4**.

Our definition of **EVAL$** is attractive because for functions which always terminate, such as **PLUS**, we get theorems of the form:

```
(EQUAL (EVAL$ T (LIST ′PLUS X Y) A)
       (PLUS (EVAL$ T X A)
             (EVAL$ T Y A)))
```

The advantage of this will become apparent later.

EVAL\$ and **V&C\$** are extremely powerful programming tools as they permit one to pass around "terms" as objects in the language. One can define many useful general purpose functions using **EVAL\$** or **V&C\$**.

For example, the following function sums values of the expression **EXP** as the variable **V** takes as its value the successive elements of **LST**:

Definition.
```
(SIGMA V LST EXP)
   =
(IF (LISTP LST)
    (PLUS (EVAL$ T EXP (LIST (CONS V (CAR LST))))
          (SIGMA V (CDR LST) EXP))
    0)
```

Note that (a) this function is not total (although we compute its value in all the cases in which it terminates) and (b) it is acceptable under the principle of definition.

Here is an example of **SIGMA** to compute the sum, as **I** ranges from **1** to **3**, of I^2:

```
    (SIGMA 'I '(1 2 3) '(TIMES I I))
      =
    (PLUS (TIMES 1 1)
          (PLUS (TIMES 2 2)
                (PLUS (TIMES 3 3)
                      0)))
      =
    14.
```

In addition to being useful as a programming aid, many beautiful theorems can be proved about **SIGMA**. For example

```
    (EQUAL (SIGMA V (APPEND L1 L2) EXP)
           (PLUS (SIGMA V L1 EXP)
                 (SIGMA V L2 EXP)))

    (EQUAL (SIGMA V L (LIST 'PLUS EXP1 EXP2))
           (PLUS (SIGMA V L EXP1)
                 (SIGMA V L EXP2)))
```

It is here that one of the main attractions of our **EVAL\$** is apparent. Had we defined **EVAL\$** to be the **CAR** of **V&C\$** the latter formula would not be a theorem—on the left-hand side, the nontermination of **EXP1** would prevent **EXP2** from making its contribution to the sum, while on the right-hand side, **EXP2** makes its contribution. But arranging for the latter formula to be a theorem permits the convenient manipulation of quantified expressions.

EVAL\$ and **V&C\$** can also be used to define and investigate the properties of partial functions. For example, suppose we arranged for

```
(FORMALS 'LEN) = ' (L)

(BODY 'LEN) = ' (IF (NULL L)
                    (QUOTE 0)
                    (ADD1 (LEN (CDR L)))) .
```

Recall that the specious acceptance of a similar "definition" earlier led to a contradiction.

However, by evaluating ' **(LEN** ' **(1 2 3))** with **EVAL\$** we can obtain the desired answer **3**. And we can *prove* that the **V&C\$** of ' **(LEN** ' **(1 2 3** . **ABC))** is **F**. That is, the function doesn't terminate on a list ending with ' **ABC**. We can indeed prove the general result that **LEN** terminates iff the argument list ends with **NIL**.

How can we arrange for the **FORMALS** and **BODY** of ' **LEN** to be as assumed above? We make a special provision for this by recognizing when a function has been defined by a top-level call to **EVAL\$** on a **QUOTE**d body and an environment that passes the formals in unaltered. Thus, the **FORMALS** and **BODY** of ' **LEN** are as shown above if **LEN** is defined with

Definition.
```
(LEN L)
  =
(EVAL$ T '(IF (NULL L)
              (QUOTE 0)
              (ADD1 (LEN (CDR L))))
          (LIST (CONS 'L L)))) .
```

We are the first to admit the hackish nature of this mechanism of defining **FORMALS** and **BODY** when the body used in the definition is such an **EVAL\$** expression. The rationale behind our choice of this mechanism follows.

First, note that unlike the mere assumptions that the **FORMALS** and **BODY** of ' **LEN** are as desired, this mechanism actually introduces the function symbol **LEN** into the logic. Not only can we talk about the result of interpreting expressions such as ' **(LEN X)** with **EVAL\$** or **V&C\$**, but we can talk about such terms as **(LEN X)**. In the event that the recurrence implicit in the computation terminates, the value of ' **(LEN X)** obtained by interpretation (under the appropriate assignment to ' **X**) is in fact **(LEN X)**. That is, if **X** ends in a **NIL**, then

```
(EVAL$ T '(LEN X) (LIST (CONS 'X X)))
```

is **(LEN X)**.

However, matters are confusing if the computation fails to terminate. The **V&C$** of **'(LEN '(1 2 3 . ABC))** is provably **F**. But the **EVAL$** of **'(LEN '(1 2 3 . ABC))** is provably **0**—because the **APPLY$** of **'LEN** to **'(1 2 3 . ABC)** is **0**. However, the term **(LEN '(1 2 3 . ABC))** is provably equal to **1** (because the **EVAL$** in the defining axiom for **'LEN APPLY$**s **ADD1** to the **APPLY$** of **'LEN** to **'(2 3 . ABC)**, which is **0**). Meanwhile, the evaluation of all three of these expressions in the execution environment runs forever.

In [11] we explain the formal axiomatization of **V&C$** at length, and we show several termination and nontermination proofs using **V&C$**.

2.11. The General Purpose Quantifier

The function **SIGMA**, shown above, is only one of many useful "quantifiers." In addition to summing the value of some term over a list, we may wish to take the product, check that the term is true on every element or on some element, find the maximum, collect the successive values into a new list, etc. We call all of these concepts "quantifiers" because they involve the notion of a "bound" variable which takes on the values in some specified domain. Using **EVAL$** we define a general purpose bounded quantifier function, called **FOR** and modeled on Teitelman's iterative statement, **FOR**, in Interlisp [35].

The term

```
(FOR 'I L '(MEMBER I S)
     'SUM '(TIMES I I)
     (LIST (CONS 'S S)))
```

may be read "for **I** in **L** when **I** is member of **S** sum I^2." The final argument to the **FOR** is an association list that maps from the "free variables" in the quantified expressions to their values. In this case, the alist maps from the **LITATOM**'s to the variable **S**.

(FOR VAR LST COND OP BODY ALIST)
        In common use, **VAR** is a **LITATOM** denoting a variable, **LST** is a list, **COND** and **BODY** are both the quotations of terms, **OP** is one of the keywords below indicating the operation to be performed, and **ALIST** is an association list. The definition of **FOR** is recursive: if **LST** is empty, **FOR** returns an "initial value" that is determined by **OP**. Other-

wise **LST** is some element **e** followed by some remaining elements **tl**. **FOR** binds **VAR** in **ALIST** to **e** and evaluates the **COND** expression in that environment. If the value of the **COND** expression is non-**F**, **FOR** evaluates **BODY** and performs the indicated "quantifier operation" on the value of **BODY** and the result of recursing on **tl**. Otherwise, if the value of the **COND** expression is **F**, **FOR** does not evaluate **BODY** and returns the result of recursing on **tl**.

The permitted operations and the values of the corresponding **FOR** statements are as follows:

ADD-TO-SET	Return the list of successive evaluations of **BODY**, with duplicates eliminated.
ALWAYS	Return **T** if every evaluation of **BODY** returns non-**F**; otherwise return **F**.
APPEND	Return the concatenation of the successive evaluations of **BODY**.
COLLECT	Return the list of successive evaluations of **BODY**.
COUNT	Return the number of times **BODY** evaluated to non-**F**.
DO-RETURN	Return the first evaluation of **BODY**—that is, return the value of **BODY** on the first element of the range for which **COND** evaluates to non-**F**.
EXISTS	Return **T** if there is an element of the range on which **BODY** evaluates to non-**F**.
MAX	Return the maximum of the evaluations of **BODY**.
SUM	Return the sum, as with **PLUS**, of the evaluations of **BODY**.
MULTIPLY	Return the product, as with **TIMES**, of the evaluations of **BODY**.
UNION	Return the list obtained by unioning together the successive evaluations of **BODY**.

The syntax contains some syntactic sugar for writing **FOR** expressions. While the function **FOR** takes six arguments we permit "applications" of **FOR** to both five and seven "arguments." In such ill-formed applications, some of the "arguments" are "noise" words. Others are terms which are replaced by their quotations. In addition, the five and seven argument versions omit the association list mapping the quotation of free variables in the quantified expressions to their values.

Table 2.5

term	value
`(EXPLODE 'TREE)`	`= '(T R E E)`

`(FOR X IN '(CAT DOG MAN OX POT)`
`    WHEN`
`    (MEMBER 'O (EXPLODE X))`
`    COLLECT X)`
	`= '(DOG OX POT)`

`(FOR X IN '(CAT HIT HEN)`
`    COLLECT (EXPLODE X))`
	`= '((C A T)`
	`    (H I T)`
	`    (H E N))`

`(FOR X IN '(CAT HAT DOG)` `    APPEND (EXPLODE X))`	`= '(C A T H A T D O G)`
`(FOR X IN '(CAT HOT DOG)` `    UNION (EXPLODE X))`	`= '(C A H T D O G)`

`(FOR X IN '(CAT HAT MAT)`
`    ALWAYS`
`    (MEMBER 'A (EXPLODE X))`
	`= T`

`(FOR X IN '(CAT HAT HEN)`
`    WHEN`
`    (MEMBER 'H (EXPLODE X))`
`    DO-RETURN`
`    (CADR (EXPLODE X)))`
	`= 'A`

An example of the seven argument use of **FOR** is

```
(FOR X IN L
     WHEN (LESSP X 100)
     SUM (TIMES A B X)).
```

This abbreviates

```
(FOR 'X L
     '(LESSP X (QUOTE 100))
     'SUM '(TIMES A (TIMES B X))
     (LIST (CONS 'A A)
           (CONS 'B B)))
```

The five argument use of **FOR** permits one to drop the **WHEN** keyword and the following condition in situations when the condition is **T**.

Table 2.5 contains some examples of **FOR** statments and their values. The function **EXPLODE**, used in Table 2.5, is defined as follows:

Definition.
```
(EXPLODE WRD)
    =
(FOR X IN (UNPACK WRD) COLLECT (PACK (CONS X 0))).
```

In [11] we carefully explain our axiomatization of **FOR** and some of the alternative methods we considered. In addition, we list many "schematic" theorems proved about **FOR**.

3   Formalization Within the Logic

Given the descriptions of the primitive functions in the logic it is easy to see that the value of

    (APPEND NIL '(4 5 6))

is **'(4 5 6)**, and the value of

    (APPEND '(1 2 3) '(4 5 6))

is

    '(1 2 3 4 5 6).

Another way to phrase the last example is that the value of

    (EQUAL (APPEND '(1 2 3) '(4 5 6))
           '(1 2 3 4 5 6))

is **T**.

Now what is the value of **(APPEND NIL Y)**? In general, we cannot answer such a question unless we know the values of the variables involved, in this case, **Y**. But whatever the value of **Y**, the value of **(APPEND NIL Y)** is the same as that of **Y**. That is,

    (EQUAL (APPEND NIL Y) Y)

has the value **T**, regardless of the value of **Y**.

Similarly, the value of

```
(EQUAL (APPEND (APPEND X Y) Z)
       (APPEND X (APPEND Y Z)))
```

is **T**, regardless of the values of **X**, **Y**, and **Z**.

The obvious question is "Can you prove it?" It is easy to *test* these assertions by executing the given expressions under sample assignments to the variables. But is it possible to demonstrate that the value must always be **T**? If all we have to work with is the informal descriptions of the logic as a programming language, as given in the previous chapter, the answer to these questions is "no, we can't prove it, but would you like to see another test?"

In the next chapter we present the logic again but do so formally. We define the *language* precisely so that you know exactly what is legal to write down. We give *axioms* that completely describe each function, and we give *rules of inference* with which the axioms can be manipulated. A *theorem* is any formula that is either an axiom or can be derived from theorems using the rules of inference. It happens that every theorem is always true, regardless of the values of the variables. More precisely, if **t** is some theorem containing the variables v_1, ..., v_n, then regardless of what values we assign to v_1, ..., v_n, the value of **t** in any model of our axioms is non-**F**.

So, if for some reason you wish to determine whether some formula has the value **T** in all models, you can try proving it. Technically speaking, this is not always possible. That is, there are formulas that are true in all models but that cannot be proved. That is what Gödel's incompleteness theorem tells us. But you are extremely unlikely to happen upon a truth that is not a theorem and for all practical purposes you should proceed as though every truth in the logic has a proof.

Why might you want to know whether some formula is always true? Suppose you are writing a "program" (i.e., function) in the logic and you need to compute **(APPEND A (APPEND B C))**. Suppose you have already computed **(APPEND A B)**, and it is the value of the variable **AB**. Then you might use **(APPEND AB C)**, i.e., **(APPEND (APPEND A B) C)**, for **(APPEND A (APPEND B C))**. This is a legitimate thing to do, *if* you know that **APPEND** is associative. That is, if you know that

```
(EQUAL (APPEND (APPEND X Y) Z)
       (APPEND X (APPEND Y Z)))
```

always evaluates to **T**.

The situation just described is a simple example of a very deep problem: *formalization*. When confronted with a practical computing question of the form "Have I done this correctly?" it is often possible to convert it into a formal question of the form "Is this formula a theorem?" We offer no mechanical assistance in this process; indeed, there is a sense in which no mechanical assistance is possible: the question bridges the gap between the informal and the formal and, by necessity, any mechanical help must confine itself to the formal side of the chasm.[10]

Almost invariably, when confronted with the challenge to formalize a problem, new users of our logic are baffled. How can anything as complicated or as abstract as your problem be couched in the simple, nearly constructive system described here? It is hard enough to formalize concepts in a truly powerful mathematical system such as set theory. To do it in a logic with no quantification, no mutual recursion, no infinite objects, no sets, no abstraction, no higher order variables, and a very "constructive" sense of partial functions is, it would seem, impossible. For the authors of the system to then inveigh against the addition of axioms as being too dangerous simply seems to doom the system to total uselessness. These impressions notwithstanding, many complicated and abstract problems have been formalized within the logic. This chapter explains how it is done.

It is not necessary to be able to prove theorems in order to formalize problems. It is necessary to have a clear understanding of what formulas in the logic "mean"—a topic that is often illuminated by the axioms and rules of inference. But we believe the primer gives a description of the language adequate for the discussion of formalization. Furthermore, the discussion of formalization clarifies some of the issues and may motivate some readers to undertake the necessary study of Chapter 4. Readers who disagree may wish to read Chapter 4 first and then return to this chapter.

This chapter is organized as follows. First, we show a few recursive definitions, in the spirit of those offered in the primer, to illustrate the use of the logic as a programming language. However, we basically assume in this book that you are sufficiently familiar with programming to use recursion and inductive data structures to implement solutions to elementary programming problems. Of more concern in this chapter is the expression of relationships and the definitions of concepts that most readers think of as being "mathematical" rather than "computational." Thus, the second section of the chapter illustrates the formal statement of some familiar mathematical relationship such as associativity, transitivity, etc. We describe how we deal with some of the omissions from our logic: mutual recursion, unbounded quantification, sets, and infinities. We then

---

[10]We take the view that anything that is codified in a programming language—be it a low level machine code or a high level language like Prolog—is formal. Researchers trying to bring the informal world within the grasp of computing machines are, in our view, merely formalizing a fragment of that world. Regardless of the extent of their success, there will necessarily be a gap between that which has been formally modeled and that which we personally want or desire or intend of our programs.

deal with two problems uniquely associated with features of our logic (rather than omissions from it), namely the use of **V&C$** to discuss termination questions and the statement of general purpose "schematic" theorems about **FOR**. Finally, we discuss two commonly occurring formalization problems: nondeterminism and language semantics. The latter problem is discussed in the more general framework of the formalization of other formal systems within ours.

3.1. Elementary Programming Examples

In section 2.5 (page 28) of the primer, we showed how the primitive shells are used to represent sequences, words, tables, and trees. In section 2.7 (page 37), we gave definitions for list concatenation, **APPEND**; table lookup, **ASSOC**; tree flattening, **FLATTEN**; and term substitution, **SUBST**. These are typical examples of uses of the logic as a programming language. They are also examples of formalization. Is "list concatenation" **APPEND**? We cannot answer the question, nor can we tell you how to invent the formal definition of **APPEND** in response to the challenge "Formalize list concatenation." In lieu of definite answers, we offer more examples. In this section we'll implement in the logic push down stacks, finite queues, and an insertion sort function.

3.1.1. Push Down Stacks

Problem. Formalize push down stacks on which only numbers are pushed. Since we are dealing with an applicative programming language a stack is an object and the operations on it are functions that return "new" objects with certain functional relations to the input. Informally we want the following five functions:

PUSH	Construct the stack obtained by pushing a given number onto a given stack of numbers.
EMPTY	Return the empty stack of numbers.
TOP	Return the topmost element of a given stack of numbers.
POP	Return the stack obtained by popping the topmost element off a given stack of numbers.
STACKP	Return **T** or **F** according to whether the given argument is a stack of numbers.

This informal specification can be formalized by the following invocation of the shell principle:

Shell Definition.
Add the shell **PUSH** of 2 arguments,
with base object **EMPTY**,
recognizer **STACKP**,
accessors **TOP** and **POP**
type restrictions **(ONE-OF NUMBERP)** and **(ONE-OF STACKP)**
default functions **ZERO** and **EMPTY**.

We leave to the reader the difficult question ''Is that really what is meant by the informal specification?''

Several observations are in order however. Let **STK** be the push down stack constructed by **(PUSH 3 (PUSH 2 (PUSH 1 (EMPTY))))**, that is, the stack obtained by pushing **1**, then **2**, and then **3** onto the empty stack. Then **(TOP STK)** is **3**, the top of the stack. **(POP STK)** is **(PUSH 2 (PUSH 1 (EMPTY)))**, the result of popping the **3**. **(STACKP STK)** is **T**.

Several ''pathological'' cases are included in the formalization, for better or for worse. **(PUSH T STK)** produces the same stack as **(PUSH 0 STK)** because **T** is not a number and so **PUSH** ''coerces'' it to the first default object **0**. **(TOP (EMPTY))** is **0** because **TOP** returns the first default object when called on a non-stack or on the empty stack. **(POP F)** is **(EMPTY)** because **POP** returns the second default object when called on a non-stack or the empty stack.

3.1.2. *Finite Queues*

Problem. Formalize finite queues. Informally, we want the following functions:

MAKE-QUEUE	Return an empty finite queue of a given maximum size.
ENQUEUE	Add a new element to the front of a given finite queue.
DEQUEUE	Given a finite queue, return the finite queue with the last element removed.
ELE	Return the last element of a given finite queue.
EMPTY-QUEUEP	Return **T** or **F** according to whether a given finite queue is empty.
FULL-QUEUEP	Return **T** or **F** according to whether a given finite queue is full.
QUEUEP	Return **T** or **F** according to whether the argument is a finite queue.

The basic idea behind our formalization is that a finite queue is a pair, <list, max> where **list** is a list of the elements currently in the queue, ordered from oldest to newest, and **max** is the maximum size of the queue. We cannot use the shell principle alone to formalize this approach because we have no way, within the shell principle, to enforce the constraint that the length of **list** is less than or equal to **max**. Therefore, we will use the shell principle to get a "new" kind of ordered pair, called a **PROTO-QUEUE**, and we will formalize queues in terms of it. By ordering **list** as indicated we can formalize **ENQUEUE** by **APPEND**ing the new element to the **list**, **DEQUEUE** by taking the **CDR**, and **ELE** by taking the **CAR**.

Here is the formalization of **PROTO-QUEUE**s:

Shell Definition.
Add the shell **PROTO-QUEUE** of 2 arguments,
recognizer **PROTO-QUEUEP**,
accessors **QLIST** and **QMAX**
type restrictions **(NONE-OF)** and **(ONE-OF NUMBERP)**
default functions **ZERO**, and **ZERO**.

   MAKE-QUEUE is then defined as

Definition.
```
(MAKE-QUEUE MAX)
   =
(PROTO-QUEUE NIL MAX).
```

   We can define **QUEUEP** to be

Definition.
```
(QUEUEP X)
   =
(AND (PROTO-QUEUEP X)
     (LEQ (LENGTH (QLIST X))
          (QMAX X))),
```

where

Definition.
```
(LENGTH X)
   =
(IF (NLISTP X)
    0
    (ADD1 (LENGTH (CDR X)))).
```

   We can define **EMPTY-QUEUEP** and **FULL-QUEUEP** as follows:

Definition.
```
(EMPTY-QUEUEP Q)
     =
(AND (QUEUEP Q)
     (NLISTP (QLIST Q)))
```

Definition.
```
(FULL-QUEUEP Q)
    =
(AND (QUEUEP Q)
     (EQUAL (LENGTH (QLIST Q))
            (QMAX Q))).
```

What should **ENQUEUE**, **DEQUEUE**, and **ELE** do on "illegal" arguments such as non-queues or full queues or empty queues? Do we implement them with "run-time" checks and make them return special answers in "illegal" situations? For example, we could define **ENQUEUE** so that if its argument were not a **QUEUEP** or were full, it returned **F**. If we do not include run-time checks, the functions may return "garbage" in illegal situations. Our own personal bias is to avoid run-time checks, use the functions in a way that is consistent with their intended specifications, and prove that every use is appropriate. Here then are the definitions:

Definition.
```
(ENQUEUE E Q)
    =
(PROTO-QUEUE (APPEND (QLIST Q)
                     (LIST E))
            (QMAX Q)).
```

Observe that if **Q** is not a **QUEUEP** or is full, we return a non-**QUEUEP** in which the list component is longer than the maximum size.

Definition.
```
(DEQUEUE Q)
    =
(PROTO-QUEUE (CDR (QLIST Q))
            (QMAX Q)).
```

We intend for **DEQUEUE** to be used only on nonempty **QUEUEP**s. If **Q** is not even a **PROTO-QUEUEP**, **DEQUEUE** actually returns the empty **QUEUE** of size 0. If **Q** is a **PROTO-QUEUE** but not a **QUEUEP**—meaning its list component is too long—**DEQUEUE** shortens the list by 1, and the answer may or may not be a **QUEUEP**. If **Q** is a **QUEUEP** but is empty, **DEQUEUE** returns an empty **QUEUEP** of the same size.

Definition.
```
(ELE Q)
   =
(CAR (QLIST Q)).
```

Observe that if **Q** is not a **PROTO-QUEUEP** or is the empty **QUEUEP**, **ELE** returns **0**. If **Q** is a **PROTO-QUEUEP** that fails to be a **QUEUEP**, **ELE** returns the first element of its list component.

Once again the hard question is left to the reader: "Is that what we mean by finite queues?"

3.1.3. Insertion Sort

Problem. Define a function that sorts lists of numbers into ascending order. Our approach will be to define an insertion sort function.

The function **INSERT** takes a number **N** and an ordered list of numbers **L** and returns the list obtained by inserting **N** into **L** "at the right place," i.e., immediately before the first element of **L** that is greater than or equal to **N**:

Definition.
```
(INSERT N L)
   =
(IF (NLISTP L)
    (LIST N)
    (IF (LEQ N (CAR L))
        (CONS N L)
        (CONS (CAR L) (INSERT N (CDR L))))).
```

Thus, **(INSERT 5 ' (2 4 5 6))** is **' (2 4 5 5 6)**.

The main function, **SORT**, takes a list **L** and recursively sorts its **CDR**, when nonempty, and then **INSERT**s the **CAR** of **L** into the result

Definition.
```
(SORT L)
   =
(IF (NLISTP L)
    NIL
    (INSERT (CAR L) (SORT (CDR L)))).
```

Thus, **(SORT ' (4 2 5 1 5 6))** is **' (1 2 4 5 5 6)**.

3.2. Elementary Mathematical Relationships

We now turn to the problem of expressing elementary relationships between functions as theorems in the logic. Below are formulas expressing familiar facts of arithmetic:

```
(EQUAL (PLUS I J)                    ; Commutativity of PLUS
       (PLUS J I))

(EQUAL (PLUS (PLUS I J) K)           ; Associativity of PLUS
       (PLUS I (PLUS J K)))

(EQUAL (PLUS I 0)                    ; Right Identity of PLUS
       I)

(EQUAL (TIMES X (PLUS I J))          ; Distributivity of TIMES
       (PLUS (TIMES X I)             ; over PLUS
             (TIMES X J)))

(IMPLIES (AND (LESSP I J)            ; Transitivity of LESSP
              (LESSP J K))
         (LESSP I K))
```

Consider the first formula. The formula is a theorem and thus it is "always true." That is, no matter what values we choose for **I** and **J**, the sum **I** plus **J** is the same as that of **J** plus **I**. In other words, **PLUS** is a commutative function. In more traditional notation this might be written: $\forall$ i $\forall$ j i+j = j+i. Such elementary facts of arithmetic are so often expressed formally (i.e., as formulas) that it is not difficult to write them in our notation, once you get used to our prefix syntax and the absence of quantifiers. One way to think of the quantifier situation is that all formulas are (implicitly) universally quantified over all variables on the far outside of the formula.

However, one must be especially careful of the formalization of familiar concepts. One of the five formulas above is not a theorem. Do you know which one?

It is the third. Normally, when we say "**0** is the right identity of plus" we implicitly restrict our attention to numeric arguments. What is the sum of **T** and **0**? In a strictly typed language such questions don't arise. But in our language they do and they have answers: the sum of **T** and **0** is **0**, not **T**. An accurate statement of our version of the right identity law is

Theorem.
```
(IMPLIES (NUMBERP I) (EQUAL (PLUS I 0) I))
```

or, perhaps more conveniently,

Theorem.
(EQUAL (PLUS I 0) (FIX I)).

Often it is necessary to define new concepts simply to state the desired properties of given ones. For example, suppose we wished to formalize the notion that **SORT** produces ordered output. To express this as a formula we must define the "predicate" that checks whether a list is ordered. One suitable definition is

Definition.
```
(ORDEREDP L)
   =
(IF (NLISTP L)                    ; An empty list is ordered.
    T

    (IF (NLISTP (CDR L))          ; A list of length 1 is too.
        T
                                  ; Otherwise, check that
                                  ; the first two elements
                                  ; are in the right relation
        (AND (LEQ (CAR L)         ; and that the rest of L
                  (CADR L))       ; is ordered.

             (ORDEREDP (CDR L)))))
```

Thus, **(ORDEREDP ′(1 2 2 5 27 99))** is **T**, but **(ORDEREDP ′(1 2 2 5 27 17 99))** is **F**.

The formalization of "**SORT** produces ordered output" is then

Theorem.
(ORDEREDP (SORT L)).

Of course, is **ORDEREDP** really what we mean by "ordered"? That is the hard problem. Furthermore, even if we are convinced that **ORDEREDP** is correctly defined, there is the additional problem: "If a function *does* produce ordered output, do I know it is a correct sort function?" The answer is "no." For example, the function

Definition.
(FAST-SORT L) = NIL.

has the property that it produces ordered output.

Generally, when we say a function is a "sort function" we mean that it permutes its input into order.

This raises the question "How do we formalize the notion that one list is a permutation of another?'' We define **PERM** so that it scans the first list and attempts to find each element as a member of the second list. If some element is not found, the two lists are not permutations of one another. When an element is found in the second list, that occurrence of the element is deleted from the second list so that it is not used to account for duplications in the first list.

Definition.
```
(PERM X Y)
   =
(IF (NLISTP X)
    (NLISTP Y)
    (AND (MEMBER (CAR X) Y)
         (PERM (CDR X)
               (DELETE (CAR X) Y)))).
```

(DELETE E L) deletes the first occurrence of **E** in **L**:

Definition.
```
(DELETE E L)
   =
(IF (NLISTP L)
    L
    (IF (EQUAL E (CAR L))
        (CDR L)
        (CONS (CAR L) (DELETE E (CDR L)))))).
```

Again, is **(PERM X Y)** what we mean by the informal remark that **X** is a permutation of **Y**? We can test **PERM** of course and see that **(PERM '(1 2 3 4) '(3 1 2 4))** is **T**, and **(PERM '(1 2 3 4) '(3 1 1 4))** is **F**. In addition, we can prove theorems about **PERM**, for instance that it is reflexive and transitive:

Theorem.
```
(PERM X X)
```

Theorem.
```
(IMPLIES (AND (PERM X Y)
              (PERM Y Z))
         (PERM X Z))
```

But in the end, we are left with the fundamental formalization question.

If we accept both **ORDEREDP** and **PERM**, then a more complete correctness conjecture for **SORT** is

Theorem.
```
(AND (PERM L (SORT L))
     (ORDEREDP (SORT L))).
```

3.3. Dealing with Omissions

3.3.1. Mutual Recursion

The logic formally prohibits mutual recursion. However, as discussed in the primer, the prohibition can be effectively skirted by defining a single function whose body is a syntactic combination of the mutually recursive definitions. See page 38 of the primer for the details.

3.3.2. Quantification

Most users have been exposed to predicate calculus and have some familiarity with the unbounded universal quantifier, ∀ (pronounced "for all"), and the unbounded existential quantifier, ∃ (pronounced "for some"). In the attempt to formalize an intuitive statement many users therefore go through a stage in which they write down or at least think of quantified versions of the terms in our logic. They then convert these quantified sentences into terms which are inter-provable in the two systems. This is not an entirely precise remark because we haven't formalized a version of our logic containing ∀ and ∃, but the idea should be clear.

The most commonly used observation is that if you want to prove ∀x p(x) in predicate calculus, you should prove **(p x)** in our system, where **(p x)** is the translation into our language of the predicate p(x). That is, the axioms, defini-tions, and theorems of our logic can be thought of as having implicit universal quantification on the far outside. For example

Problem. State that **TIMES** is commutative.
  In the imagined extension of the logic to include ∀ we wish to prove

    ∀I ∀J (EQUAL (TIMES I J) (TIMES J I)).

But this is provable in the imagined extension of the logic precisely if

    (EQUAL (TIMES I J) (TIMES J I))

is provable in the logic provided. As we have seen before, if this term is a theorem, then *for all* values of **I** and **J** the two **TIMES** expressions are equiv-alent.

  This example is deceptively simple because it suggests that universal quan-tification, at least, can simply be ignored. This is not the case and great care is called for when eliminating universal quantifiers from any position other than the outside of a formula. We return to this in a moment, but first we discuss the similarly simple case of an outermost existential quantifier.

Problem. State that there exists a right zero for **TIMES**.

By "a right zero for **TIMES**" we mean a number, **z**, such that **(TIMES I z) = 0**, for all **I**. Thus, the existence conjecture is

$$\exists \mathtt{z}\ \forall \mathtt{I}\ \mathtt{(EQUAL\ (TIMES\ I\ Z)\ 0)}. \qquad [1]$$

Since we do not have quantification, we are forced to exhibit a suitable **z**. That is, we drop the $\exists \mathtt{z}$ and replace all free occurrences of **z** by a term that has the alleged property. A suitable term is **0**:

$$\forall \mathtt{I}\ \mathtt{(EQUAL\ (TIMES\ I\ 0)\ 0)}.$$

If we proved this, the law of $\exists$-introduction in predicate calculus would immediately let us prove [1]. By the previous observations about universal quantifiers on the outside, we can drop the $\forall \mathtt{I}$ above and are left with

Theorem.
(EQUAL (TIMES I 0) 0)

as a formalization of the statement that there exists a right zero for **TIMES**.

Problem. State that **0** is the unique right zero for **TIMES**.

If by this remark we mean "If z is a right zero for **TIMES** then z is **0**," the remark is not valid. **0** is not the only right zero for **TIMES**. **T** is also a right zero:

Theorem.
(EQUAL (TIMES I T) 0).

So by "**0** is unique" here we must mean "**0** is the only number" or "**0** is unique up to coercion by **FIX**."

That said, a suitable rendering in the imagined extension of the logic is

$$\mathtt{(IMPLIES\ [}\forall \mathtt{I}\ \mathtt{(EQUAL\ (TIMES\ I\ Z)\ 0)]} \qquad [2]$$
$$\mathtt{(EQUAL\ (FIX\ Z)\ 0))}.$$

The hypothesis says "**z** is a right zero," and the conclusion says "**z** is (coerced to) **0**."

Very often, new users make the mistake of simply dropping the universal quantifier in the hypothesis, producing, in this case,

$$\mathtt{(IMPLIES\ (EQUAL\ (TIMES\ I\ Z)\ 0)} \qquad [3]$$
$$\mathtt{(EQUAL\ (FIX\ Z)\ 0))}.$$

But formula [3], while in our language, is not at all equivalent to [2] and, indeed, is not a theorem! To see that [3] is not a theorem, evaluate it with **I** equal to **0** and **Z** equal to **47**. The hypothesis, **(EQUAL (TIMES 0 47) 0)**, is true but the conclusion, **(EQUAL (FIX 47) 0)**, is false. Hence, the implication is false.

What is wrong? The problem is that you simply cannot drop a universal quantifier in the hypothesis. The hypothesis in [2] is very strong. Given a **Z**, the hypothesis

    [∀I (EQUAL (TIMES I Z) 0)]

says that **(TIMES I Z)** is 0 for all **I**. The hypothesis **(EQUAL (TIMES I Z) 0)** in [3] is much weaker. Given an **I** and a **Z** it says **(TIMES I Z)** is 0—it doesn't say that **Z** is a right zero for **TIMES**.

More generally, in predicate calculus, $((\forall x\ p) \to q)$ is not equivalent to $\forall x(p \to q)$. The tendency simply to ignore universal quantifiers is encouraged by the fact that $(p \to (\forall x\ q))$ is equivalent to $\forall x\ (p \to q)$, provided x is not free in p, and the fact that it is conventional to have implicit universal quantification of all free variables on the far outside of any theorem.

So how do we formalize [2] within the logic? In the case where the universal quantification is over a finite domain, for example, had the hypothesis read "for all **I** between **N** and **M**, ...," the standard approach is to replace it with a **FOR** statement or with a call of a recursively defined function that checks the alleged property of **I** for each value in the domain. This approach is not applicable here because we are dealing with an unbounded universal quantifier.

Two common techniques are used, both of which rely upon an understanding of predicate calculus and Skolemization. The first is to use the fact that if x is not free in q, then $((\forall x\ p) \to q)$ is equivalent to $\exists x\ (p \to q)$. Thus, we can render [2] as

    ∀Z ∃I (IMPLIES (EQUAL (TIMES I Z) 0)
                   (EQUAL (FIX Z) 0)).

What does this formula say? It says that for any **Z** you can find an **I** such that if **(TIMES I Z)** is 0, then **Z** is (coerced to) **0**. To render that into our logic we must exhibit a suitable **I** given any **Z**. In particular, we define a "witness function," **I-WITNESS**, drop the existential quantifier, ∃**I**, and replace all free **I**s by **(I-WITNESS Z)**.

    ∀Z (IMPLIES (EQUAL (TIMES (I-WITNESS Z) Z) 0)
                (EQUAL (FIX Z) 0)).

What is a suitable definition of **(I-WITNESS Z)**? It must be a number such that if **Z** is a right zero for it, then **Z** is a right zero for everything. Clearly, we could define **I-WITNESS** to be the constant function that returns **1**—in this case the witness need not take account of which particular **Z** is being considered.

Eliminating **I-WITNESS** altogether, replacing the call by **1**, and dropping the universal quantifier as previously explained, we get the following formula as a formalization of [2]:

Theorem.
```
(IMPLIES (EQUAL (TIMES 1 Z) 0)
         (EQUAL (FIX Z) 0)).
```

To many readers the following statement, which is stronger than [2], is a more convincing formalization of the uniqueness of the right zero for **TIMES**:

Theorem.
```
(IFF (EQUAL (TIMES I J) 0)
     (OR (EQUAL (FIX I) 0)
         (EQUAL (FIX J) 0))).
```

This formula says that the product of two numbers is **0** iff one of the two arguments is **0**.

A second approach to formalizing [2] is to Skolemize the formula and appeal to the deduction law of predicate calculus. In particular, [2] is provable in predicate calculus iff

Theorem.
```
(EQUAL (FIX (Z)) 0)
```

can be proved assuming the new

Axiom.
```
(EQUAL (TIMES I (Z)) 0)
```

where **Z** is a new, undefined function symbol of no arguments. This is an unusual way to formalize the problem because instead of producing a formula to prove, we produce a sequence of logical acts that if admissible in our logic assures us that the desired formula is a theorem of another logic. This approach is commonly used in program verification. See for example our work on the verification of Fortran [6]. For practical reasons we do not recommend this approach to handling universally quantified hypotheses because our theorem prover is not designed to deduce consequences from arbitrary axioms.

Finally, let us consider one more quantification problem.

Problem. State the unique prime factorization theorem. Traditionally, a natural number p is *prime* iff p>1 and the only divisors of p are 1 and p. A *prime factorization* of a number n is a set of pairs $\{<p_1,i_1>, ..., <p_k,i_k>\}$ with the property that each p_j is prime, each i_j is greater than 0, p_i is p_j iff i is j, and the product $p_1^{i_1}*...*p_k^{i_k}$ is n. The theorem that every natural number has a unique prime factorization is then: for every natural number n there exists a prime factorization, and if both s_1 and s_2 are prime factorizations of n then $s_1 = s_2$.

Note that the notion of prime, as traditionally defined, involves an unbounded universal quantifier: no number besides 1 and p divides p. Rather than attempt to capture that unbounded quantifier, we adopt the definition of prime that says "no number less than p divides p, except 1." We can define this concept recursively since the quantification is now over the finite domain of numbers less than p.

Definitions.
```
(PRIME P)
   =
(AND (NOT (ZEROP P))
     (NOT (EQUAL P 1))
     (PRIME1 P (SUB1 P)))
```

where

```
(PRIME1 X Y)
   =
(IF (ZEROP Y)
    F
    (IF (EQUAL Y 1)
        T
        (AND (NOT (DIVIDES Y X))
             (PRIME1 X (SUB1 Y))))) .
```

This is not, *a priori*, the same concept as *prime* above, for there may be some **PRIME**s that fail to be *prime* because they are divisible by any of the unbounded number of naturals greater than themselves. We accept that **PRIME** is *prime* only after we have proved that no number is divisible by a number greater than itself.

Rather than use sets of pairs to define prime factorizations we use lists of primes.

We say **S** is a **PRIME-FACTORIZATION** of **N** iff **S** is a list of **PRIME**s and the product of the elements of **S** is **N**:

Definition.
```
(PRIME-FACTORIZATION S N)
   =
(AND (FOR X IN S ALWAYS (PRIME X))
     (EQUAL N (FOR X IN S MULTIPLY X)))
```

Note that here, too, the quantification is bounded so our **FOR** function is adequate.

Use of the **FOR** quantifier is unnecessary. An alternative approach is to define the functions **PRODUCT** and **PRIME-LIST** so that they recursively determine what the product is and whether **L** is a list of primes.

Definitions.
```
(PRIME-LIST L)
   =
(IF (NLISTP L)
    T
    (AND (PRIME (CAR L))
         (PRIME-LIST (CDR L))))

(PRODUCT L)
   =
(IF (NLISTP L)
    1
    (TIMES (CAR L)
           (PRODUCT (CDR L)))).
```

By defining factorizations to be lists of primes we avoid the use of sets, but this returns to haunt us when we must state uniqueness. Our statement of uniqueness is that two lists of primes with the same product are equal up to order, which is to say, they are permutations of each other. We state the uniqueness part of the main theorem as follows:

Theorem.
```
(IMPLIES (AND (PRIME-FACTORIZATION S1 N)
              (PRIME-FACTORIZATION S2 N))
         (PERM S1 S2)).
```

Finally, we must state the existence part of the theorem without using an existential quantifier. This we do by defining a "witness function," **PRIME-FACTORS**, that takes any given positive number **N** and returns an alleged factorization. The existence theorem is then

Theorem.
```
(IMPLIES (AND (NUMBERP N)
              (NOT (EQUAL N 0)))
         (PRIME-FACTORIZATION (PRIME-FACTORS N) N)).
```

That is, we not only prove there exists a factorization, we exhibit a constructive function for obtaining one.

The definition we use for **PRIME-FACTORS** is irrelevant to the intended understanding of the existence theorem. In fact, the definition is relatively complicated: we define the notion of the greatest factor of a number and then we define the prime factors as follows. The prime factors of **0** and **1** is the empty list; the prime factors of a prime is the singleton list containing the prime;

and the prime factors of any other number **n** is obtained by appending the prime factors of the greatest factor, **m**, of **n**, to the prime factors of the quotient of **n** by **m**. That this is an admissible definition follows from the observations that both **m** and the quotient of **n** by **m** are smaller than **n**. The reason we defined **PRIME-FACTORS** this way was to make the proof of the existence theorem easier. It is trivial to show that **(PRIME-FACTORS N)** yields a list of primes. It is also relatively straightforward to show that the product of the prime factors is **N**, given that the greatest factor of **N** divides **N** if **N** is not prime.

In summary, we use recursion to capture the standard quantifiers, proving bounds on the universal quantification when necessary. Of course, **FOR** can be used in straightforward cases. We use lists where sets are traditionally used. Within this setting we have proved such deep results as Fermat's theorem [9], Wilson's theorem [29], and Gauss's law of quadratic reciprocity.[11] Such standard mathematical techniques as modulo arithmetic, the pigeon hole principle, and one-to-one mappings have been formalized, proved, and successfully used in other proofs.

3.3.3. Infinities

Problem. State the theorem that there are an infinite number of primes.

One formalization of this idea is that for every prime **P** there exists a prime bigger than **P**—and of course, there *is* at least one prime, witness **7**. To eliminate the quantifier define the function **BIGGER-PRIME** which takes a number **N** and returns a prime bigger than **N**. Then prove

Theorem.
```
(IMPLIES (PRIME P)
         (AND (PRIME (BIGGER-PRIME P))
              (LESSP P (BIGGER-PRIME P)))))
```

An appropriate **BIGGER-PRIME** can be defined by searching through the numbers from **P+1** to **P!-1**. That at least one of those is prime follows from the fact that no prime less than or equal to **P** divides **P!-1**. Thus, if **P!-1** is itself not prime, its greatest prime factor is greater than **P**.

If the above theorem is not enough, it can be used as the main stepping stone to another: To each natural number there corresponds a unique prime. Again, the existential quantifier is eliminated by a constructive function, **NTH-PRIME**, with the following two properties:

---

[11]See the **"gauss"** section of the file **basic.events** on the theorem prover's directory.

Theorem.
```
(IMPLIES (NUMBERP N)
         (PRIME (NTH-PRIME N)))
```

and

Theorem.
```
(IMPLIES (AND (NUMBERP N)
              (NUMBERP M)
              (EQUAL (NTH-PRIME N)
                     (NTH-PRIME M)))
         (EQUAL N M))
```

Another kind of infinity with which we frequently deal has to do with processes that "run forever."

Problem. Formalize a "message flow modulator," a device that sits on a communications line and filters the incoming messages into two streams according to some predicate.

Some formalists in computer science are very fond of using infinite sequences to represent the three message streams. However, for very many purposes finite sequences suffice. For example, we might formalize the modulator as a function **MFM** that takes a single message **msg** as its argument and returns a pair <**tag**, **msg**> as its result, where **tag** indicates to which output stream the outgoing message is assigned. The system is then formalized as

Definition.
```
(SYSTEM S)
   =
(IF (NLISTP S)
    NIL
    (CONS (MFM (CAR S))
          (SYSTEM (CDR S))))).
```

Here we formalize the system as a function which takes an incoming stream of messages, **S**, and produces a list of pairs, each of which is of the form <**tag**, **msg**> indicating a destination and the associated input message.[12]

We might then prove the theorem that the messages sent to tag **I** are a subset of the incoming messages:

```
(SUBSETP (FOR PAIR IN (SYSTEM S)
```

---

[12]The function **SYSTEM** could have been defined equivalently as **(FOR MSG IN S COLLECT (MFM MSG))**. However, the recursive definition more easily accommodates the complexities of more realistic models.

```
            WHEN (EQUAL I (CAR PAIR))
            COLLECT (CDR PAIR))
      S)
```

Many people object to this formalization of the system because it suggests that only a finite number of messages come down the communications line. We have two views on the matter, depending on how ornery we're feeling. The first is that, indeed, no communications line yet has had an infinite number of messages on it and no communications line is ever going to. The second view is that the variable **S** in the model is not to be thought of as the entire history of the communications line but merely some initial segment of it, and the answer returned by **(SYSTEM S)** is not the entire output of the system but only the output in response to that initial segment. The theorem means that the messages output to tag **I** *so far* are a subset of the incoming messages *so far*.

3.4. Dealing with Features

In this section we discuss two rather peculiar features of the logic: the interpreter, **V&C\$**, and the bounded quantifier, **FOR**. The reader should see [11] for a deeper discussion of these functions. Much of this section is extracted or paraphrased from that paper.

3.4.1. Termination Theorems with V&C\$

Problem. Prove the termination properties of the partial function described by

```
(APP X Y)
   ⇐
(IF (EQUAL X (QUOTE NIL))
    Y
    (CONS (CAR X) (APP (CDR X) Y))).
```

The recurrence described here is similar to **APPEND**'s but the termination condition is that **X** is **NIL** rather than that **X** is not a **LISTP**. Note that if the first argument of **APP** is **0**, the computation of **APP** runs forever:

```
(APP 0 Y)
   ⇐
(CONS 0 (APP 0 Y))
   ⇐
(CONS 0 (CONS 0 (APP 0 Y)))
```

$\Longleftarrow$

(CONS 0 (CONS 0 (CONS 0 (APP 0 Y))))

$\Longleftarrow$

. . .

And in general, since the **CDR** of a non-**LISTP** is **0**, if the first argument to **APP** does not end in **NIL** the computation runs forever. That is the first "termination property" of **APP**. The second is that when it terminates, **APP** returns the same thing as **APPEND**. We wish to formalize these two statements.

An easy subproblem is to formalize what we mean by "ends in **NIL**." We define **PROPERP** to recognize those lists that end in **NIL**:

Definition.
(PROPERP L)

=

(IF (NLISTP L)
    (EQUAL L NIL)
    (PROPERP (CDR L))).

That is, a non-**LISTP** is **PROPERP** only if it is **NIL**, and a **LISTP** is **PROPERP** precisely when its **CDR** is.

Now how do we get a handle on termination?

Consider for a moment the proposed definition similar to description of **APP** above:

Definition?
(APP X Y)

=

(IF (EQUAL X NIL)
    Y
    (CONS (CAR X)
          (APP (CDR X) Y))).

This equation is inadmissible under the principle of definition because there is no measure of the arguments that decreases in a well-founded sense. Were the above equation an axiom we could derive

(APP 0 1) = (CONS 0 (APP 0 1)),

contradicting the theorem Y ≠ (CONS X Y).

To investigate the termination properties of **APP** we cannot add the equation "defining" **APP** as an axiom! We use **V&C$** instead.

First, we define **APP** using **EVAL$** as follows:

Definition.
```
(APP X Y)
  =
(EVAL$ T '(IF (EQUAL X (QUOTE NIL))
              Y
              (CONS (CAR X)
                    (APP (CDR X) Y)))
         (LIST (CONS 'X X)
               (CONS 'Y Y))).
```

As noted in the primer (page 52) and explained in detail in Chapter 4 (page 135), one effect of this definition is to add the following axioms:

Axioms.
```
(SUBRP 'APP) = F

(FORMALS 'APP) = '(X Y)

(BODY 'APP)
  =
'(IF (EQUAL X (QUOTE NIL))
     Y
     (CONS (CAR X)
           (APP (CDR X) Y)))
```

Now recall that **V&C$** takes (the quotation of) a term and an association list assigning values to (the quotations of) variable symbols. **V&C$** returns either a pair, <**v**, **c**>, indicating the value and cost of the evaluation of the term, or else returns **F** if no cost is sufficient. Thus, the intuitive idea that an expression "runs forever" is here formalized by the assertion that the **V&C$** of the expression is **F**.

Here then is the statement of the first termination property of **APP** that **(APP X Y)** terminates if and only if **X** is proper:

Theorem.
```
(IFF (V&C$ T '(APP X Y)
            (LIST (CONS 'X X)
                  (CONS 'Y Y)))
     (PROPERP X))
```

Note that we had to quote the expression, **(APP X Y)** and supply the map between the quoted variables **'X** and **'Y** and the variables **X** and **Y**.

The second termination property of **APP** is that if **(APP X Y)** terminates its value is **(APPEND X Y)**. The hypothesis that the expression terminates is just that the **V&C$** of it is non-**F**. The delivered value is the **CAR** of the pair returned by **V&C$**. Thus, here is an appropriate formalization:

Theorem.
```
(IMPLIES (V&C$ T ' (APP X Y)
                (LIST (CONS 'X X)
                      (CONS 'Y Y)))
         (EQUAL (CAR (V&C$ T ' (APP X Y)
                            (LIST (CONS 'X X)
                                  (CONS 'Y Y))))
                (APPEND X Y))).
```

Problem. State that **(RUSSELL)** does not terminate, where

```
(RUSSELL) ⇐ (NOT (RUSSELL)).
```

The solution is exactly analogous to that above. Define **RUSSELL** as

Definition.
```
(RUSSELL)
    =
(EVAL$ T ' (NOT (RUSSELL)) NIL)
```

so as to add the appropriate axioms for **FORMALS** and **BODY**. Then the statement that **(RUSSELL)** doesn't terminate is

Theorem.
```
(EQUAL (V&C$ T ' (RUSSELL) NIL)
       F).
```

Problem. Formalize the termination properties of the 91-function, where

```
(F91 X)
    ⇐
(IF (LESSP 100 X)
    (DIFFERENCE X 10)
    (F91 (F91 (PLUS X 11)))).
```

It turns out that this function is total and computes **(G91 X)**, where

Definition.
```
(G91 X)
    =
(IF (LESSP 100 X)
    (DIFFERENCE X 10)
    91).
```

To formalize this, we define **F91** as

Definition .
```
(F91 X)
  =
(EVAL$ T '(IF  (LESSP '100 X)
               (DIFFERENCE X '10)
               (F91 (F91 (PLUS X '11))))
       (LIST (CONS 'X X))) .
```

Then

Theorem .
```
(AND (V&C$ T '(F91 X) (LIST (CONS 'X X)))
     (EQUAL
      (CAR (V&C$ T '(F91 X) (LIST (CONS 'X X))))
      (G91 X))) .
```

The first conjunct states that **F91** is total. The second states that its value is that of **G91**.

In [11] we show how such theorems can be proved within the logic. Leading the theorem prover to such proofs is often difficult. We have done it for the theorems mentioned here but do not yet have enough experience to pass on reliable advice. The interested reader should see the **"quant"** section of the example file **basic.events**.

3.4.2. Schematic Theorems about FOR

Suppose the user of the logic desires to discuss the list obtained by doubling the elements of **L**. One way to proceed is to define **(DOUBLE-LIST L)** as follows:

Definition.
```
(DOUBLE-LIST L)
  =
(IF (NLISTP L)
    NIL
    (CONS (TIMES 2 (CAR L))
          (DOUBLE-LIST (CDR L)))).
```

For example, **(DOUBLE-LIST '(1 2 3 4)) = '(2 4 6 8)**.

A useful theorem about **DOUBLE-LIST** is that it "distributes" over **APPEND**:

Theorem.
```
(DOUBLE-LIST (APPEND A B))
  =
(APPEND (DOUBLE-LIST A)
        (DOUBLE-LIST B)).
```

However, suppose that in addition, the user wished to refer to the list obtained by adding 1 to every element of **L**. In the spirit that led to the definition of **DOUBLE-LIST** the user would have to define the function **ADD1-LIST**, so that **(ADD1-LIST '(1 2 3 4)) = '(2 3 4 5)**. Should it be necessary to use the fact that **ADD1-LIST** distributes over **APPEND**, that fact would have to be proved. One is tempted to say "proved again." But since **DOUBLE-LIST** and **ADD1-LIST** are different function symbols, the first lemma cannot be used to shorten the proof of the second.

An alternative is to use the quantifier **FOR** and write such expressions as

```
(for X in L collect (TIMES 2 X))
```

and

```
(for X in L collect (ADD1 X)).
```

The first expression is equivalent to **(DOUBLE-LIST L)** and the second is equivalent to **(ADD1-LIST L)**.

It is possible to state very general lemmas about quantifiers. Consider for example the schematic form

```
(for V in (APPEND A B) collect body(V))
  =
(APPEND (for V in A collect body(V))
        (for V in B collect body(V))),
```

where *body* is understood here to be a second order variable. (Our formalization does not introduce such variables or other new syntactic classes. We adopt this notation now only for expository purposes in the same spirit in which we earlier

used ∀ and ∃ in our formulas.) This lemma is easy to prove because no time is
wasted considering special properties of the particular *body* used. This lemma is
more useful than the fact that **DOUBLE-LIST** distributes over **APPEND** since it
also handles the analogous property for **ADD1-LIST** and other such functions.

The introduction of quantifiers has three major attractions: First, quantifiers
are conceptually clarifying. Logical relationships that would otherwise be
buried inside of recursive definitions are lifted out into the open. The users and
readers of the logic need no longer invent and remember names for many
"artificial" recursive functions. Second, it is possible to state general purpose,
schematic theorems about quantifiers, thus reducing the number of theorems
needed. Third, these schematic theorems are generally easier to prove than the
corresponding theorems about recursively defined instances of the quantifiers,
because irrelevant concepts have been abstracted out of the theorems. Thus,
quantifiers are a boon to the reader, to the writer, and to the theorem prover.
However, you have to know how to use them and that is what this section is
about.

Problem. State that summation distributes over **APPEND**. That is, formalize
the following schematic theorem:

>   (for V in (APPEND A B) sum *body*(V))
>   =
>   (PLUS (for V in A sum *body*(V))
>   (for V in B sum *body*(V))),

Recall the abbreviation conventions for **FOR**. In particular,

>   (for X in (APPEND U V)
>   when (MEMBER X B)
>   sum (TIMES X C))

is formally represented in the logic and in the implementation by

>   (FOR 'X (APPEND U V)
>   '(MEMBER X B)
>   'SUM '(TIMES X C)
>   (LIST (CONS 'B B) (CONS 'C C))).

Note that in the abbreviated form of **FOR** the bound variable symbol **X**, the
conditional expression **(MEMBER X B)**, the operator **sum**, and the body
(TIMES X C), are written as terms but become quoted constants in the formal
representation.

To state a general purpose "schematic" theorem it is necessary to write down
a **FOR** expression in which the bound variable, condition, operation, and/or body
are all arbitrary terms satisfying given conditions, rather than constants. Thus,

schematic theorems about **FOR** use the unabbreviated, formal form of **FOR**, namely **(FOR var range cond op body alist)**.

The schematic theorem expressing the idea that summation distributes over **APPEND** is as follows:

Theorem.
```
(EQUAL (FOR V (APPEND A B) COND 'SUM BODY ALIST)
       (PLUS (FOR V A COND 'SUM BODY ALIST)
             (FOR V B COND 'SUM BODY ALIST))).
```

Note that the equation holds no matter what the bound variable symbol is and no matter what the conditional and body expressions are. For example, the following concrete use of **FOR**, written in the abbreviated form

```
(for I in (APPEND L1 L2) sum (TIMES 2 I))
```

is just an abbreviation for[13]

```
(FOR 'I (APPEND L1 L2) '(TRUE)
     'SUM '(TIMES 2 I) NIL).
```

We can instantiate the "schematic" theorem above, replacing **V**—the bound variable—by **'I**, **A** and **B** by **L1** and **L2** respectively, **COND** by **'(TRUE)**, **BODY** by **'(TIMES 2 I)**, and **ALIST** by **NIL**, and derive immediately the equivalence of the concrete **FOR** with

```
(PLUS (FOR 'I L1 '(TRUE) 'SUM '(TIMES 2 I) NIL)
      (FOR 'I L2 '(TRUE) 'SUM '(TIMES 2 I) NIL)),
```

which, in abbreviated form is

```
(PLUS (for I in L1 sum (TIMES 2 I))
      (for I in L2 sum (TIMES 2 I))),
```

as one would have expected.

Problem. Formalize the statement that summation of a **PLUS** expression is the **PLUS** of the summations. Or, in everyday mathematics,

$$\sum_{i=0}^{n} g(i) + h(i) = \sum_{i=0}^{n} g(i) + \sum_{i=0}^{n} h(i);$$

If we had higher order variables g and h we could write

---

[13]The use of **'(TRUE)** in the abbreviated term is actually incorrect. The term abbreviated contains the expression **'(QUOTE *1*TRUE)** instead of **'(TRUE)**. These two have the same value under **EVAL$**. See page 118.

```
(for I in L sum (PLUS g(I)  h(I)))
   =
(PLUS (for I in L sum g(I))
      (for I in L sum h(I))).
```

However, in our logic we don't have such variables, but we don't need them here. It is sufficient simply to use the unabbreviated form of **FOR** and use ordinary variable symbols **G** and **H** to describe (the quotation of) an arbitrary **PLUS** expression:

Theorem.
```
(EQUAL (FOR V L COND 'SUM (LIST 'PLUS G H) ALIST)
       (PLUS (FOR V L COND 'SUM G ALIST)
             (FOR V L COND 'SUM H ALIST))).
```

Again, note that this theorem can be instantiated so as to let us distribute the summation over the two branches of the body below:

```
(for I in L sum (PLUS I (SQ I)))
```

The important thing to consider is that the body of the above **for** is actually `'(PLUS I (SQ I))` or, put another way, `(LIST 'PLUS 'I '(SQ I))`.

In stating some classic quantifier manipulation theorems it is necessary to put elaborate syntactic constraints on the form of the body expression. Here is a simple example:

Problem. Formalize the theorem that the summation of an expression not involving the bound variable is a constant. In particular, we would like the formal version of the theorem that permits us to reduce $\sum_{i \in s} n$ to simply |s|*n.

To do this we must define the notion that the body does not "involve" the bound variable. Suppose we have defined **(FREE-VARS T X)** to be the variables in the (quotation of a) term **X**. Then the first cut at a formalization of the goal is

```
(IMPLIES (NOT (MEMBER V (FREE-VARS T N)))
         (EQUAL (FOR V S '(TRUE) 'SUM N ALIST)
                (TIMES (LENGTH S) N)))
```

However, this is incorrect because what is being summed by the **FOR** is the **EVAL$** of N under successive extensions to **ALIST** produced by binding **V**. Thus, instead of **N** in **(TIMES (LENGTH S) N)** we should write **(EVAL$ T N ALIST)**. An accurate statement of the rule is then

Theorem.
```
(IMPLIES (NOT (MEMBER V (FREE-VARS T N)))
```

```
(EQUAL (FOR V S ' (TRUE) 'SUM N ALIST)
       (TIMES (LENGTH S)
              (EVAL$ T N ALIST))))
```

Note that this theorem can be used to simplify a concrete **FOR** provided the conditional expression in the **FOR** is ' **(TRUE)** and the bound variable does not occur in the body. The restriction on the conditional expression can be relaxed by replacing **LENGTH** with the quantifier statement that counts the number of times the conditional is true in **S**.

We conclude our discussion of **FOR** by exhibiting the formalization of the concept of **FREE-VARS**. This is particularly appropriate because it forces us to consider the form of the quotations of terms, a topic with which the user must be familiar if accurate schematic theorems are to be written.

The definition of **FREE-VARS** recursively explores terms in the same way that **EVAL$** does. When **X** is treated as a term there are four cases: **X** is a variable symbol (i.e., **(LITATOM X)**), **X** is a **QUOTE**d constant, (i.e., **(LISTP X)** and the **CAR** of **X** is ' **QUOTE**), **X** is a function application (i.e., **(LISTP X)** but the **CAR** is not ' **QUOTE**), and **X** is of any other form (e.g., a **NUMBERP**). In the case that **X** is a function application we must recursively collect the variables in all of the arguments, and so we are dealing with another case of mutual recursion. Here is a suitable definition:

Definition .
```
(FREE-VARS FLG X)
   =
(IF (EQUAL FLG 'LIST)
    (IF (NLISTP X)
        NIL
        (UNION (FREE-VARS T (CAR X))
               (FREE-VARS 'LIST (CDR X))))

(IF (LITATOM X)
    (LIST X)
(IF (NLISTP X)
    NIL
(IF (EQUAL (CAR X) 'QUOTE)
    NIL
    (FREE-VARS 'LIST (CDR X))))))))
```

Perhaps the most interesting thing about this definition is that it is not necessary for **FREE-VARS** to "know about" **FOR**. The reason is that **FOR** is just like every other function in our logic. It does not really introduce a "bound" variable or have terms as its arguments. Is **I** among the free variables of **(for I in L sum (PLUS I X))**? That is to say, is ' **I** a member of the list

returned by **FREE-VARS** on the quotation of the **for** term? The answer is no.
The formal term abbreviated by **(for I in L sum (PLUS I X))** is
**(FOR 'I L '(TRUE) 'SUM '(PLUS I X) (LIST (CONS 'X
X)))**. The quotation of this term is **'(FOR 'I L '(TRUE) 'SUM
'(PLUS I X) (LIST (CONS 'X X)))**. The result of **FREE-VARS** on
this is **'(L X)**.

In [11] we show many schematic theorems about **FOR**. In the **"quant"**
section of the example file **basic.events** we show the events leading to the
proofs of those theorems. The reader interested in using **FOR** is urged to look at
those events.

3.5. Nondeterminism

Problem. Define a nondeterministic merge function which merges two input
streams (finite lists) into a single output stream.

Below is an alleged definition of the concept

Definition .
```
(MERGE A B)
   =
(IF (NLISTP A)
    B
(IF (NLISTP B)
    A
(IF (RANDOM-BOOL)
    (CONS (CAR A)
          (MERGE (CDR A) B))
    (CONS (CAR B)
          (MERGE A (CDR B)))))))
```
where **RANDOM-BOOL** is an undefined function.

The trouble with this definition is that **(RANDOM-BOOL)** is a constant. It is
either **F** or non-**F**. Indeed,

Theorem .
```
(IMPLIES (AND (LISTP A)
              (LISTP B))
         (OR (EQUAL (MERGE A B) (APPEND A B))
             (EQUAL (MERGE A B) (APPEND B A)))) .
```

Is this a property of a nondeterministic merge function? Probably not.

A typical patch is to make **RANDOM-BOOL** a function of **A** and **B**. Thus, at
each stage in the recursion, an element of **A** or an element of **B** is chosen as an

undefined function of the current values of **A** and **B**. This function can produce more varied output than the previous one, depending on the properties of **RANDOM-BOOL**. But the mere fact that the element chosen at each stage is a function of the current inputs permits some deductions about the function's behavior. For example, there is no definition of **RANDOM-BOOL** that makes **(MERGE ' (A) ' (B)) =' (A B)** and **(MERGE ' (C A) ' (B)) =' (C B A)**, even though both desired outputs are legal merges of the inputs. The reason is that once **(MERGE ' (C A) ' (B))** chooses to output **C** and recurses to **(MERGE ' (A) ' (B))**, the recursive call must yield **' (A B)**.

Clearly, **MERGE** can be patched again so that more ''state'' is given to **RANDOM-BOOL** to prevent this too. Indeed, the following definition of **MERGE** has the desired property:

Definition.
```
(MERGE A B)
  =
(MERGE1 A B (ORACLE A B))
```

where

Definition.
```
(MERGE1 A B ORACLE)
  =
(IF (NLISTP A)
    B
(IF (NLISTP B)
    A
(IF (CAR ORACLE)
    (CONS (CAR A)
          (MERGE (CDR A) B (CDR ORACLE)))
    (CONS (CAR B)
          (MERGE A (CDR B) (CDR ORACLE))))))))
```

and **ORACLE** is an undefined function.

The basic idea is to provide the nondeterminacy by providing an additional input, the variable **ORACLE** in **MERGE1**, that is entirely responsible for the ''nondeterministic choices'' and to leave the value of that input unconstrained.

It is the case that for any set of triples <**a**, **b**, **x**> with the property that **x** is an interleaving of **a** and **b**, there exists a definition of the function **ORACLE** sufficient to make **(MERGE a b)** = **x** for every triple in the set. This can be proved within the logic for all finite sets of triples. (Quick! How do you capture the notion ''there exists a definition of **ORACLE**?'')

For a more elaborate example of the use of oracles, see the hardware verification work of [20]. There, it is necessary to model the response of memory to read/write requests. Oracles are used to permit arbitrary delays.

Perhaps the biggest philosophical obstacle in the attempt to define **MERGE** as a function is that it must be a function. In particular, **(MERGE A B)** is always equal to **(MERGE A B)**.[14] A related remark can be made that some people may find reassuring: **(MERGE1 A B ORACLE1)** need not be the same as **(MERGE1 A B ORACLE2)**. Despite the obviousness of these observations we have seen informed users of the logic fail to make similar ones.

For example, suppose you are writing an interpreter within the logic for a programming language like Lisp (see the next section). Suppose your interpreter has the notion of an "environment" by which some program variables are assigned values. Let **(LOOKUP SYM ENV)** be the expression you use to denote the value of the program variable **SYM** in the environment. How do you define **LOOKUP** to cope with the possibility that a program variable is "unbound," i.e., not assigned a value in the environment? One possibility is to declare an undefined function symbol, **UNDEF**, and to return **(UNDEF)** as the value of such a **LOOKUP**. That captures some of the desired features: it will be impossible to prove much about the type or value of unbound variables. But one consequence of this approach is that all unbound program variables are thus specified to have the same (otherwise undetermined) value. That is, **(UNDEF)** equals **(UNDEF)**.

There are three conventional ways out: (a) change the problem so that non-deterministic behavior is eliminated, e.g., in the programming language example, adopt the specification that all variables have the initial value **0**; (b) model the nondeterminism in a trivial, deterministic way but avoid asking questions that depend upon your trivial convention, e.g., define the notion of a well-formed program (in which unbound variables never arise) and include among the hypotheses of all your theorems the constraint that the programs are well-formed; or (c) model the nondeterminism carefully and accurately, e.g., include an oracle in the environment.

3.6. Embedded Formal Systems

An increasingly common use of our system is in the definition of what we will call "interpreters" for other systems. We give six brief examples ranging from an interpreter for a simple physical system, through more obviously formal systems such as the Tower of Hanoi problem, hardware design, and programming languages, to purely formal systems such as lambda-calculus and set theory.

---

[14]Isn't that a silly thing to have to say?

3.6.1. Real Time Control

The simple real time control problem discussed in [14] is to show that a certain control program keeps a vehicle on a straight-line course in a varying crosswind. We formalized the problem with an interpreter that is essentially a simulator for (a drastic simplification of) the physical system. The interpreter takes two arguments. The first is the "state" of the vehicle and the world—the vehicle position and velocity and the wind velocity. The second is a "wind history"—a list of wind velocity increments describing how the wind changes at discrete time units over some finite time interval. The interpreter determines the final state of the vehicle by "simulating" each state change, that is, by calculating for each sampling unit the new wind velocity, the resulting position of the vehicle, the associated sensor reading, the response of the control program, and the effect on the vehicle's velocity. Two theorems are proved about the simulated vehicle: the vehicle does not wander outside of a certain corridor if the wind changes "smoothly," and the vehicle homes to the proper course if the wind stays steady for a certain amount of time. For the events necessary to lead the theorem prover to these proofs, see the **"controller"** section of the example file **basic.events**.

3.6.2. Towers of Hanoi

The Towers of Hanoi is a child's puzzle with which you are probably familiar. It is played on a board with three pegs and a stack of disks each of which has a peg-sized hole in the center and a diameter different that of all other disks. Initially the disks are arranged in a stack on a single peg so that no disk sits atop one that is smaller. The object of the game is to move the disks one at a time so as to reassemble the initial stack on one of the two initially empty pegs without ever placing a disk atop one that is smaller. Writing a computer program to "solve" this problem is a typical exercise in programming language courses when introducing recursion. We wished to write a function that solves the problem, and we wished to prove that it is correct.

In our formalization, the function called **HANOI** takes as input three pegs, **A**, **B**, and **C**, and a number **n** and generates a list of "moves" that supposedly is sufficient to move a tower of **n** disks from peg **A** to peg **C** using peg **B** for temporary storage. A "move" is just a pair <**i**, **j**> whose interpretation is that the top disk on peg **i** is to be moved to peg **j**. To state the correctness of **HANOI** we defined an "interpreter" for a list of moves. The interpreter takes as arguments a "state" and a "move list" and returns either the final state or **F** indicating that an illegal move was attempted. A state is simply a triple of lists, each list representing the configuration of a given peg by showing the diameters of the disks on that peg. The interpreter is defined to carry out each move on the state successively, checking each time that the designated source peg is non-empty and that its top disk is smaller than the top disk, if any, on the designated destination peg. The theorem proved was that if the initial state was as expected—i.e., there is a well-formed tower on peg **A** and the other pegs are empty—then the final state, after playing out the moves delivered by **(HANOI A B C N)**, is non-**F** and configured as desired—i.e., the tower is on peg **C** and the other pegs are empty.[15] The assurance that **HANOI** never put a disk on top of a smaller one is not stated explicitly in the theorem but rather follows from the definition of the interpreter.

3.6.3. Hardware Verification

Combinational logic can be modeled by propositional expressions. That is, **(AND S1 S2)** can be thought of as a circuit that takes two input bits, **S1** and **S2**, and delivers their logical **AND**. However, consider modeling a device, such as a cpu, that contains state-holding components that are changed over time by combinational logic. Such a model of a microcoded cpu is presented in [20]. Essentially a register-transfer model is used, except the model is formalized as a recursively defined function. All but one of the arguments of the function represent state-holding components in the device, such as the registers of the processor, the microaddress register, the memory, etc. One argument is an oracle that represents the values found on various input lines at each clock cycle over some time interval, as well as "nondeterministic" parameters determining memory response time. The definition of the function is such that if the oracle is exhausted, the entire state is returned. Otherwise, the function recurses, using combinational logic expressions (and, where appropriate, input from the oracle) to determine the new value of every state holding component. The theorem proved about this machine is that, under a certain abstraction, it is equivalent to a machine-code interpreter.

---

[15]Actually, the statement of the theorem is rather delicate because one must know that **A**, **B**, and **C** are distinct peg numbers. The proof was carried out by Matt Kaufmann of the Institute for Computing Science, University of Texas.

3.6.4. Programming Languages

We have expressed the semantics of a variety of programming languages in the logic by the definition of interpreters for them. For example, in [10] we define Pure Lisp and prove the unsolvability of its halting problem (see also the **"unsolv"** section of the example file **basic.events**). In [13] we define Turing Machines and prove the Turing completeness of Pure Lisp (see also the **"tmi"** section of **basic.events**). In the **"proveall"** section of **basic.events** we define an interpreter for a simple assembly language and verify the correctness of a program that sums the naturals from **1** to **N** (see the event named **CORRECTNESS-OF-INTERPRETED-SIGMA**). In [11] we show how theorems about partial functions can be proved with **V&C$** (see also the **"quant"** section of **basic.events**).

The basic idea in all of these interpreters is that we define a function in the logic that takes a ''program'' and a ''state'' and returns a state after executing the program. States may be as simple as the list of current variable bindings or as complicated as a microprocessor state with registers, flags, program status words, memory, etc.

In all of these examples except those involving **V&C$** each interpreter contains a ''clock''—an argument that is decremented when the interpreter definition recurses for the sole purpose of making the definition admissible. There is no doubt that the presence of a clock complicates the *statement* of theorems about an interpreted language, but it is not at all clear that the clock complicates the *proof* of such statements. In particular, to say that eventually some state will be reached or that the final state is so-and-so, does not *a priori* require the expression of exactly when it will happen. But the proof of such a statement often involves induction on the length of the computation, and it is necessary to be quite precise about that in order to get the induction to go through. Despite the provision of **V&C$** in the system, we recommend the use of clocked interpreters for many simple formalization problems.

It should be noted that the logic can be used to address program correctness problems without necessarily formalizing the language semantics in the logic. For example, in [6] we present a verification condition generator (vcg) for a subset of ANSI Fortran 66 and 77. A verification condition generator is a program that takes two inputs, a program and a specification, and generates formulas, called ''verification conditions,'' that, if theorems, establish that the program satisfies its specification. The language semantics are embedded in the vcg program, and the logic is used simply to express specifications and the verification conditions. We present a vcg for a much simpler language in [4].

3.6.5. *Lambda Calculus*

The Church-Rosser theorem for lambda calculus says that if a lambda-expression x can be reduced to two expressions y and z then there is a w such that both y and z reduce to w. Briefly, the formalization of the lambda calculus used in [31] proceeds along the following lines. Represent lambda-expressions as list or shell constants, e.g., ' **(LAMBDA (X) (X X))** is such a constant. Define what is meant by α- and β-*steps* by defining predicates that determine whether one lambda-expression is obtained from another by the appropriate transformation. Define the concept that one lambda-expression *reduces* to another via a given finite sequence of lambda-expressions, each obtained from the previous by an α- or β-step. The theorem is then: if **X**, **Y**, and **Z** are lambda-expressions and **X** reduces to **Y** via the sequence **S1** and **X** reduces to **Z** via the sequence **S2** then there exist a lambda-expression **W** and sequences **S3** and **S4** such that **Y** reduces to **W** via **S3**, and **Z** reduces to **W** via **S4**. The existential quantifiers are then eliminated by defining functions for constructing the alleged **W**, **S3**, and **S4**. For the complete details see the **"church-rosser"** section of **basic.events**.

Once again we see a trade-off between difficulty of statement and difficulty of proof: key steps in the proof, namely, the construction of **W**, **S3**, and **S4**, are taken during the formalization of the problem.

3.6.6. *Gödel's Incompleteness Theorem*

To state Gödel's incompleteness theorem it was necessary to formalize within our logic another logic. The object logic was Shoenfield's first order logic with Cohen's axioms for hereditarily finite set theory, Z2. The formalization was done by representing *formulas* in the object logic by list- and shell-constants and then defining within our logic a proof checker for the object logic. That is, the function defined the concept that **P** is a *proof* of **X**. The theorem was then formalized by saying that there exists a closed formula, **X**, of the object logic such that if **P1** is a proof of **X** or **P2** is a proof of its negation, then there exist proofs **P3** and **P4** of both **X** and its negation. The existential quantifiers are again removed by defining the appropriate functions. The details are given in [32] and in the example file **goedel.events**.

4   A Precise Description of the Logic

4.1. Apologia

Traditionally, logicians keep their formal systems as simple as possible. This is desirable because logicians rarely use the formal systems themselves. Instead, they stay in the metatheory and (informally) prove results about their systems.

The system described here is intended to be used to prove interesting theorems. To state interesting theorems it must be possible to add axioms that define interesting objects and concepts. Logically speaking, the main theorem and all the intermediate lemmas are proved in the single final theory. But practically speaking, the theory "evolves" over time as the user repeatedly extends it with new axioms and derives intermediate results.

Practical considerations are apparent throughout the theory presented here. The set of variable and function symbols is influenced by conventions of half a dozen different Lisp systems. The set of axioms is unnecessarily large from the purely logical viewpoint. For example, it includes axioms for both the natural numbers and ordered pairs. A general purpose quantifier over finite domains is provided, even though recursively defined functions suffice. An interpreter for the logic is embedded in the logic, and every "new" function symbol must be axiomatically tied to the interpreter. Our metalanguage is greatly complicated by the necessity of describing the correspondence between terms and objects.

Nowhere is concern for pragmatics more apparent than in the rules of inference. The statement of the induction principle is quite complicated, but it generates simple proofs. In addition, among the rules of inference are two "extension" principles—the "shell principle" for introducing new data types and the "definitional principle" for introducing new functions.

But while the logic is complicated compared to most mathematical logics, it is simple compared to most programming languages and many specification languages. If our presentation of it makes it seem "too complicated" it is perhaps merely that we are presenting all of the details.

4.2. Outline of the Presentation

In presenting our logic we follow the well-established tradition of incremental extension. We begin by defining a very simple syntax, called the *formal syntax*, of the language. A much richer syntax, called the *extended syntax*, which contains succinct abbreviations for constants such as numbers, lists, and trees, is defined only after we have axiomatized the primitive data types of the logic.

Using the formal syntax we present the axioms and rules of inference for propositional calculus with equality, the foundation of our theory. Next we embed propositional calculus and equality in the term structure of the logic by defining functional analogues of the propositional operators. We then present the shell principle and use it to add the axioms for natural numbers, ordered pairs, literal atoms, and negative integers.

At this point we have enough formal machinery to explain and illustrate the extended formal syntax.

We then present our formalization of the ordinals up to ε_0. The "less-than" relation on these ordinals plays a crucial role in our principles of mathematical induction and recursive definition.

Next we add axioms defining many useful functions.

Then we embed the semantics of the theory in the theory by axiomatizing an interpreter for the logic as a function. In order to do this it is necessary to set up a correspondence between the terms in the formal syntax and certain constants in the logic, called the "quotations" of those terms. Roughly speaking, the quotation of a term is a constant in the logic whose value under the interpreter is equal to the term.

We complete the set of axioms by defining our general purpose quantifier function, which, much like the "mapping" functions of Lisp, includes among its arguments objects denoting terms which are evaluated with the interpreter.

Finally, we state the principles of inductive proof and recursive definition.

We frequently pause during the presentation to illustrate the concepts discussed. However, we do not attempt to motivate the development or explain "how" certain functions "work" or the role they play in the subsequent development. We assume that the reader interested in such asides will have first read the primer, Chapter 2. Familiarity with the primer is completely unnecessary to follow the precise development of the theory.

We classify our remarks into seven categories:

- **Terminology**: In paragraphs with this label we define syntactic notions that let us state our axioms or syntactic conventions precisely. The concept defined is *italicized*.

- **Abbreviation**: In paragraphs with this label we extend the previously agreed upon syntax by explaining how some string of characters is, henceforth, to be taken as shorthand for another.

- **Example**: We illustrate most of the terminology and abbreviations in paragraphs with this label. Technically, these paragraphs contain no new information, but they serve as a way for the reader to check his understanding.

- **Axiom** or **Defining Axiom**: A formula so labelled is an axiom of our system. Axioms of the latter sort are distinguished because they uniquely define a function. We have numbered every axiom uniquely.

- **Shell Definition**: A paragraph so labelled schematically specifies a set of axioms of our system.

- **Rule of Inference**: A paragraph so labelled describes a rule of inference of our system.

- **Note**: Assorted remarks, such as alternative views, are collected in paragraphs with this label.

4.3. Formal Syntax

Terminology. A sequence of characters, s, is a *symbol* if and only if s is nonempty, each character in s is a member of the set

```
{A  B  C  D  E  F  G  H  I  J  K  L  M
 N  O  P  Q  R  S  T  U  V  W  X  Y  Z
 0  1  2  3  4  5  6  7  8  9
 $  ^  &  *  _  -  +  =  ~  {  }  ?  <  >},
```

and the first character of s is a letter, i.e., in the set

```
{A  B  C  D  E  F  G  H  I  J  K  L  M
 N  O  P  Q  R  S  T  U  V  W  X  Y  Z}.
```

Examples. **PLUS**, **ADD1**, and **PRIME-FACTORS** are symbols. ***1*TRUE**,

123, **A/B** and **#.FOO** are not symbols.

Terminology. The *variable symbols* and *function symbols* of our language are the symbols other than **T**, **F**, and **NIL**.

Terminology. Associated with every function symbol is a nonnegative integer called the *arity* of the symbol. The arity indicates how many argument terms must follow each application of the function symbol. The arity of each function symbol in the Ground Zero logic is given in the table below. We also include brief descriptive comments in the hopes that they will make subsequent examples more meaningful.

Table 4.1

symbol	arity	comment
ADD1	1	successor function for natural numbers
ADD-TO-SET	2	adds an element to a list if not present
AND	2	logical and
APPEND	2	list concatenation
APPLY-SUBR	2	application of primitive fn to arguments
APPLY$	2	application of fn to arguments
ASSOC	2	association list lookup
BODY	1	body of a fn definition
CAR	1	first component of ordered pair
CDR	1	second component of ordered pair
CONS	2	constructs ordered pairs
COUNT	1	size of an object
DIFFERENCE	2	natural difference of two natural numbers
EQUAL	2	equality predicate
EVAL$	3	interpreter for the logic
FALSE	0	false object
FALSEP	1	predicate for recognizing **FALSE**
FIX	1	coerces argument to **0** if not numeric
FIX-COST	2	increments cost if argument is non-**F**
FOR	6	general purpose quantifier
FORMALS	1	list of formal arguments of a function
GEQ	2	greater than or equal on natural numbers
GREATERP	2	greater than on natural numbers
IF	3	if-then-else
IFF	2	if and only if
IMPLIES	2	logical implication
LEQ	2	less than or equal on natural numbers
LESSP	2	less than on natural numbers

`LISTP`	1	recognizes ordered pairs
`LITATOM`	1	recognizes literal atoms
`MAX`	2	maximum of two natural numbers
`MEMBER`	2	membership predicate
`MINUS`	1	constructs negative of a natural number
`NEGATIVEP`	1	recognizes negatives
`NEGATIVE-GUTS`	1	absolute value of a negative
`NLISTP`	1	negation of **LISTP**
`NOT`	1	logical negation
`NUMBERP`	1	recognizes natural numbers
`OR`	2	logical or
`ORDINALP`	1	recognizes ordinals
`ORD-LESSP`	2	less than on ordinals up to ε_0
`PACK`	1	constructs a **LITATOM** from ASCII codes
`PAIRLIST`	2	pairs corresponding elements
`PLUS`	2	sum of two natural numbers
`QUANTIFIER-INITIAL-VALUE`		
	1	initial value of a quantifier
`QUANTIFIER-OPERATION`		
	3	operation performed by quantifier
`QUOTIENT`	2	natural quotient of two natural numbers
`REMAINDER`	2	mod
`STRIP-CARS`	1	list of **CAR**s of argument list
`SUB1`	1	predecessor function on natural numbers
`SUBRP`	1	recognizes primitive function symbols
`SUM-CDRS`	1	sum of **CDR**s of elements of argument list
`TIMES`	2	product of two natural numbers
`TRUE`	0	true object
`TRUEP`	1	recognizes **TRUE**
`UNION`	2	union of two lists
`UNPACK`	1	explodes a **LITATOM** into ASCII codes
`V&C$`	3	determines value and cost of an expr
`V&C-APPLY$`	2	determines value and cost of fn application
`ZERO`	0	0
`ZEROP`	1	recognizes 0 and nonnatural numbers

The arity of each user-introduced function symbol is declared when the symbol is first used as a function symbol.

Terminology. A *term* is either a variable symbol or else is a sequence consisting of a function symbol of arity n followed by n terms.

Note. Observe that we have defined a term as a tree structure rather than a character sequence. Of interest is how we display such trees.

Terminology. To *display* a symbol, we merely write down the characters in it, with "white space" on each side. By *white space* we mean an arbitrary, possibly empty, string of spaces, tabs, carriage returns, and "comments." By *comment* we mean any string of characters beginning with a semicolon and ending with a carriage return and not containing any other carriage returns. To *display* a term that is a variable symbol, we display the symbol. To *display* a non-variable term with function symbol **fn** and arguments terms t_1, ..., t_n, we write down an open parenthesis, a display of **fn**, nonempty white space, a display of t_1, nonempty white space, ..., a display of t_n, white space, and a close parenthesis.

Examples. The following are (displays of) terms:

```
(ZERO)

(ADD1 X)

(PLUS (ADD1 X) (ZERO))

(IF B
    (ZERO)
    (ADD1 X))

    (IF B                (ZERO)   ;This term is identical to
                         (ADD1    ;the term above but is
X))                               ;displayed differently.
```

Terminology. Our axioms are presented as formulas in propositional calculus with equality. The formulas are constructed from terms, as defined above, using the equality symbol and the symbols for "or" and "not". More precisely, an *atomic formula* is any string of the form **t1=t2**, where **t1** and **t2** are terms. A *formula* is either an atomic formula, or else of the form **(¬form1)**, where **form1** is a formula, or else of the form **(form1 ∨ form2)**, where **form1** and **form2** are both formulas. Parentheses are omitted when no ambiguity arises.

Abbreviations. We abbreviate **(¬ t1 = t2)** by **(t1≠t2)**. If **form1** and **form2** are formulas then **(form1 → form2)** is an abbreviation for **((¬form1) ∨ form2)** and **(form1 ∧ form2)** is an abbreviation for **(¬((¬form1) ∨ (¬form2)))**.

4.3.1. Terminology about Terms

Terminology. To talk about terms, it is convenient to use so-called "metavariables" that are understood by the reader to stand for certain variables, function symbols, or terms. In this book we use lower case words to denote metavariables.

Example. If **f** denotes the function symbol **PLUS**, and **t** denotes the term **(ADD1 Y)**, then **(f t X)** denotes the term **(PLUS (ADD1 Y) X)**.

Terminology. If **i** is a nonnegative integer, then we let **Xi** denote the variable symbol whose first character is **X** and whose other characters are the decimal representation of **i**.

Example. If **i** is **4**, **Xi** is the variable symbol **X4**.

Terminology. A term **t** is a *call* of **fn** with *arguments* a_1, ..., a_n iff **t** has the form **(fn** a_1 **...** a_n**)**.

Terminology. If a term **t** is a call of **fn** we say **fn** is the *top function symbol* of **t**. A function symbol **fn** *is called in* a term **t** iff either **t** is a call of **fn** or **t** is a nonvariable term and **fn** is called in an argument of **t**. The set of *subterms* of a term **t** is {**t**} if **t** is a variable symbol and otherwise is the union of {**t**} together with the union of the subterms of the arguments of **t**. The *variables* of a term **t** is the set of variable subterms of **t**.

Examples. The term **(PLUS X Y)** is a call of **PLUS** with arguments **X** and **Y**. **PLUS** is called in **(IF A (PLUS X Y) B)**. The set of subterms of **(PLUS X Y)** is { **(PLUS X Y) X Y**}. The set of variables of **(PLUS X Y)** is {**X Y**}.

4.3.2. Terminology about Theories

Notes. Theories evolve over time by the repeated application of extension principles. For example, to construct our logic we start with propositional calculus with equality and extend it by adding the axioms for the natural numbers. Then we extend it again to get ordered pairs and again to get symbols... We eventually start adding axioms defining functions such as Peano sum, product, etc. When we stop, the user of the theorem prover starts by invoking the extension principles to add his own data types and concepts.

Each extension principle preserves the consistency of the original logic, provided certain "admissibility" requirements are met. In order to describe these requirements it is necessary that we be able to talk clearly about the sequence of steps used to create the "current" extension.

Terminology. Formula **t** *can be proved directly from* a set of axioms A if and only if **t** may be derived from the axioms in A by applying the rules of inference of propositional calculus with equality and instantiation (see page 101) and the principle of induction (see page 139).

Terminology. There are three kinds of *axiomatic acts*: (a) an application of the shell principle (page 105), (b) an application of the principle of definition (page 140), and (c) the addition of an arbitrary formula as an axiom.

Terminology. Each such act *adds* a set of axioms. The axioms added by an application of the first two acts are described in the relevant subsections. The axioms added by the addition of an arbitrary formula is the singleton set consisting of the formula.

Terminology. A *history* h is a finite sequence of axiomatic acts such that either (a) h is empty or (b) h is obtained by concatenating to the end of a history h′ an axiomatic act that is "admissible" under h′. An arbitrary axiom is admissible under any h′. The specification of the shell and definitional principles define "admissibility" in those instances.

Terminology. The *axioms* of a history h is the union of the axioms added by each act in h.

Terminology. A function symbol **fn** is *new* in a history h iff **fn** is called in no axiom of h, **fn** is not a **CAR/CDR** symbol (see below), and **fn** is not in the set {**QUOTE, LIST, T, F, NIL**}.

Terminology. We say a symbol **fn** is a *CAR/CDR symbol* if there are at least three characters in **fn**, the first character in **fn** is **C**, the last character is **R**, and each other character is either an **A** or a **D**.

Examples. The symbol **CADDR** is a **CAR/CDR** symbol. We will eventually introduce an abbreviation that "defines" such symbols to stand for nests of **CAR**s and **CDR**s. Because **CADDR** is a **CAR/CDR** symbol it is not new. The definitional principle requires that the function symbol defined be "new." Hence, it is impossible to define **CADDR**. Similarly, it is impossible to define five other perfectly acceptable symbols: **QUOTE, LIST, T, F**, and **NIL**. All of these prohibited symbols will be involved in our abbreviation conventions.

4.4. Embedded Propositional Calculus and Equality

Notes. Our logic is a quantifier-free first order extension of propositional calculus with equality, obtained by adding axioms and rules of inference. Any classical formalization of propositional calculus and equality will suit our purposes. So that this book is self-contained we have included as the first subsection below, one such formalization, namely that of Shoenfield [33].

We then add axioms to define the functional analogues of the propositional operators and the equality relation. This effectively embeds propositional calculus and equality into the term structure of the logic. That is, we can write down and reason about terms that contain propositional connectives, equality, and case analysis. For example, we can write

```
(IF (EQUAL N 0)
    1
    (TIMES N (FACT (SUB1 N))))
```

which is a term equal to **1** if **N** is **0** and equal to **(TIMES N (FACT (SUB1 N)))** otherwise. The ability to write such terms is very convenient later when we begin defining recursive functions.

4.4.1. Propositional Calculus with Equality

Shoenfield's system consists of one axiom schema and four inference rules. A *propositional axiom* is any formula of the form

Axiom Schema.
((¬ a) ∨ a).

The four rules of inference are

Rules of Inference.

Expansion: derive (**a** ∨ **b**) from **b**;

Contraction: derive **a** from (**a** ∨ **a**);

Associativity: derive ((**a** ∨ **b**) ∨ **c**) from (**a** ∨ (**b** ∨ **c**)); and

Cut: derive (**b** ∨ **c**) from (**a** ∨ **b**) and ((¬**a**) ∨ **c**).

To formalize equality we also use Shoenfield's approach, which involves three axiom schemas. A *Reflexivity Axiom* is any formula of the form

Axiom Schema
`(a = a).`

For every function symbol **fn** of arity **n** we add an "equality axiom"

Axiom.
```
((X1=Y1)  →
   (...          →
      ((Xn=Yn)  →

      (fn X1 ... Xn) = (fn Y1 ... Yn))...))
```

Finally, we add

Axiom.
```
((X1=Y1)  →  ((X2=Y2)  →  ((X1=X2)  →  (Y1=Y2)))).
```

This axiom is the only instance we need of Shoenfield's "equality axiom (schema) for predicates."

Note. Finally, we add the rule of inference that any instance of a theorem is a theorem. To make this precise we first define substitution.

Terminology. A finite set s of ordered pairs is said to be a *substitution* provided that for each ordered pair <**v**, **t**> in s, **v** is a variable, **t** is a term, and no other member of s has **v** as its first component. The *result of substituting* a substitution s *into* a term or formula **x** (denoted **x**/s) is the term or formula obtained by simultaneously replacing, for each <**v**, **t**> in s, each occurrence of **v** as a variable in **x** with **t**. We sometimes say **x**/s is the *result of instantiating* **x** with s. We say that **x′** is an *instance* of **x** if there is a substitution s such that **x′** is **x**/s.

Example. If s is {<**X**, (**ADD1 Y**)> <**Y**, **Z**> <**G**, **FOO**>} then s is a substitution. If **p** is the term

```
(PLUS     X     (G Y     X))
```

then **p**/s is the term

```
(PLUS (ADD1 Y) (G Z (ADD1 Y))).
```

Note that even though the substitution contains the pair <**G**, **FOO**> the occurrence of **G** in **p** was not replaced by **FOO** since **G** does not occur as a variable in **p**.

Rule of Inference. *Instantiation*:
Derive **a**/s from **a**.

Note. Without further ado we will take advantage of the traditional results of propositional calculus and equality reasoning. We will use such derived rules of inference as

- **Modus Ponens**: derive **q** from **p** and **p**→**q**.

- **The Tautology Theorem**: any propositional tautology is a theorem.

- **The Deduction Law**: derive **p**→**q** from a proof of **q** in which **p** is assumed as given but neither that assumption nor any formula derived from it is instantiated.

- **Case Analysis**: if **p** can be proved under each of a set of exhaustive cases, **p** is a theorem.

- **Substitution of Equals for Equals**: If **t**=**s** has been proved and the formula **q** is obtained from the formula **p** by replacing some occurrences of **t** by **s**, then **q** is provable iff **p** is provable.

4.4.2. The Axioms for TRUE, FALSE, IF, and EQUAL

Abbreviation. We will abbreviate the term **(TRUE)** with the symbol **T** and the term **(FALSE)** with the symbol **F**.

Axiom 1.
T ≠ **F**

Axiom 2.
X = **Y** → **(EQUAL X Y)** = **T**

Axiom 3.
X ≠ **Y** → **(EQUAL X Y)** = **F**

Axiom 4.
X = **F** → **(IF X Y Z)** = **Z**

Axiom 5.
X ≠ **F** → **(IF X Y Z)** = **Y**.

4.4.3. The Propositional Functions

Defining Axiom 6.
`(TRUEP X) = (EQUAL X T)`

Defining Axiom 7.
`(FALSEP X) = (EQUAL X F)`

Defining Axiom 8.
`(NOT P)`
`=`
`(IF P F T)`

Defining Axiom 9.
`(AND P Q)`
`=`
`(IF P (IF Q T F) F)`

Defining Axiom 10.
`(OR P Q)`
`=`
`(IF P T (IF Q T F))`

Defining Axiom 11.
`(IMPLIES P Q)`
`=`
`(IF P (IF Q T F) T)`

Abbreviation. When we refer to a term **t** as a formula, one should read in place of **t** the formula $t \neq F$.

Example. The term

`(IMPLIES (AND (P X) (Q Y)) (R X Y)),`

if used where a formula is expected (e.g., in the allegation that it is a theorem), is to be read as

`(IMPLIES (AND (P X) (Q Y)) (R X Y))` $\neq$ **F**.

Given the foregoing axioms and the rules of inference of propositional calculus and equality, the above formula can be shown equivalent to

$$((P\ X) \neq F \ \wedge \ (Q\ Y) \neq F) \quad \rightarrow \quad (R\ X\ Y) \neq F$$

which we could abbreviate

$$((P \ X) \ \wedge \ (Q \ Y)) \quad \rightarrow \quad (R \ X \ Y).$$

Note. The definitional principle, to be discussed later, permits the user of the logic to add new defining axioms under admissibility requirements that insure the unique satisfiability of the defining equation. The reader may wonder why we did not invoke the definitional principle to add the defining axioms above—explicitly eliminating the risk that they render the system inconsistent. In fact, we completely avoid use of the definitional principle in this presentation of the logic. There are two reasons. First, the definitional principle also adds an axiom (the non-**SUBRP** axiom) that connects the defined symbol to the interpreter for the logic—an axiom we do not wish to have for the primitives. Second, the admissibility requirements of the definitional principle are not always met in the development of the logic.

4.5. The Shell Principle and the Primitive Data Types

Note. The shell principle permits the extension of the logic by the addition of a set of axioms that define a new data type. Under the conditions of admissibility described, the axioms added are guaranteed to preserve the consistency of the logic. The axioms are obtained by instantiating a set of axiom schemas described here. In order to describe the axiom schemas it is first necessary to establish several elaborate notational conventions. We then define the shell principle precisely. Then we invoke the shell principle to obtain the axioms for the natural numbers, the ordered pairs, the literal atoms, and the negative integers.

4.5.1. Conventions

Terminology. We say **t** is the **fn** *nest around* **b** *for* **s** iff **t** and **b** are terms, **fn** is a function symbol of arity 2, **s** is a finite sequence of terms, and either (a) **s** is empty and **t** is **b** or (b) **s** is not empty and **t** is (**fn** t_1 t_2) where t_1 is the first element of **s** and t_2 is the **fn** nest around **b** for the remaining elements of **s**. When we write (**fn** t_1 ... t_n) @**b** where a term is expected, it is an abbreviation for the **fn** nest around **b** for t_1, ..., t_n.

Examples. The **OR** nest around **F** for **A**, **B**, and **C** is the term (**OR A** (**OR B** (**OR C F**))), which may also be written (**OR A B C**) @**F**.

Terminology. Each application of the shell principle introduces several "new" function symbols. The invocation explicitly names one symbol as the *constructor* and another as the *recognizer*. Zero or more other symbols are named as *accessors*, and one may be named as the *base* function symbol for that shell.

Terminology. The *constructor function symbols of* a history h consists exactly of the constructor function symbols of applications of the shell principle in h. The *recognizer function symbols* of a history h is the union of {**TRUEP, FALSEP**} with the set consisting exactly of the recognizer function symbols of the applications of the shell principle in h. The *base function symbols* of a history h is the union of {**TRUE, FALSE**} with the set consisting exactly of the base function symbols of the applications of the shell principle in h for which a base function symbol was supplied.

Terminology. We say **r** is the *type* of **fn** iff either (a) **r** is given as the type of **fn** in Table 4.2 or (b) **fn** is a constructor or base function symbol introduced in the same axiomatic act in which **r** was the recognizer function symbol.

Table 4.2

fn	type of fn
TRUE	TRUEP
FALSE	FALSEP

Terminology. A *type restriction over* a set of function symbols s is a nonempty finite sequence of symbols where the first symbol is either the word **ONE-OF** or **NONE-OF** and each of the remaining are elements of s.

Terminology. A function symbol **fn** *satisfies* a type restriction (**flg** s_1 ... s_n) iff either **flg** is **ONE-OF** and **fn** is among the s_i or **flg** is **NONE-OF** and **fn** is not among the s_i.

Terminology. We say **t** is the *type restriction term for* a type restriction (**flg** r_1 ... r_n) *and* a variable symbol **v** iff **flg** is **ONE-OF** and **t** is (OR (r_1 v) ... (r_n v))@F or **flg** is **NONE-OF** and **t** is (NOT (OR (r_1 v) ... (r_n v))@F).

Examples. Let tr_1 be (**ONE-OF LISTP LITATOM**). Then tr_1 is a type restriction over the set {**NUMBERP LISTP LITATOM**}. The function symbol **LISTP** satisfies tr_1 but the function symbol **NUMBERP** does not. The type restriction term for tr_1 and X1 is (OR (LISTP X1) (OR (LITATOM X1) F)). Let tr_2 be (**NONE-OF NUMBERP**). Then tr_2 is a type restriction over the set {**NUMBERP LISTP LITATOM**}. The function symbol **LISTP** satisfies **tr**$_2$ but the function symbol **NUMBERP** does not. The type restriction term for **tr**$_2$ and **X2** is **(NOT (OR (NUMBERP X2) F))**.

4.5.2. The Shell Principle

Rule of Inference. Shell Principle

The axiomatic act

Shell Definition.
Add the shell **const** *of* **n** *arguments*
with (optionally, base function **base**,
recognizer function **r**,
accessor functions **ac**$_1$, . . . , **ac**$_n$,
type restrictions **tr**$_1$, . . . , **tr**$_n$, *and*
default functions **dv**$_1$, . . . , **dv**$_n$,

is admissible under the history h provided

(a) **const** is a new function symbol of **n** arguments,
(**base** is a new function symbol of no arguments,
if a base object is supplied), **r**, **ac**$_1$, ..., **ac**$_n$
are new function symbols of one argument, and
all the above function symbols are distinct;

(b) each **tr**$_i$ is a type restriction over the recognizers
of h together with the symbol **r**;

(c) for each **i**, **dv**$_i$ is either **base** or one of the
base functions of h; and

(d) for each **i**, if **dv**$_i$ is **base** then **r** satisfies **tr**$_i$
and otherwise the type of **dv**$_i$ satisfies **tr**$_i$.

If the **tr**$_i$ are not specified, they should each be assumed to be **(NONE-OF)**.
If admissible, the act adds the following axioms:

(1)   **(OR (EQUAL (r X) T)**
          (EQUAL (r X) F))

(2)   **(r (const X1 ... Xn))**

(3)   **(r (base))**

(4)   **(NOT (EQUAL (const X1 ... Xn) (base)))**

(5)   **(IMPLIES (AND (r X)**
 (NOT (EQUAL X (base))))
 (EQUAL (const (ac$_1$ X) ... (ac$_n$ X))
 X))

For each **i** from 1 to **n**, the following formula

(6)   **(IMPLIES trt$_i$**
 (EQUAL (ac$_i$ (const X1 ... Xn))
 Xi))

where **trt$_i$** is the type restriction term for **tr$_i$** and **Xi**.

For each **i** from 1 to **n**, the following formula

(7)   **(IMPLIES (OR (NOT (r X))**
 (OR (EQUAL X (base))
 (AND (NOT trt$_i$)
 (EQUAL X
 (const X1 ... Xn)))))
 (EQUAL (ac$_i$ X) (dv$_i$)))

where **trt$_i$** is the type restriction term for **tr$_i$** and **Xi**.

(8)   **(NOT (r T))**

(9)   **(NOT (r F))**

For each recognizer, **r'**, in the recognizer functions of h the formula

(10)   **(IMPLIES (r X) (NOT (r' X)))**

(11)   **(IMPLIES (r X)**
 (EQUAL (COUNT X)
 (IF (EQUAL X (base))
 (ZERO)
 (ADD1
 (PLUS
 (COUNT (ac$_1$ X))
 ...
 (COUNT (ac$_n$ X)))@(ZERO)))))

(12) The **SUBRP** axiom for each of the symbols **const, base** (if supplied), **r**, ac_1, ..., ac_n. We define the ''**SUBRP** axiom'' on page 133.

In the special case that no **base** is supplied, **T** should be used for all occurrences of **(r (base))** above, and **F** should be used for all terms of the form **(EQUAL x (base))** above.

4.5.3. Natural Numbers—Axioms 12.n

Shell Definition.
Add the shell **ADD1** of one argument
with base function **ZERO**,
recognizer function **NUMBERP**,
accessor function **SUB1**,
type restriction **(ONE-OF NUMBERP)**,
default function **ZERO**.

Note. In Appendix II we explicitly list the axioms added by this invocation of the shell principle. Each axiom has a number of the form **12.**n, where n indicates the corresponding axiom schema of the shell principle.

Axiom 13.
(NUMBERP (COUNT X))

Axiom 14.
(EQUAL (COUNT T) (ZERO))

Axiom 15.
(EQUAL (COUNT F) (ZERO))

Defining Axiom 16.
```
(ZEROP X)
   =
(OR (EQUAL X 0) (NOT (NUMBERP X)))
```

Defining Axiom 17.
(FIX X) = (IF (NUMBERP X) X 0)

Defining Axiom 18.
```
(PLUS X Y)
   =
(IF (ZEROP X)
    (FIX Y)
    (ADD1 (PLUS (SUB1 X) Y)))
```

4.5.4. Ordered Pairs—Axioms 19.n

Shell Definition.
Add the shell **CONS** of two arguments
with recognizer function **LISTP**,
accessor functions **CAR** and **CDR**,
default functions **ZERO** and **ZERO**.

Note. In Appendix II we explicitly list the axioms added by this invocation of the shell principle. Each axiom has a number of the form **19.**n, where n indicates the corresponding axiom schema of the shell principle.

4.5.5. Literal Atoms—Axioms 20.n

Shell Definition.
Add the shell **PACK** of one argument
recognizer function **LITATOM**,
accessor function **UNPACK**,
default function **ZERO**.

Note. In Appendix II we explicitly list the axioms added by this invocation of the shell principle. Each axiom has a number of the form **20.**n, where n indicates the corresponding axiom schema of the shell principle.

4.5.6. Negative Integers—Axioms 21.n

Shell Definition.
Add the shell **MINUS** of one argument
with recognizer function **NEGATIVEP**,
accessor function **NEGATIVE-GUTS**,
type restriction **(ONE-OF NUMBERP)**,
default function **ZERO**.

Note. In Appendix II we list explicitly the axioms added by this invocation of the shell principle. Each axiom has a number of the form **21.**n, where n indicates the corresponding axiom schema of the shell principle.

4.6. Explicit Value Terms

Note. This section is technically an aside in the development of the logic. We define a particularly important class of terms in the logic, called the "explicit value terms." Intuitively, the explicit value terms are the "canonical constants" in the logic. It is almost the case that every constant term—every variable-free term—can be mechanically reduced to a unique, equivalent explicit value. The only terms not so reducible are those involving (at some level in the definitional hierarchy) undefined functions or calls of metafunctions such as **V&C\$**. Thus, the explicit value terms are the terms upon which we can "compute" in the logic. They are the basis for our encoding of the terms as objects in the logic, and elaborate syntactic conventions are adopted in the extended syntax to permit their succinct expression.

Terminology. We say **tr** is the ith *type restriction for a constructor function symbol* **fn** of arity n iff $1 \leq i \leq n$, and **tr** is the ith type restriction specified in the axiomatic act in which **fn** was introduced.

Examples. The first type restriction for **ADD1** is **(ONE-OF NUMBERP)**. The second type restriction for **CONS** is **(NONE-OF)**.

Terminology. We say **t** is an *explicit value term* in a history h iff **t** is a term and either (a) **t** is a call of a base function symbol in h, or (b) **t** is a call of a constructor function symbol **fn** in h on arguments $a_1, ..., a_n$ and for each $1 \leq i \leq n$, a_i is an explicit value term in h and the type of the top function symbol of a_i satisfies the ith type restriction for the constructor function **fn**. We frequently omit reference to the history h when it is obvious by context.

Examples. The following are explicit value terms:

(ADD1 (ADD1 (ZERO)))

(CONS (PACK (ZERO)) (CONS (TRUE) (ADD1 (ZERO)))))

The term **(ADD1 X)** is not an explicit value, since **X** is neither a call of a base function symbol nor a call of a constructor. The term **(ADD1 (TRUE))** is not an explicit value, because the top function symbol of **(TRUE)** does not satisfy the type restriction, **(ONE-OF NUMBERP)**, for the first argument of **ADD1**.

4.7. The Extended Syntax—Abbreviations I

Notes. The extended syntax differs from the formal syntax only in that it permits certain abbreviations. These primarily concern notation for shell constants such as numbers, literal atoms, and lists. In addition, the extended syntax provides some abbreviations for commonly used function nests (e.g., **CAR** and **CDR** combinations and **CONS** sequences) and for the general purpose bounded quantifier function **FOR**. We delay the presentation of the quantifier abbreviations until after we have axiomatized **FOR** (see section 4.11, page 136) but discuss all other aspects of the extended syntax in this section.

The approach we take to describing the extended syntax is as follows. We first define a class of tree structures, called "s-expressions," that includes all the terms and other structures as well. We explain how such s-expressions are displayed. We avoid entirely the business of parsing character strings into s-expressions. We then provide a mapping from some s-expressions to terms in the formal syntax. Any s-expression that maps to a term is a legal expression in the extended syntax and abbreviates the term to which it maps. All other s-expressions are ill-formed expressions in the extended syntax. We apologize to readers expecting a definition of our syntax presented in a formal grammar. We have three reasons for proceeding in this fashion. First, despite the apparent simplicity of our syntax, it is actually very complicated; for example, we have yet to see an accurate description of how to read the closely related **QUOTE** or "dot" notation of Lisp. Second, we not only wish to specify the legal expressions in the extended syntax but also to map them to terms in the formal syntax. We think it unlikely that an accurate formal presentation of our syntax and its meaning would be any more clear than the informal but precise one offered here; furthermore, it would be much less accessible to most readers. Finally, this presentation is closely related to the actual implementation of the syntax in the user interface to our theorem prover. Particularly, in our implementation the user's terms are read by the Lisp reader and parsed into Lisp s-expressions. Those s-expressions are then checked for well-formedness and converted into the internal representation of terms. The s-expressions of the implementation are the s-expressions here. Our avoidance of parsing issues here is well motivated: there are many different ways the experienced Lisp user can make the Lisp reader produce a given s-expression. On the other hand, the novice user can type according to our rules and get the expected results.

4.7.1. S-Expressions and Their Display

Terminology. A sequence of characters, s, is a *word* if and only if s is non-empty and each character in s is a member of the set

```
{A  B  C  D  E  F  G  H  I  J  K  L  M
 N  O  P  Q  R  S  T  U  V  W  X  Y  Z
 0  1  2  3  4  5  6  7  8  9
 $  ^  &  *  _  -  +  =  ~  {  }  ?  <  >},
```

Note. All of our symbols are words, but the set of words is larger because it includes such non-symbols as ***1*TRUE**, **123**, and **1AF**.

Terminology. An *s-expression* is either a word, a nonempty sequence of s-expressions, or a sequence of length at least three whose second-to-last element is the character . (pronounced "dot") and all of whose other elements are s-expressions. An s-expression of the third kind (containing a dot as its second-to-last element) is called a *dotted s-expression*.

Terminology. To *display* an s-expression that is a word, we write down white space, the word, and white space. To *display* the dot character we write down white space, the dot character, and white space. To *display* a nonword s-expression consisting of the elements $t_1, ..., t_n$, (t_{n-1} might be the dot character here, but otherwise all t_i are s-expressions) we write down an open parenthesis, white space, a display of t_1, nonempty white space, a display of t_2, nonempty white space, ..., a display of t_n, white space, and a close parenthesis. In addition, an alternative display of some s-expressions is permitted. To display an s-expression of length two whose first element is the word **QUOTE** and whose second element is the s-expression **x**, we may write down white space, the character ' (pronounced "single gritch") followed by white space, followed by a display of **x**.

Example. Below we show some (displays of) s-expressions:

```
(EQUAL X                        ;White space includes
       (QUOTE (A B . C)))  ;comments.

(EQUAL X (QUOTE (A B . C)))

(EQUAL X '(A B . C))

(TIMES I J K)
```

```
(FN 123 (QUOTE *1*TRUE))

((1AB B**3 C) 12R45 (ADD1))
```

The first, second, and third are different displays of the same s-expression. It will turn out that all but the last s-expression above abbreviate terms, provided **FN** is a function of arity 2. The last s-expression above does not abbreviate a term.

4.7.2. Some Preliminary Terminology

Terminology. The *NUMBERP corresponding* to a nonnegative integer n is the term **(ZERO)** if n is 0, and otherwise is the term **(ADD1 t)**, where **t** is the **NUMBERP** corresponding to n-1. The *NEGATIVEP corresponding* to a negative integer n is the term **(MINUS t)**, where **t** is the **NUMBERP** corresponding to -n.

Examples. The **NUMBERP** corresponding to **2** is **(ADD1 (ADD1 (ZERO)))**. The **NEGATIVEP** corresponding to **-1** is **(MINUS (ADD1 (ZERO)))**.

Terminology. If **fn** is a **CAR/CDR** symbol, we call the sequence of characters in **fn** starting with the 2nd and concluding with the next to last the *A/D sequence* of **fn**.

Terminology. If **s** is a character sequence of **A**'s and **D**'s, the *CAR/CDR nest* for **s** around a term **b** is the term **t** defined as follows. If **s** is empty, **t** is **b**. Otherwise, **s** consists of either an **A** or **D** followed by a sequence **s'**. Let **t'** be the **CAR/CDR** nest for **s'** around **b**. Then **t** is **(CAR t')** or **(CDR t')**, according to whether the first character of **s** is **A** or **D**.

Example. The symbol **CADDAAR** is a **CAR/CDR** symbol. Its **A/D** sequence is the sequence **ADDAA**. The **CAR/CDR** nest for **ADDAA** around **L** is **(CAR (CDR (CDR (CAR (CAR L)))))**.

Terminology. We say a term **e** is the *explosion of* a sequence of ASCII characters, **s**, iff either (a) **s** is empty and **e** is **(ZERO)** or (b) **s** is a character **c** followed by some sequence **s'** and **e** is **(CONS i e')** where **i** is the **NUMBERP** corresponding to the ASCII code for **c** and **e'** is the explosion of **s'**.

Example. The ASCII codes for the characters **A**, **B**, and **C** are **65**, **66**, and **67** respectively. Let t_{65}, t_{66}, and t_{67} denote, respectively, the **NUMBERP**s corresponding to **65**, **66**, and **67**. For example, t_{65} here denotes a nest of **ADD1**s 65 deep with a **(ZERO)** at the bottom. Then the explosion of **ABC** is the formal term

$$(\text{CONS } t_{65} \ (\text{CONS } t_{66} \ (\text{CONS } t_{67} \ (\text{ZERO})))).$$

Terminology. We say the term **e** is the *LITATOM corresponding to* a symbol **s** iff **e** is the term **(PACK e')** where **e'** is the explosion of **s**.

Example. The **LITATOM** corresponding to the symbol **ABC** is

$$(\text{PACK } (\text{CONS } t_{65} \ (\text{CONS } t_{66} \ (\text{CONS } t_{67} \ (\text{ZERO}))))),$$

where t_{65}, t_{66}, and t_{67} are as in the last example.

4.7.3. Well-Formed S-Expressions and Their Translations

Notes. The terminology we have developed is sufficient for defining what it means for an s-expression to be "well-formed" and what its "translation" is, for all s-expressions except those employing **QUOTE** notation or abbreviated **FOR**s. Rather than define the concepts necessary to pin down these conventions, we now jump ahead in our development of the syntax and define "well-formed" and "translation." Such a presentation here necessarily involves four undefined concepts—the notions of well-formedness and translation of both **QUOTE** and **FOR** expressions. However, by providing the definition at this point in the development we can use some s-expressions to illustrate and motivate the discussion of **QUOTE** notation.

Terminology. Below we define two concepts: what it means for an s-expression **x** to be a *well-formed term in the extended syntax* and, for well-formed s-expressions, what is the *translation* into a term in the formal syntax. These definitions are made implicitly with respect to a history because **QUOTE** notation permits the abbreviation of explicit values, a concept which, recall, is sensitive to the history. Our style of definition is to consider any s-expression **x** and announce whether it is well-formed or not and if so, what its translation is.

- If **x** is a word then
  - If **x** is a sequence of digits, optionally signed by + or − and optionally followed by the dot (decimal point) character, **x** is well-formed. In this case, **x** is the decimal representation of some integer, **n**, and the formal term to which **x** translates is the **NEGATIVEP** or **NUMBERP** corresponding to **n**, according

to whether **n** is negative or not.

- If **x** is the symbol **T**, it is well-formed and its translation is the formal term **(TRUE)**.

- If **x** is the symbol **F**, it is well-formed and its translation is the formal term **(FALSE)**.

- If **x** is the symbol **NIL**, it is well-formed and its translation is the **LITATOM** corresponding to **NIL**.

- If **x** is any other symbol, it is well-formed and its translation is the formal term **x**.

- Otherwise, **x** is a non-symbol word and it is not well-formed.

- If **x** is a dotted s-expression or if its first element is not a symbol, it is not well-formed.

- If the first element of **x** is the symbol **QUOTE**, then **x** is well-formed iff it is of the form **(QUOTE e)** (also displayed **'e**) and **e** is an explicit value descriptor (see the next subsection). If well-formed, the translation of **x** is the explicit value term denoted by **e** (see the next subsection).

- Otherwise, **x** is of the form $(\mathbf{fn}\ \mathbf{x_1}\ \ldots\ \mathbf{x_n})$, where **fn** is a symbol other than **QUOTE** and each $\mathbf{x_i}$ is an s-expression. If some $\mathbf{x_i}$ is not well-formed, then **x** is not well-formed. Otherwise, let $\mathbf{t_i}$ be the translation of $\mathbf{x_i}$ below:

  - If **fn** is in the set {**NIL T F**}, **x** is not well-formed.

  - If **fn** is the symbol **LIST** then **x** is well-formed and its translation is the **CONS** nest around the translation of **NIL** for $\mathbf{t_1}, \ldots, \mathbf{t_n}$.

  - If **fn** is a **CAR/CDR** symbol, then **x** is well-formed iff **n** is 1 and, if well-formed, its translation is the **CAR/CDR** nest around $\mathbf{t_1}$ for the **A/D** sequence of **fn**.

  - If **fn** is a function symbol of arity **n**, then **x** is well-formed and its translation is the formal term $(\mathbf{fn}\ \mathbf{t_1}\ \ldots\ \mathbf{t_n})$.

  - If **fn** is the symbol **FOR**, then **x** is well-formed iff **x** is an abbreviated **FOR** (see page 137). If well-formed, the translation of **x** is the **FOR** expression denoted by **x** (see page 137).

  - If **fn** is in the set {**AND OR PLUS TIMES**} and n>2, then **x** is well-formed and its translation is the **fn** nest around $\mathbf{t_n}$ for $\mathbf{t_1}, \ldots, \mathbf{t_{n-1}}$.

• Otherwise, **x** is not well-formed.

Examples. Table 4.3 shows well-formed s-expressions on the left and their translations to formal terms on the right.

Table 4.3

s-expression	translation
T	(TRUE)
2	(ADD1 (ADD1 (ZERO)))
(CADR X)	(CAR (CDR X))
(PLUS I J K)	(PLUS I (PLUS J K))

Certain formal terms, such as the translation of **NIL**, are exceedingly painful to write down because they contain deep nests of **ADD1**s. Table 4.4 also contains translations, except this time the right-hand column is, technically, not a formal term but rather another well-formed s-expression with the same translation. In particular, in Table 4.4 we use decimal notation in the right-hand column, but otherwise confine ourselves to formal syntax.

Table 4.4

s-expression	s-expression with same translation	

NIL	(PACK
	  (CONS 78
	    (CONS 73
	      (CONS 76 0))))	

(LIST 1 2 3)	(CONS 1
	  (CONS 2
	    (CONS 3
	      (PACK
	        (CONS 78
	          (CONS 73
	            (CONS 76 0))))))))
		; first element
		; second element
		; third element
		;NIL

4.7.4. QUOTE Notation

Notes and Example. In this subsection we define what we mean by an "explicit value descriptor" and the "explicit value denoted" by such a descriptor. These are the concepts used to define the well-formedness and meaning of s-expressions of the form **(QUOTE e)**.

Each explicit value term can be written in **QUOTE** notation. That is, for each explicit value term **t** there is an s-expression **e** such that the s-expression **(QUOTE e)** (otherwise displayed as **' e**) is well-formed and translates to **t**. We call **e** the "explicit value descriptor" of **t**. For example, consider the s-expression

```
(CONS 1
      (CONS (PACK
             (CONS 65 (CONS 66 (CONS 67 0))))
            (CONS 2 3))).
```

This s-expression is well-formed and translates to an explicit value. Call that explicit value term **t**. The explicit value descriptor for **t** is the s-expression **(1 ABC 2 . 3)**. The s-expression **' (1 ABC 2 . 3)** is well-formed and translates to **t**.

Our **QUOTE** notation is derived from the Lisp notation for data structures composed of numbers, symbols, and ordered pairs, but is complicated by the need to denote structures containing user-defined shell constants. That is, after the theory has been extended by the addition of a new shell, it is possible to build constants containing both primitive shells and user-defined ones, e.g., lists of stacks. Unlike Lisp's **QUOTE** notation, the notation described here permits such constants to be written down, via an "escape" mechanism.[16]

Following the precedent set for well-formedness and translation, we proceed in a top-down fashion to define what we mean by an "explicit value descriptor" and its "denoted explicit value" without first defining the terminology to discuss the "escape" mechanism. Immediately following the definition below we illustrate the use of **QUOTE** notation on primitive shell constants, e.g., lists, numbers, and literal atoms. We define the escape mechanism for user-declared shells in the next subsection.

Terminology. Below we define two concepts: what it is for an s-expression **e** to be an *explicit value descriptor* and, for explicit value descriptors, what is the *denoted explicit value term*. These definitions are made with respect to a history which is used implicitly below. Our style of definition is to consider any

---

[16]Lisp provides the much more powerful "backquote" feature.

s-expression **e** and announce whether it is an explicit value descriptor or not and if so, what its denoted explicit value term is.

- If **e** is a word, then

  - If **e** is a sequence of digits, optionally signed by **+** or **−** and optionally followed by the dot (decimal point) character, **e** is an explicit value descriptor. In this case, **e** is the decimal representation of some integer, **n**, and the explicit value term denoted by **e** is the **NEGATIVEP** or **NUMBERP** corresponding to **n**, according to whether **n** is negative or not.

  - If **e** is the word ***1*TRUE**, **e** is an explicit value descriptor and denotes the explicit value **(TRUE)**.

  - If **e** is the word ***1*FALSE**, **e** is an explicit value descriptor and denotes the explicit value **(FALSE)**.

  - If **e** is a symbol, **e** is an explicit value descriptor and denotes the **LITATOM** corresponding to **e**.

  - Otherwise, **e** is not an explicit value descriptor.

- If the first element of **e** is the word ***1*QUOTE**, **e** is an explicit value descriptor iff it is an explicit value escape descriptor (see the next subsection). If so, it has the form **(*1*QUOTE fn** e_1 **...** e_n**)**, where **fn** is a constructor or base function symbol of arity **n** and each e_i is an explicit value descriptor denoting an explicit value t_i. The explicit value denoted by **e** is then **(fn** t_1 **...** t_n**)**. (That this is, indeed, an explicit value is assured by the definition of ''explicit value escape descriptor.'')

- If **e** is a dotted s-expression of length 3, i.e., **(**e_1 **.** e_2**)**, then **e** is an explicit value descriptor iff each e_i is an explicit value descriptor. If so, let t_i be the explicit value denoted by e_i. Then the explicit value denoted by **e** is **(CONS** t_1 t_2**)**.

- If **e** is an s-expression of length 1, i.e., **(**e_1**)**, **e** is an explicit value descriptor iff e_1 is an explicit value descriptor. If so, let t_1 be the explicit value denoted by e_1 and let **nil** be the explicit value denoted by **NIL**. Then the explicit value denoted by **e** is **(CONS** t_1 **nil)**.

- Otherwise, either **e** is a dotted s-expression of length greater than 3 or **e** is a non-dotted s-expression of length greater than 1. Let e_1 be the first element of **e** and let e_2 be the sequence consisting of the remaining elements of **e**. Observe that e_1 and e_2 are both s-expressions. **e** is an explicit value descriptor iff each **e**$_i$ is an explicit value descriptor. If so, let **t**$_i$ be the explicit value denoted by **e**$_i$. Then the explicit value denoted by **e** is $(\texttt{CONS } \texttt{t}_1 \texttt{ t}_2)$.

Examples. Table 4.5 illustrates the **QUOTE** notation. In particular, the left-hand column is a well-formed s-expression. The right-hand column is another well-formed s-expression that has the same translation as the corresponding entry in the left-hand column.

Table 4.5

s-expression in QUOTE notation	s-expression with same translation
'123	123
'ABC	(PACK '(65 66 67 . 0))
'(65 66 67 . 0)	(CONS 65 (CONS 66 (CONS 67 0)))

'(PLUS I J)	(CONS 'PLUS
	    (CONS 'I
	        (CONS 'J NIL)))

(QUOTE (PLUS I J))	(CONS 'PLUS
	    (CONS 'I
	        (CONS 'J NIL)))

'((I . 2) (J . 3))	(LIST (CONS 'I 2) (CONS 'J 3))

'((A . *1*TRUE)
 	
  (B . T))
	(LIST
	    (CONS 'A (TRUE))
	    (CONS 'B
	        (PACK (CONS 84 0))))

Note. Of particular note is the possible confusion of the meaning of the symbol **T** (and, symmetrically, of **F**) in s-expressions. If **T** is used "outside a **QUOTE**" it denotes **(TRUE)**. If **T** is used "inside a **QUOTE**" it denotes the literal atom whose "print name" is the single character **T**. If the user wishes to include **(TRUE)** among the elements of a **QUOTE**d list, he should write the non-symbol ***1*TRUE** "inside the **QUOTE**."

The reason we resorted to an explicitly recursive description of well-formedness and translation should now be apparent. The interpretation of an s-expression (such as **T**) depends upon the context in which the s-expression occurs.

If the s-expression **(QUOTE ABC)** (sometimes displayed **'ABC**) is used as a term it denotes **(PACK ' (65 66 67 . 0))**. That is, the translation of the former is the latter. However, if the s-expression **(QUOTE ABC)** is used as an explicit value descriptor, it denotes a list of length 2 whose **CAR** is **QUOTE** and whose **CADR** is **'ABC**. **'ABC** is used as an explicit value descriptor when **''ABC** is used as a term. See Table 4.6. The translation of **'ABC** is a literal

Table 4.6

s-expression	s-expression with same translation
'ABC	**(PACK ' (65 66 67 . 0))**

''ABC	**' (QUOTE ABC)**
	 =
	 (CONS 'QUOTE (CONS 'ABC NIL))
	 =
	 (CONS
	   (PACK ' (81 85 79 84 69 . 0))
	   (CONS
	     (PACK ' (65 66 67 . 0))
	     (PACK ' (78 73 76 . 0))))

atom; the translation of **''ABC** is a list whose first element is the literal atom **'QUOTE**.

Here is another example illustrating the subtlety of the situation. The innocent reader may have, by now, adopted the convention that whenever he sees **(CADR X)** he reads **(CAR (CDR X))**. This is incorrect. When **(CADR X)** is used as a term, i.e., when we are interested in its translation into a formal term, it denotes **(CAR (CDR X))**. But if **(CADR X)** is "inside a **QUOTE**" it is not being used as a term but rather as an explicit value descriptor. In particular, the translation of **' (CADR X)** is a list whose first element is the atom **'CADR**, not a list whose first element is **'CAR**. The translations of **' (CADR X)** and **' (CAR (CDR X))** are different. Similarly the translation of **' 1** is not the same as that of **' (ADD1 (ZERO))**; the first is a number, the second is a list.

4.7.5. *1*QUOTE Escape Mechanism for User Shells

Notes and Example. In this section we describe how to use the ***1*QUOTE** convention to write down user-declared shell constants. In particular, we define the notion of the "explicit value escape descriptor" used above.

Roughly speaking, an explicit value escape descriptor is an s-expression of the form (***1*QUOTE fn** e$_1$ ... e$_n$) where **fn** is a shell constructor or base function and the e$_i$ are explicit value descriptors denoting its arguments. Thus, if **PUSH** is a shell constructor of two arguments and **EMPTY** is the corresponding base function then (***1*QUOTE PUSH 3 (*1*QUOTE EMPTY)**) is an explicit value escape descriptor, and hence an explicit value descriptor, that denotes (**PUSH 3 (EMPTY)**). We restrict the legal escape descriptors so that the mechanism cannot be used to write down alternative representations of constants that can be written in the conventional **QUOTE** notation. For example, (***1*QUOTE CONS 1 2**) is *not* an explicit value escape descriptor because if it were it would be an alternative representation of (**CONS 1 2**). Furthermore, we must restrict the escape descriptors so that they indeed denote explicit values. Is (**PUSH 3 (EMPTY)**) an explicit value? The answer depends upon the type restrictions for the **PUSH** shell. To answer this question it is necessary to know the current history.

Terminology. The s-expression **e** is an *explicit value escape descriptor* with respect to a history h iff **e** has the form (***1*QUOTE fn** e$_1$ ... e$_n$) and each of the following is true:

- **fn** is a constructor or base function symbol of arity **n** in history h;

- **fn** is not **ADD1**, **ZERO**, or **CONS**;

- each e$_i$ is an explicit value descriptor with corresponding denoted term t$_i$ in h;

- if **fn** is a constructor, the top function symbol of each t$_i$ satisfies the corresponding type restriction for **fn**;

- if **fn** is **PACK**, t$_1$ is not the explosion of any symbol; and

- if **fn** is **MINUS**, t$_1$ is (**ZERO**).

Notes and Examples. We now illustrate the use of the ***1*QUOTE** escape mechanism. Suppose we are in a history obtained by extending the current one with the following:

Shell Definition.
Add the shell **PUSH** of 2 arguments,
with base object **EMPTY**,
recognizer **STACKP**,
accessors **TOP** and **POP**
type restrictions **(ONE-OF NUMBERP)** and **(ONE-OF STACKP)**
default functions **ZERO**, and **EMPTY**.

Table 4.7 contains some example s-expressions employing the ***1*QUOTE**
mechanism.

Table 4.7

s-expression	s-expression with same translation
'(A (*1*QUOTE MINUS 0))	(LIST 'A (MINUS 0))

'((*1*QUOTE PUSH 2
    (*1*QUOTE PUSH 3
      (*1*QUOTE EMPTY)))
  FOO . 45)
	(CONS
	  (PUSH 2
	   (PUSH 3 (EMPTY)))
	 (CONS 'FOO 45))

'(*1*QUOTE PACK
   (97 98 99 . 0))
	(PACK
	  '(97 98 99 . 0))

*1*QUOTE can be used not only to denote constants of "new" types but also
to write down "unusual" constants of the primitive types, namely **(MINUS 0)**
and "**LITATOM**s corresponding to non-symbols."

That we want unique representation is due to efficiency considerations in the
mechanization of the logic. However, that implementation decision did not *have*
to be visible to the user of the logic. However, it is our opinion that the user
who makes extensive use of metafunctions suffers if the syntax hides too much
of the internal representation of terms.

Note also that the terms denoted by ***1*QUOTE** expressions are often more
simply written without the use of the **QUOTE** notation at all. We include the
*1*QUOTE "escape" because it is occasionally necessary to write large list
constants that contain unusual structures (such as a **STACKP**) deep inside. Were
it not for the ***1*QUOTE** escape, it would be necessary to avoid the use of
QUOTE notation in the containing structure.

4.7.6. The Definition of the Extended Syntax

Terminology. The *extended syntax* consists of the well-formed s-expressions as defined on page 115.

Henceforth, all terms in this book are in the extended syntax.

Abbreviation. When an expression in the extended syntax is used as a term, it is an abbreviation for its translation. When an expression in the extended syntax is used as a formula, it is an abbreviation for $t \neq$ **(FALSE)**, where **t** is the translation of the expression.

Note. In Appendix I we exhibit a parser for the extended syntax as a function defined within the logic.

4.8. Ordinals

Defining Axiom 22.
```
(LESSP X Y)
   =
(IF (ZEROP Y)
    F
    (IF (ZEROP X)
        T
        (LESSP (SUB1 X) (SUB1 Y))))
```

Axiom 23.
```
(IMPLIES (NOT (ZEROP I))
         (LESSP (SUB1 I) I))
```

Note. **Axiom 23** permits us to apply the induction principle to prove the fundamental properties of **LESSP**, **PLUS**, and **COUNT**, which in turn permit us to induct in more sophisticated ways.

Defining Axiom 24.
```
(ORD-LESSP X Y)
   =
(IF (NOT (LISTP X))
    (IF (NOT (LISTP Y))
        (LESSP X Y)
        T)
    (IF (NOT (LISTP Y))
        F
```

```
(IF (ORD-LESSP (CAR X) (CAR Y))
    T
    (AND (EQUAL (CAR X) (CAR Y))
         (ORD-LESSP (CDR X) (CDR Y))))))))
```

Defining Axiom 25.
```
(ORDINALP X)
   =
(IF (LISTP X)
    (AND (ORDINALP (CAR X))
         (NOT (EQUAL (CAR X) 0))
         (ORDINALP (CDR X))
         (OR (NOT (LISTP (CDR X)))
             (NOT (ORD-LESSP (CAR X) (CADR X)))))
    (NUMBERP X)))
```

Examples. See page 41 in the primer for a table of example ordinals.

4.9. Useful Function Definitions

4.9.1. Boolean Equivalence

Defining Axiom 26.
```
(IFF P Q)
   =
(IF P
    (IF Q T F)
    (IF Q F T))
```

4.9.2. Natural Number Arithmetic

Defining Axiom 27.
```
(GREATERP I J) = (LESSP J I)
```

Defining Axiom 28.
```
(LEQ I J) = (NOT (LESSP J I))
```

Defining Axiom 29.
```
(GEQ I J) = (NOT (LESSP I J))
```

Defining Axiom 30.
```
(MAX I J) = (IF (LESSP I J) J (FIX I))
```

Defining Axiom 31.
```
(DIFFERENCE I J)
   =
(IF (ZEROP I)
    0
    (IF (ZEROP J)
        I
        (DIFFERENCE (SUB1 I) (SUB1 J))))
```

Defining Axiom 32.
```
(TIMES I J)
   =
(IF (ZEROP I)
    0
    (PLUS J (TIMES (SUB1 I) J)))
```

Defining Axiom 33.
```
(QUOTIENT I J)
   =
(IF (ZEROP J)
    0
    (IF (LESSP I J)
        0
        (ADD1 (QUOTIENT (DIFFERENCE I J) J))))
```

Defining Axiom 34.
```
(REMAINDER I J)
   =
(IF (ZEROP J)
    (FIX I)
    (IF (LESSP I J)
        (FIX I)
        (REMAINDER (DIFFERENCE I J) J)))
```

4.9.3. List Processing

Defining Axiom 35.
```
(NLISTP X) = (NOT (LISTP X))
```

Defining Axiom 36.
```
(APPEND L1 L2)
   =
(IF (LISTP L1)
    (CONS (CAR L1) (APPEND (CDR L1) L2))
    L2)
```

Defining Axiom 37.
```
(MEMBER X L)
   =
(IF (NLISTP L)
    F
    (IF (EQUAL X (CAR L))
        T
        (MEMBER X (CDR L)))))
```

Defining Axiom 38.
```
(UNION L1 L2)
   =
(IF (LISTP L1)
    (IF (MEMBER (CAR L1) L2)
        (UNION (CDR L1) L2)
        (CONS (CAR L1) (UNION (CDR L1) L2)))
    L2)
```

Defining Axiom 39.
```
(ADD-TO-SET X L)
   =
(IF (MEMBER X L)
    L
    (CONS X L))
```

Defining Axiom 40.
```
(ASSOC X ALIST)
   =
(IF (NLISTP ALIST)
    F
    (IF (EQUAL X (CAAR ALIST))
        (CAR ALIST)
        (ASSOC X (CDR ALIST)))))
```

Defining Axiom 41.
```
(PAIRLIST L1 L2)
   =
(IF (LISTP L1)
    (CONS (CONS (CAR L1) (CAR L2))
          (PAIRLIST (CDR L1) (CDR L2)))
    NIL)
```

4.10. The Formal Metatheory

Note. In this section we describe the interpreter for the logic. We start by presenting the notion of the "quotation" of terms. Roughly speaking, the quotation of a term is an explicit value that has a structure isomorphic to that of the term; for example, the quotation of **(PLUS X Y)** is the explicit value **' (PLUS X Y)**. An important property of quotations is that, for most terms, the interpreted value of the quotation under a certain standard assignment is equal to the term. For example, the value of **' (PLUS X Y)** as determined by our interpreter, when **' X** has the value **X** and **' Y** has the value **Y**, is **(PLUS X Y)**. After defining quotations we define the interpreter. Finally, we describe the **SUBRP** and non-**SUBRP** axioms that tie **QUOTE**d symbols to the interpreter.

4.10.1. The Quotation of Terms

Note. The "quotation" of an explicit value term may be rendered either by nests of constructor function applications or by embedding the term in a **QUOTE** form. This makes the notion of "quotation" depend upon the notion of "explicit value," which, recall, involves a particular history h from which the constructor and base functions are drawn. This is the only sense in which the notion of "quotation" depends upon a history.

Terminology. We say **e** is a *quotation* of **t** (in some history h which is implicit throughout this definition) iff **e** and **t** are terms and either (a) **t** is a variable symbol and **e** is the **LITATOM** corresponding to **t**, (b) **t** is an explicit value term and **e** is **(LIST 'QUOTE t)**, or (c) **t** has the form **(fn a₁ ... aₙ)** and **e** is **(CONS efn elst)** where **efn** is the **LITATOM** corresponding to **fn** and **elst** is a "quotation list" (see below) of **a₁ ... aₙ**. Note that clauses (b) and (c) are not mutually exclusive.

Terminology. We say **elst** is a *quotation list of* **tlst** (in some history h which is implicit throughout this definition) iff **elst** is a term and **tlst** is a sequence of terms, and either (a) **tlst** is empty and **elst** is **NIL** or (b) **tlst** consists of a term **t** followed by a sequence **tlst'** and **elst** is **(CONS e elst')** where **e** is a quotation of **t** and **elst'** is a quotation list of **tlst'**.

Examples. In Table 4.8 we give some terms and examples of their quotations.

Note. To describe the axioms for the **BODY** function, we wish to say something like "for each defined function symbol, **fn**, **(BODY 'fn)** is the quotation of

Table 4.8

term	quotation displayed in the extended syntax
ABC	' ABC
(ZERO)	' (ZERO)
(ZERO)	' (QUOTE 0)
(PLUS 3 (TIMES X Y))	' (PLUS (QUOTE 3) (TIMES X Y))

the body of the definition of **fn**.'' But note that explicit values, e.g., **(ZERO)** above, have multiple quotations. (Indeed, all terms containing explicit values have multiple quotations.) Consequently, we cannot speak of ''the'' quotation of a term. To get around this we define the notion of the ''preferred quotation.'' The preferred quotation of **(ZERO)** is **' (QUOTE 0)**. In general, the definitions of ''preferred quotation'' and ''preferred quotation list,'' below, are strictly analogous to the definitions of ''quotation'' and ''quotation list,'' above, except that explicit values must be encoded in **' QUOTE** form. This is done by making clauses (b) and (c) of the definition of ''quotation'' be mutually exclusive with clause (b) the superior one.

Terminology. We say **e** is the *preferred quotation* of **t** (in some history h which is implicit throughout this definition) iff **e** and **t** are terms and either (a) **t** is a variable symbol and **e** is the **LITATOM** corresponding to **t**, (b) **t** is an explicit value term and **e** is **(LIST 'QUOTE t)**, or (c) **t** has the form **(fn a_1 ... a_n)**, **t** is not an explicit value, and **e** is **(CONS efn elst)** where **efn** is the **LITATOM** corresponding to **fn** and **elst** is the ''preferred quotation list'' (see below) of $a_1 ... a_n$.

Terminology. We say **elst** is the *preferred quotation list of* **tlst** (in some history h which is implicit throughout this definition) iff **elst** is a term and **tlst** is a sequence of terms, and either (a) **tlst** is empty and **elst** is **NIL** or (b) **tlst** consists of a term **t** followed by a sequence **tlst'** and **elst** is **(CONS e elst')** where **e** is the preferred quotation of **t** and **elst'** is the preferred quotation list of **tlst'**.

4.10.2. V&C$ and EVAL$

Note. The axiomatization of **V&C$** and **EVAL$** are rather subtle. In the primer, starting on page 45, we explain many of the constraints and "design decisions." In addition, the interested reader is urged to see [11].

Defining Axiom 42.
```
(FIX-COST VC N)
    =
(IF VC
    (CONS (CAR VC) (PLUS N (CDR VC)))
    F)
```

Defining Axiom 43.
```
(STRIP-CARS L)
    =
(IF (NLISTP L)
    NIL
    (CONS (CAAR L) (STRIP-CARS (CDR L))))
```

Defining Axiom 44.
```
(SUM-CDRS L)
    =
(IF (NLISTP L)
    0
    (PLUS (CDAR L) (SUM-CDRS (CDR L))))
```

Note. We now "define" **V&C$**. This axiom defines a partial function and would not be admissible under the definitional principle. Because of its complexity we include comments in the axiom.

Defining Axiom 45.
```
(V&C$ FLG X VA)
    =
(IF (EQUAL FLG 'LIST)

    ;X is a list of terms. Return a list of value-cost
    ;"pairs"—some "pairs" may be F.

    (IF (NLISTP X)
        NIL
        (CONS (V&C$ T (CAR X) VA)
              (V&C$ 'LIST (CDR X) VA)))
```

; Otherwise, consider the cases on the **X**.

```
(IF  (LITATOM X)                          ; Variable
     (CONS (CDR (ASSOC X VA)) 0)

(IF  (NLISTP X)                           ; Constant
     (CONS X 0)

(IF  (EQUAL (CAR X) 'QUOTE)               ; QUOTEd
     (CONS (CADR X) 0)

(IF  (EQUAL (CAR X) 'IF)                  ; IF-expr
```

; If the test of the **IF** is defined, test the value and
; interpret the appropriate branch. Then, if the branch
; is defined, increment its cost by that of the test plus
; one. If the test is undefined, **X** is undefined.

```
(IF  (V&C$ T (CADR X) VA)
     (FIX-COST
      (IF  (CAR (V&C$ T (CADR X) VA))
           (V&C$ T (CADDR X) VA)
           (V&C$ T (CADDDR X) VA))
      (ADD1 (CDR (V&C$ T (CADR X) VA))))
     F)
```

; Otherwise, **X** is the application of a **SUBRP** or
; defined function. If some argument is undefined, so is **X**.

```
(IF  (MEMBER F (V&C$ 'LIST (CDR X) VA))
     F

(IF  (SUBRP (CAR X))                      ; SUBRP
```

; Apply the primitive to the values of the arguments and
; let the cost be one plus the sum of the argument costs.

```
(CONS (APPLY-SUBR (CAR X)
                  (STRIP-CARS
                      (V&C$ 'LIST (CDR X) VA)))
      (ADD1 (SUM-CDRS
                  (V&C$ 'LIST (CDR X) VA))))
```

```
                                        ; Defined fn

    ; Interpret the BODY on the values of the arguments
    ; and if that is defined increment the cost by one plus
    ; the sum of the argument costs.

    (FIX-COST
     (V&C$ T (BODY (CAR X))
               (PAIRLIST
                 (FORMALS (CAR X))
                 (STRIP-CARS (V&C$ 'LIST (CDR X) VA))))
       (ADD1
         (SUM-CDRS
           (V&C$ 'LIST (CDR X) VA)))))))))))
```

Note. Having defined **V&C$** we can now define the general purpose "apply" function in terms of it:

Defining Axiom 46.
```
(V&C-APPLY$ FN ARGS)
   =
(IF (EQUAL FN 'IF)
 (IF (CAR ARGS)
     (FIX-COST (IF (CAAR ARGS)
                   (CADR ARGS)
                   (CADDR ARGS))
               (ADD1 (CDAR ARGS)))
     F)
 (IF (MEMBER F ARGS)
     F
     (IF (SUBRP FN)
         (CONS (APPLY-SUBR
                  FN
                  (STRIP-CARS ARGS))
               (ADD1 (SUM-CDRS ARGS)))
         (FIX-COST
           (V&C$ T
                  (BODY FN)
                  (PAIRLIST (FORMALS FN)
                            (STRIP-CARS ARGS)))
           (ADD1 (SUM-CDRS ARGS)))))))
```

Note. A trivial consequence of the definitions of **V&C$** and **V&C-APPLY$** is that the following is a theorem:

Theorem.
```
(V&C$ FLG X VA)
    =
(IF (EQUAL FLG 'LIST)
    (IF (NLISTP X)
        NIL
        (CONS (V&C$ T (CAR X) VA)
              (V&C$ 'LIST (CDR X) VA)))
    (IF (LITATOM X) (CONS (CDR (ASSOC X VA)) 0)
        (IF (NLISTP X) (CONS X 0)
            (IF (EQUAL (CAR X) 'QUOTE)
                (CONS (CADR X) 0)
                (V&C-APPLY$
                  (CAR X)
                  (V&C$ 'LIST (CDR X) VA))))))
```

Note. We finally define the functions **APPLY$** and **EVAL$**:

Defining Axiom 47.
```
(APPLY$ FN ARGS)
    =
(CAR (V&C-APPLY$ FN (PAIRLIST ARGS 0)))
```

Defining Axiom 48.
```
(EVAL$ FLG X A)
    =
(IF (EQUAL FLG 'LIST)
  (IF (NLISTP X)
      NIL
      (CONS (EVAL$ T (CAR X) A)
            (EVAL$ 'LIST (CDR X) A)))
  (IF (LITATOM X) (CDR (ASSOC X A))
      (IF (NLISTP X) X
          (IF (EQUAL (CAR X) 'QUOTE) (CADR X)
              (APPLY$ (CAR X)
                      (EVAL$ 'LIST (CDR X) A))))))
```

4.10.3. The SUBRP and non-SUBRP Axioms

Notes. We now axiomatize the functions **SUBRP**, **APPLY-SUBR**, **FORMALS**, and **BODY** and define what we mean by the "**SUBRP**" and "non-**SUBRP** axioms."

The function **SUBRP** is Boolean:

Axiom 49.
```
(OR (EQUAL (SUBRP FN) T) (EQUAL (SUBRP FN) F))
```

The three functions **SUBRP**, **FORMALS**, and **BODY** "expect" **LITATOM**s as arguments, i.e., the quotations of function symbols. We tie down the three functions outside their "expected" domain with the following three axioms:

Axiom 50.
```
(IMPLIES (NOT (LITATOM FN)) (EQUAL (SUBRP FN) F))
```

Axiom 51.
```
(IMPLIES (NOT (LITATOM FN)) (EQUAL (FORMALS FN) F))
```

Axiom 52.
```
(IMPLIES (NOT (LITATOM FN)) (EQUAL (BODY FN) F))
```

Note. In a similar spirit, we define the **FORMALS** and **BODY** of **SUBRP**s to be **F**, and we define the result of applying a non-**SUBRP** with **APPLY-SUBR** to be **F**:

Axiom 53.
```
(IMPLIES (SUBRP FN) (EQUAL (FORMALS FN) F))
```

Axiom 54.
```
(IMPLIES (SUBRP FN) (EQUAL (BODY FN) F))
```

Axiom 55.
```
(IMPLIES (NOT (SUBRP FN)) (EQUAL (APPLY-SUBR FN X) F))
```

Note. In section 4.12 we enumerate the primitive **SUBRP**s and non-**SUBRP**s. For each we will add either the "**SUBRP** axiom" or the "non-**SUBRP** axiom," which we now proceed to define.

Terminology. We say term **t** is the n*th CDR nest around* the term **x** iff **n** is a natural number and either (a) **n** is 0 and **t** is **x** or (b) **n**>0 and **t** is (CDR t') where **t'** is the n-1st **CDR** nest around **x**. When we write (CDR^n x) where a term is expected it is an abbreviation for the nth **CDR** nest around **x**.

Example. (CDR^2 A) is (CDR (CDR A)).

Terminology. The *SUBRP axiom* for **fn**, where **fn** is a function symbol of arity **n**, is

```
(AND (EQUAL (SUBRP 'fn) T)
     (EQUAL (APPLY-SUBR 'fn L)
            (fn (CAR (CDR⁰ L))
```

```
                    . . .
            (CAR (CDR^{n-1} L)))))
```

where **' fn** is the **LITATOM** corresponding to **fn**.

Example. The **SUBRP** axiom for **PLUS** is

```
(AND (EQUAL (SUBRP 'PLUS) T)
     (EQUAL (APPLY-SUBR 'PLUS L)
            (PLUS (CAR L) (CAR (CDR L)))))
```

Terminology. The *standard alist* for a sequence of variable symbols **args** is **NIL** if **args** is empty and otherwise is **(CONS (CONS 'v v) alist')** where **v** is the first symbol in **args**, **'v** is the **LITATOM** corresponding to **v**, and **alist'** is the standard alist for the sequence of symbols obtained by deleting **v** from **args**.

Example. The standard alist for **X**, **ANS**, and **L** is

```
(LIST (CONS 'X X)
      (CONS 'ANS ANS)
      (CONS 'L L))
```

Terminology. The *non-SUBRP axiom* for **fn**, **args**, and **body**, where **fn** is a function symbol, **args** is a sequence of variable symbols, and **body** is a term, is

```
(AND (EQUAL (SUBRP 'fn) F)
     (EQUAL (FORMALS 'fn) eargs)
     (EQUAL (BODY 'fn) ebody))
```

where **' fn** is the **LITATOM** corresponding to **fn**, **eargs** is the quotation list for **args**, and **ebody** is the preferred quotation of **body** unless **body** has the form **(EVAL$ flg ebody' alist)** where

1. **flg** is an explicit value other than **' LIST**;

2. **ebody'** is an explicit value that is a quotation of some term **body'**;

3. **alist** is the standard alist on **args**; and

4. the set of variables in **body'** is a subset of those in **args**,

in which case **ebody** is the preferred quotation of **body'**.

Examples. The non-**SUBRP** axiom for **ADD2**, **(X Y)**, and **(PLUS 2 X Y)** is

```
(AND (EQUAL (SUBRP 'ADD2) F)
     (EQUAL (FORMALS 'ADD2) '(X Y))
     (EQUAL (BODY 'ADD2)
            '(PLUS (QUOTE 2) (PLUS X Y)))).
```

The non-**SUBRP** axiom for **RUS**, **( )** , and

```
(EVAL$ T '(ADD1 (RUS)) NIL)
```

is

```
(AND (EQUAL (SUBRP 'RUS) F)
     (EQUAL (FORMALS 'RUS) NIL)
     (EQUAL (BODY 'RUS) '(ADD1 (RUS)))).
```

4.11. Quantification

Note. The reader is urged to see [11] for a motivated development of our axiomatization of **FOR**.

4.11.1. The Definition of FOR and its Subfunctions

Defining Axiom 56.
```
(QUANTIFIER-INITIAL-VALUE OP)
  =
(CDR (ASSOC OP '((ADD-TO-SET . NIL)
                 (ALWAYS . *1*TRUE)
                 (APPEND . NIL)
                 (COLLECT . NIL)
                 (COUNT . 0)
                 (DO-RETURN . NIL)
                 (EXISTS . *1*FALSE)
                 (MAX . 0)
                 (SUM . 0)
                 (MULTIPLY . 1)
                 (UNION . NIL))))
```

Defining Axiom 57.
```
(QUANTIFIER-OPERATION OP VAL REST)
  =
(IF (EQUAL OP 'ADD-TO-SET) (ADD-TO-SET VAL REST)
(IF (EQUAL OP 'ALWAYS)     (AND VAL REST)
(IF (EQUAL OP 'APPEND)     (APPEND VAL REST)
```

```
(IF  (EQUAL OP 'COLLECT)       (CONS VAL REST)
(IF  (EQUAL OP 'COUNT)         (IF VAL (ADD1 REST) REST)
(IF  (EQUAL OP 'DO-RETURN)     VAL
(IF  (EQUAL OP 'EXISTS)        (OR VAL REST)
(IF  (EQUAL OP 'MAX)           (MAX VAL REST)
(IF  (EQUAL OP 'SUM)           (PLUS VAL REST)
(IF  (EQUAL OP 'MULTIPLY)      (TIMES VAL REST)
(IF  (EQUAL OP 'UNION)         (UNION VAL REST)
                               0)))))))))))
```

Defining Axiom 58 .
```
(FOR V L COND OP BODY A)
   =
(IF  (NLISTP L)
     (QUANTIFIER-INITIAL-VALUE OP)
     (IF (EVAL$ T COND (CONS (CONS V (CAR L)) A))
         (QUANTIFIER-OPERATION OP
             (EVAL$ T BODY (CONS (CONS V (CAR L)) A))
             (FOR V (CDR L) COND OP BODY A))
         (FOR V (CDR L) COND OP BODY A)))
```

4.11.2. The Extended Syntax for FOR—Abbreviations II

Note. This section completes the precise specification of the extended syntax by defining when an s-expression is an ''abbreviated **FOR**'' and the ''**FOR** expression denoted'' by such an s-expression.

Terminology. An s-expression **x** of the form (**FOR v IN 1st WHEN cond op body**) —i.e., **x** is an s-expression of length eight whose first element is the word **FOR**, third element is the word **IN**, and fifth element is the word **WHEN**—is an *abbreviated FOR* iff each of the following is true:

  • **v** is a variable symbol,

  • **1st**, **cond**, and **body** are well-formed s-expressions whose translations are the terms **t-1st**, **t-cond**, and **t-body**, and

  • **op** is an element of the set {**ADD-TO-SET ALWAYS APPEND COLLECT COUNT DO-RETURN EXISTS MAX SUM MULTIPLY UNION**}.

The *FOR expression denoted* by such an **x** is (**FOR 'v t-1st 't-cond 'op 't-body alist**) where **'v**, **'t-cond**, **'op**, and **'t-body** are the preferred quotations (see page 129) of **v**, **t-cond**, **op**, and **t-body** respectively, and **alist** is the standard alist (see page 135) on the sequence of variable symbols obtained by deleting **v** from the union of the variable symbols of **t-cond** with those of **t-body** and then sorting the resulting set alphabetically. An s-expression of the form **(FOR x IN lst op body)** is an *abbreviated FOR* iff **(FOR x IN lst WHEN T op body)** is an abbreviated **FOR** and, if so, denotes the same **FOR** expression as that denoted by **(FOR x IN lst WHEN T op body)**. No other form of s-expression is an *abbreviated FOR*.

4.12. SUBRPs and non-SUBRPs

Note. The symbol **QUOTE**, which is treated specially by **V&C\$** and cannot be defined by the user, is not a **SUBRP**.

Axiom 59.
(NOT (SUBRP 'QUOTE)).

Axioms 60-64. We now add the non-**SUBRP** axiom for each of the following five function symbols: **APPLY\$**, **EVAL\$**, **V&C\$**, **V&C-APPLY\$**, and **FOR**. Each of these symbols was introduced with a defining axiom of the form **(fn x_1 ... x_n)** = **body**. For each of the five function symbols we add the non-**SUBRP** axiom for **fn**, **(x_1 ... x_n)**, and **body**.

Axioms 65-120. We add the **SUBRP** axiom for every other function symbol that is mentioned in an axiom of the current theory. The complete list of SUBRPs is: **ADD1, ADD-TO-SET, AND, APPEND, APPLY-SUBR, ASSOC, BODY, CAR, CDR, CONS, COUNT, DIFFERENCE, EQUAL, FALSE, FALSEP, FIX, FIX-COST, FORMALS, GEQ, GREATERP, IF, IFF, IMPLIES, LEQ, LESSP, LISTP, LITATOM, MAX, MEMBER, MINUS, NEGATIVEP, NEGATIVE-GUTS, NLISTP, NOT, NUMBERP, OR, ORDINALP, ORD-LESSP, PACK, PAIRLIST, PLUS, QUANTIFIER-INITIAL-VALUE, QUANTIFIER-OPERATION, QUOTIENT, REMAINDER, STRIP-CARS, SUB1, SUBRP, SUM-CDRS, TIMES, TRUE, TRUEP, UNION, UNPACK, ZERO,** and **ZEROP**.

4.13. Induction and Recursion

4.13.1. Induction

Rule of Inference. Induction

Suppose

   (a) **p** is a term;
   (b) **m** is a term;
   (c) $q_1, ..., q_k$ are terms;
   (d) $h_1, ..., h_k$ are positive integers;
   (e) it is a theorem that $(ORDINALP\ m)$;
      and
   (f) for $1 \leq i \leq k$ and $1 \leq j \leq h_i$, $s_{i,j}$
      is a substitution and it is a theorem that

$$(IMPLIES\ q_i\ (ORD-LESSP\ m/s_{i,j}\ m)).$$

Then **p** is a theorem if

   (1) $(IMPLIES\ (AND\ (NOT\ q_1)\ ...\ (NOT\ q_k))@T$
      $p)$

is a theorem and

for each $1 \leq i \leq k$,

   (2) $(IMPLIES\ (AND\ q_i\ p/s_{i,1}\ ...\ p/s_{i,h_i})@T$
      $p)$

is a theorem.

Notes. In informally describing an application of the induction principle to some conjecture **p** we generally say the induction is *on* the variables occurring in the term m, which is called the *measure*. An inductive proof splits the problem into **k+1** cases, a *base case*, given by formula (1) above, and **k** *induction steps*, given by the **k** formulas of form (2) above. The *cases* are given by the q_i. The ith induction step requires proving **p** under case q_i. The base case requires proving **p** under the conjunction of the negations of the q_i. In the

i^{th} induction step one may assume an arbitrary number (namely h_i) of instances, $p/s_{i,j}$, of the conjecture being proved. The jth instance for the ith case is given by substitution $s_{i,j}$. Each instance is called an *induction hypothesis*. To *justify* an induction one must show that some ordinal measure **m** of the induction variables decreases under each substitution in each respective case.

We illustrate the principle of induction in Chapter 5.

4.13.2. The Principle of Definition

Terminology. We say that a term **t** *governs* an occurrence of a term **s** in a term **b** iff (a) either **b** contains a subterm of the form **(IF t p q)** and the occurrence of **s** is in **p** or (b) if **b** contains a subterm of the form **(IF t′ p q)**, where **t** is **(NOT t′)** and the occurrence of **s** is in **q**.

Examples. The terms **P** and **(NOT Q)** govern the first occurrence of **S** in

```
(IF P
    (IF (IF Q A S)
        S
        B)
    C)
```

The terms **P** and **(IF Q A S)** govern the second occurrence of **S**.

Rule of Inference. Definition

The axiomatic act

Definition. **(f x_1 ... x_n) = body**

is admissible under the history h provided

(a) **f** is a function symbol of **n** arguments and is new in h;

(b) x_1, ..., x_n are distinct variables;

(c) **body** is a term and mentions no symbol as a variable other than x_1, ..., x_n;

(d) there is a term m such that (a) **(ORDINALP m)** can be proved directly in h, and (b) for each occurrence of a subterm of the form **(f y_1 ... y_n)**

in **body** and the terms t_1, ..., t_k governing it,
the following formula can be proved directly in h:

```
(IMPLIES  (AND  t_1  ...  t_k) @T
          (ORD-LESSP  m/s  m)),
```

where **s** is the substitution $\{<x_1, y_1>, ..., <x_n, y_n>\}$.

If admissible, we add the

Defining Axiom.
$(f\ x_1\ \ldots\ x_n)\ =\ \textbf{body}.$

In addition, we add

Axiom.
the non-**SUBRP** axiom for **f**, $(x_1,\ \ldots,\ x_n)$, and **body**.

5 Proving Theorems in the Logic

We have already proved many theorems in the logic. For example, from

Defining Axiom 36.
```
(APPEND L1 L2)
    =
(IF (LISTP L1)
    (CONS (CAR L1) (APPEND (CDR L1) L2))
    L2)
```
we have observed that

$$(APPEND\ NIL\ '(1\ 2\ 3))\ =\ '(1\ 2\ 3)$$

and

$$(APPEND\ '(1\ 2\ 3)\ '(4\ 5\ 6))\ =\ '(1\ 2\ 3\ 4\ 5\ 6)$$

These two equations are *theorems* that can be *proved* using the familiar rules of inference of propositional calculus, equality, and instantiation.

In this Chapter we illustrate many simple proofs. We start with the propositional calculus and work our way up to inductive proofs about recursive functions. Among the illustrative theorems proved are those that justify "structural induction," the most commonly used application of the induction principle in our logic.

143

5.1. Propositional Calculus with Equality

We will start with some simple propositional calculus.[17] First, we will prove the theorem $(P \lor Q) \rightarrow (Q \lor P)$. However, the formal proof of even so simple a theorem is very long if we limit ourselves to the rules of inference given, namely Expansion, Contraction, Associativity, and Cut. We therefore start by deriving several new rules of inference.

Derived Rule of Inference. *Commutativity of Or*:
Derive $(b \lor a)$ from $(a \lor b)$.

Below we derive $(b \lor a)$ from $(a \lor b)$. The proof is presented as a sequence of formulas, each of which is either an axiom or is given (in the case of a derived rule of inference) or is derived by inference rules from previous formulas. We number and justify each formula in the presentation below. Unless otherwise noted, each rule of inference takes as its single premise the formula immediately above.

Proof.
1.	$(a \lor b)$	Given
2.	$((\neg a) \lor a)$	Propositional Axiom
3.	$(b \lor a)$	Cut, lines 1 and 2
	Q.E.D.	

What exactly is going on here? We have shown that from $(a \lor b)$ we can derive $(b \lor a)$ by applying the primitive rules, namely the Propositional Axiom and Cut. Thus, in the future, if we have derived a formula of the form $(a \lor b)$ we can, in the next line, derive $(b \lor a)$ and attribute the derivation to the derived rule Commutativity of Or, in the knowledge that we could convert the resulting "proof" into a proof by substituting for that single line the steps above.

We now derive several other useful rules, using Commutativity of Or:

Derived Rule of Inference. *Or Insertion 1*:
Derive $a \lor (c \lor b)$ from $(a \lor b)$.

Proof.
1.	$(a \lor b)$	Given
2.	$(b \lor a)$	Commutativity of Or
3.	$(c \lor (b \lor a))$	Expansion
4.	$(c \lor b) \lor a$	Associativity
5.	$a \lor (c \lor b)$	Commutativity of Or
	Q.E.D.	

---

[17]Most of the proofs in this section were contributed by N. Shankar.

Derived Rule of Inference. *Or Insertion 2*:
Derive **a** ∨ **(b** ∨ **c)** from **(a** ∨ **b)**.

Proof.

1.	**(a** ∨ **b)**	Given
2.	**(b** ∨ **a)**	Commutativity of Or
3.	**b** ∨ **(c** ∨ **a)**	Or Insertion 1
4.	**(b** ∨ **c)** ∨ **a**	Associativity
5.	**a** ∨ **(b** ∨ **c)**	Commutativity of Or
	Q.E.D.	

Derived Rule of Inference. *Or-Implication*:
Derive **(a** ∨ **b)** → **c** from **a** → **c** and **b** → **c**.

Proof.

1.	**b** → **c**	Given
2.	**¬b** ∨ **c**	Abbreviation
3.	**¬(a** ∨ **b)** ∨ **(a** ∨ **b)**	Propositional Axiom
4.	**(¬(a** ∨ **b)** ∨ **a)** ∨ **b**	Associativity
5.	**b** ∨ **(¬(a** ∨ **b)** ∨ **a)**	Commutativity of Or
6.	**(¬(a** ∨ **b)** ∨ **a)** ∨ **c**	Cut, lines 5 and 2
7.	**c** ∨ **(¬(a** ∨ **b)** ∨ **a)**	Commutativity of Or
8.	**(c** ∨ **¬(a** ∨ **b))** ∨ **a**	Associativity
9.	**a** ∨ **(c** ∨ **¬(a** ∨ **b))**	Commutativity of Or
10.	**a** → **c**	Given
11.	**¬a** ∨ **c**	Abbreviation
12.	**¬a** ∨ **(c** ∨ **¬(a** ∨ **b))**	Or Insertion 2
13.	**(c** ∨ **¬(a** ∨ **b))** ∨ **(c** ∨ **¬(a** ∨ **b))**	Cut, lines 9 and 12
14.	**(c** ∨ **¬(a** ∨ **b))**	Contraction
15.	**¬(a** ∨ **b)** ∨ **c**	Commutativity of Or
16.	**(a** ∨ **b)** → **c**	Abbreviation
	Q.E.D.	

We are finally in a position to prove our first theorem!

Theorem. **(P** ∨ **Q)** → **(Q** ∨ **P)**.

Proof.

1.	**¬P** ∨ **P**	Propositional Axiom
2.	**¬P** ∨ **(Q** ∨ **P)**	Or Insertion 1
3.	**P** → **(Q** ∨ **P)**	Abbreviation
4.	**¬Q** ∨ **Q**	Propositional Axiom
5.	**¬Q** ∨ **(Q** ∨ **P)**	Or Insertion 2
6.	**Q** → **(Q** ∨ **P)**	Abbreviation
7.	**(P** ∨ **Q)** → **(Q** ∨ **P)**	Or-Implication, lines 3 and 6

Q.E.D.

A very useful derived rule is, of course,

Derived Rule of Inference. *Modus Ponens*:
Derive **b** from **a** and **(a → b)**.

Proof.

1.	**a**	Given
2.	**a ∨ b**	Expansion
3.	**a → b**	Given
4.	**¬a ∨ b**	Abbreviation
5.	**b ∨ b**	Cut, lines 2 and 4
6.	**b**	Contraction

Q.E.D.

There are, of course, many other derived rules of inference about propositional calculus. Among them are

- **The Tautology Theorem**: any propositional tautology is a theorem.[18]

- **The Deduction Law**: derive **p→q** from a proof of **q** in which **p** is assumed as given but neither that assumption nor any formula derived from it is instantiated.

- **Case Analysis**: if **p** can be proved under each of a set of exhaustive cases, **p** is a theorem.

We next prove a simple theorem about the equality predicate. We are not so much interested in the theorem as in the proof, because it illustrates the use of the deduction law and suggests the proof of the commonly used derived rule of substitution of equals for equals.

Theorem.
X=Y → (CAR (CDR X))=(CAR (CDR Y))

Proof.

1. **X=Y**   Hypothesis
2. **X1=Y1 → (CDR X1)=(CDR Y1)**
                                    Equality Axiom for **CDR**
3. **X=Y → (CDR X)=(CDR Y)**
                                    Instantiation
4. **(CDR X)=(CDR Y)**

---

[18]In fact, it is possible to formalize Schoenfield's propositional calculus within our logic and get our mechanical theorem prover to prove the tautology theorem.   See [30].

5.   **X1=Y1** → **(CAR X1) = (CAR Y1)**
$$\text{modus ponens, lines 1 and 3}$$

6.   **(CDR X) = (CDR Y)** → **(CAR (CDR X)) = (CAR (CDR Y))**
$$\text{Equality Axiom for } \textbf{CAR}$$

7.   **(CAR (CDR X)) = (CAR (CDR Y))**
$$\text{Instantiation}$$

8.   **X=Y** → **(CAR (CDR X)) = (CAR (CDR Y))**
$$\text{modus ponens, lines 4 and 6}$$
$$\text{deduction law, lines 1 and 7}$$
     Q.E.D.

By induction on the structure of terms we can derive the following powerful and widely used rule of inference:

Derived Rule of Inference. *Substitution of Equals for Equals*:
If **t=s** has been proved and formula **q** is obtained from formula **p** by replacing some occurrences of **t** by **s**, then **q** is provable iff **p** is provable.

For example, this rule lets us replace the application of a function, e.g., **(FIX A)**, by the instantiated body of the function, **(IF (NUMBERP A) A 0)**, anywhere **(FIX A)** occurs in another formula.

By combining this rule with the deduction law we can substitute **s** for selected occurrences of **t** in **concl** when trying to prove a formula of the form **t = s** → **concl**.

5.2. Theorems about IF and Propositional Functions

Theorem.   **IF cases.**
(IF X Y Z) =U   ↔   **(X≠F → Y=U)** ∧ **(X=F → Z=U)**

Proof. The proof is by case analysis on **X=F**.
    Case 1. **X = F.** By **Axiom 4**, **(IF X Y Z) = Z**. Thus, the left-hand side above is **Z=U**. The right-hand side becomes

     (F≠F → Y=U) ∧ **(F=F → Z=U)**

By propositional calculus and equality, the right-hand side is equivalent to **Z=U**.
    Case 2. **X ≠ F.** By **Axiom 5**, the left-hand side above is equivalent to **Y=U**. By propositional calculus and equality, the right-hand side also equivalent to **Y=U**. Q.E.D.

Theorem.   **IMPLIES is implication:**
(IMPLIES P Q) ≠F   ↔   **(P≠F → Q≠F)**

Proof. We will repeatedly replace the left-hand side of this equivalence by equivalent formulas until it is identical to the right-hand side.

By the definition of **IMPLIES** (**Axiom 11**), the left-hand side is equivalent to

$$\texttt{(IF P (IF Q T F) T)} \neq \texttt{F}$$

which, by **IF cases** is equivalent to

$$\texttt{(P} \neq \texttt{F} \to \texttt{(IF Q T F)} \neq \texttt{F)} \wedge \texttt{(P=F} \to \texttt{T} \neq \texttt{F)} .$$

By **Axiom 1** and propositional calculus, the above is equivalent to

$$\texttt{P} \neq \texttt{F} \to \texttt{(IF Q T F)} \neq \texttt{F} .$$

Applying **IF cases** again produces

$$\texttt{P} \neq \texttt{F} \to \texttt{[(Q} \neq \texttt{F} \to \texttt{T} \neq \texttt{F)} \wedge \texttt{(Q=F} \to \texttt{F} \neq \texttt{F)]}$$

which, by **Axiom 1** and propositional calculus with equality, is equivalent to

$$\texttt{(P} \neq \texttt{F} \to \texttt{Q} \neq \texttt{F)} .$$

Q.E.D.

Next we observe

Derived Rule of Inference. *Term based Modus Ponens*:
The term **q** may be derived as a theorem if the term **p** is a theorem and the term
(IMPLIES p q) is a theorem.

The proof is trivial, given **IMPLIES is implies.**

Theorem. NOT case
(NOT P) $\neq$ **F** $\leftrightarrow$ **P=F**

Proof. By the definition of **NOT** (**Axiom 8**), the left-hand side is equivalent to
(IF P F T) $\neq$ **F** which, by **IF cases**, is equivalent to

$$\texttt{(P} \neq \texttt{F} \to \texttt{F} \neq \texttt{F)} \wedge \texttt{(P=F} \to \texttt{T} \neq \texttt{F)} .$$

But by **Axiom 1** and propositional calculus with equality, this is equivalent to
P=F. Q.E.D.

Theorem. EQUAL is equal:
(EQUAL X Y) $\neq$ **F** $\leftrightarrow$ **X=Y**

Proof. That the left-hand side implies the right is merely the contrapositive of

Axiom 3.
X $\neq$ **Y** $\to$ **(EQUAL X Y)** = **F**.

That the right-hand side implies the left follows immediately from

Axiom 2.
`X = Y → (EQUAL X Y) = T`

and

Axiom 1.
`T≠F`.

by equality reasoning. Q.E.D.

Henceforth, we will reason about the propositional functions `EQUAL`, `IF`, `NOT`, `AND`, `OR`, and `IMPLIES` with the same casual ease we use with propositional calculus and equality.

5.3. Simple Theorems about NIL, CONS, and APPEND

Theorem. `NIL is not a LISTP`
`(LISTP NIL)=F`

Informally, the proof of this theorem is "`NIL` is an abbreviation for a `PACK` expression, `PACK` returns a `LITATOM`, and no `LITATOM` is a `LISTP`." We do it more formally below.

Proof. Recall that `NIL` is an abbreviation for

        `(PACK ' (78 73 76 . 0))`

Thus, by instantiating

Axiom 20.2.
`(LITATOM (PACK X1)),`

replacing `X1` by `' (78 73 76 . 0)`, we get

`(1)    (LITATOM NIL)`

By instantiating

Axiom 20.10.1.
`(IMPLIES (LITATOM X) (NOT (LISTP X)))`

replacing `X` by `NIL`, we get

`(2)    (IMPLIES (LITATOM NIL) (NOT (LISTP NIL)))`

Term based modus ponens on lines (1) and (2) produces

(3)   (NOT (LISTP NIL)).

By **NOT case**, instantiating **P** with **(LISTP NIL)** (and choosing only the
"→" direction of the "↔") we get

(4)   (NOT (LISTP NIL))   →   (LISTP NIL)=F.

Thus, with modus ponens on lines (3) and (4) we get

(LISTP NIL) = F.

Q.E.D.

We next prove two lemmas that make it easy to "compute" **APPEND** expressions:

Theorem. APPEND-NIL
(APPEND NIL L) = L

Proof. Instantiating the definition of **APPEND**,

Defining Axiom 36.
(APPEND L1 L2)
**   =**
(IF (LISTP L1)
**   (CONS (CAR L1) (APPEND (CDR L1) L2))**
**   L2)**

replacing **L1** by **NIL** and **L2** by **L** we get

(APPEND NIL L)
**   =**
(IF (LISTP NIL)
**   (CONS (CAR NIL) (APPEND (CDR NIL) L))**
**   L)).**

By **NIL is not a LISTP** and substitution of equals for equals we get

(APPEND NIL L)
**   =**
(IF F
**   (CONS (CAR NIL) (APPEND (CDR NIL) L))**
**   L)).**

By instantiation of

Axiom 4.
```
X = F → (IF X Y Z) = Z
```

and equality we get

```
(IF F
    (CONS (CAR NIL) (APPEND (CDR NIL) L))
    L)
  =
L.
```

Thus, by equality,

```
(APPEND NIL L) = L.
```

Q.E.D.

The second lemma about **APPEND** is

Theorem. APPEND-CONS
```
(APPEND (CONS X Y) L) = (CONS X (APPEND Y L)).
```

Proof. By instantiation of **Defining Axiom 36** (above)

```
(APPEND (CONS X Y) L)
  =
(IF (LISTP (CONS X Y))
    (CONS (CAR (CONS X Y))
          (APPEND (CDR (CONS X Y)) L))
    L).
```

But, by

Axiom 19.2.
```
(LISTP (CONS X1 X2))
```

we get **(LISTP (CONS X Y))** thus by instantiation of

Axiom 5.
```
X ≠ F → (IF X Y Z) = Y,
```

and modus ponens we get

```
(IF (LISTP (CONS X Y))
    (CONS (CAR (CONS X Y))
          (APPEND (CDR (CONS X Y)) L))
    L)
  =
(CONS (CAR (CONS X Y))
      (APPEND (CDR (CONS X Y)) L)).
```

Thus we have

```
(APPEND (CONS X Y) L)
   =
(CONS (CAR (CONS X Y))
      (APPEND (CDR (CONS X Y)) L)).
```

It remains only to appeal to

Axiom 19.6.1.
```
(EQUAL (CAR (CONS X1 X2)) X1)
```

and

Axiom 19.6.2.
```
(EQUAL (CDR (CONS X1 X2)) X2),
```

to get

```
(APPEND (CONS X Y) L) = (CONS X (APPEND Y L)).
```

Q.E.D.

With **APPEND-NIL** and **APPEND-CONS** it is easy to derive

Theorem.
```
(APPEND NIL '(1 2 3)) = '(1 2 3)
```

Proof. The theorem is an instance of **APPEND-NIL**. Q.E.D.

Theorem.
```
(APPEND '(1 2 3) '(4 5 6)) = '(1 2 3 4 5 6).
```

Proof.

```
   (APPEND '(1 2 3) '(4 5 6))
 = (CONS 1 (APPEND '(2 3) '(4 5 6)))
 = (CONS 1 (CONS 2 (APPEND '(3) '(4 5 6))))
 = (CONS 1 (CONS 2 (CONS 3 (APPEND NIL '(4 5 6)))))
 = (CONS 1 (CONS 2 (CONS 3 '(4 5 6))))
 = '(1 2 3 4 5 6).
```

The first three equalities are derived with **APPEND-CONS**, the fourth is derived with **APPEND-NIL**, and the last is an identity exploiting the **QUOTE** notation. Q.E.D.

5.4. The Associativity of APPEND

Theorem. `ASSOCIATIVITY-OF-APPEND`:
`(APPEND (APPEND A B) C) = (APPEND A (APPEND B C))`.

Proof. The proof is by induction on **A**. We split the problem into two cases according to whether **(LISTP A)**. The base case is when **A** is not a **LISTP**. The induction step is when **A** is a **LISTP**. In the induction step we assume one instance of the conjecture as an inductive hypothesis. The instance of interest is obtained by replacing **A** by **(CDR A)**. This induction is justified by the observation that **(COUNT A)** decreases under this substitution when **A** is a **LISTP**.

Having informally described the application of the induction principle we will now go through the statement and application of the principle carefully. Recall the principle:

Rule of Inference. Induction

Suppose

  (a) **p** is a term;
  (b) **m** is a term;
  (c) q_1, ..., q_k are terms;
  (d) h_1, ..., h_k are positive integers;
  (e) it is a theorem that **(ORDINALP m)**;
   and
  (f) for $1 \le i \le k$ and $1 \le j \le h_i$, $s_{i,j}$
    is a substitution and it is a theorem that

$$\text{(IMPLIES } q_i \text{ (ORD-LESSP } m/s_{i,j} \text{ m))}.$$

Then **p** is a theorem if

  (1) `(IMPLIES (AND (NOT `q_1`) ... (NOT `q_k`))@T`
         `p)`

is a theorem and

for each $1 \le i \le k$,

  (2) `(IMPLIES (AND `q_i` p/`$s_{i,1}$` ... p/`s_{i,h_i}`)@T`
         `p)`

is a theorem.

To use the principle of induction we must choose **p**, the formula we wish to prove; **m**, a "measure term" that justifies our induction; the terms **q$_i$** that distinguish the various cases of the inductive proof; the substitutions **s$_{i,j}$** that produce the inductive hypotheses; and the various limits on the number of cases, substitutions, etc. In addition, we must prove certain theorems about our choices, namely that the measure term is an **ORDINALP** and that the substitutions decrease the measure under the appropriate tests. Here are the choices we shall make to prove the associativity of **APPEND**:

(a) **p** is the term **(EQUAL (APPEND (APPEND A B) C) (APPEND A (APPEND B C)))**, the conjecture we are trying to prove;

(b) **m**, the measure, is **(COUNT A)**;

(c) **k**, the number of cases, is 1 and the case, **q$_1$**, is **(LISTP A)**;

(d) **h$_1$**, the number of induction hypotheses in the first case, is 1;

(e) It is a theorem that **(ORDINALP (COUNT A))**, since, by **Axiom 13 COUNT** returns a **NUMBERP** and from **Axiom 25** it follows that every **NUMBERP** is an **ORDINALP**; and

(f) The substitution, **s$_{1,1}$**, that determines our induction hypothesis replaces **A** by **(CDR A)**. It is a theorem that

```
(IMPLIES (LISTP A)
         (ORD-LESSP (COUNT (CDR A))
                    (COUNT A))).
```

An informal proof of the above theorem is as follows: by **Axiom 13**, **COUNT** returns a **NUMBERP** and thus, by **Axiom 24**, **ORD-LESSP** is **LESSP** on the arguments above. But by **Axiom 19.11**, the **COUNT** of **A** is one plus the sum of the **COUNT**s of **(CAR A)** and **(CDR A)**. Hence, by simple arithmetic, the **COUNT** of **(CDR A)** is **LESSP** the **COUNT** of **A**. The "simple arithmetic" needed is surprisingly elaborate if one starts at Ground Zero. In the next section we develop enough arithmetic to prove the above theorem more carefully. But for now we will continue with the proof of the associativity of **APPEND**.

Having met the requirements of the principle of induction, we may conclude that **p** is a theorem if

```
(1) (IMPLIES (AND (NOT q₁) ... (NOT qₖ)) @T
        p)
```

is a theorem and, for each $1 \leq i \leq k$,

$$(2) \quad (\text{IMPLIES } (\text{AND } q_i \ P/s_{i,1} \ \cdots \ P/s_{i,h_i}) @ T$$
$$P)$$

is a theorem. We will display and prove these formulas for the above choices of **P**, q_i, $s_{i,j}$, etc.

The base case is

```
(IMPLIES (NOT (LISTP A))
         (EQUAL (APPEND (APPEND A B) C)
                (APPEND A (APPEND B C)))).
```

We will thus assume that **A** is not a **LISTP** and prove the conclusion above by successively rewriting both sides until they are identical. The only fact used in the rewriting is that **APPEND** returns its second argument when its first is not a **LISTP**, an immediate observation from the definition of **APPEND** (**Axiom 36**). The desired conclusion is

```
(EQUAL (APPEND (APPEND A B) C)
       (APPEND A (APPEND B C)))
```

By rewriting the second **APPEND** expression, this is equivalent to

```
(EQUAL (APPEND B C)
       (APPEND A (APPEND B C))),
```

which, by rewriting the second **APPEND** expression, is equivalent to

```
(EQUAL (APPEND B C)
       (APPEND B C)).
```

Thus, the base case holds.

Only one induction step is generated by the scheme above, since **k** is 1. The induction step is

```
(IMPLIES (AND (LISTP A)
              (EQUAL (APPEND (APPEND (CDR A) B)
                             C)
                     (APPEND (CDR A)
                             (APPEND B C))))
         (EQUAL (APPEND (APPEND A B) C)
                (APPEND A (APPEND B C))))
```

We take **(LISTP A)** and

```
(EQUAL (APPEND (APPEND (CDR A) B) C)
       (APPEND (CDR A) (APPEND B C)))
```

as hypotheses and will prove the conclusion above by successively rewriting it. The conclusion is

```
(EQUAL (APPEND (APPEND A B)
               C)
       (APPEND A
               (APPEND B C))).
```

By the definition of **APPEND** and the fact that **A** is a **LISTP** we can rewrite **(APPEND A B)** to **(CONS (CAR A) (APPEND (CDR A) B))**. Thus, the conclusion becomes

```
(EQUAL (APPEND (CONS (CAR A)
                     (APPEND (CDR A) B))
               C)
       (APPEND A
               (APPEND B C))).
```

By **APPEND-CONS** the first **APPEND** expression above can be rewritten, producing

```
(EQUAL (CONS (CAR A)
             (APPEND (APPEND (CDR A) B)
                     C))
       (APPEND A
               (APPEND B C))).
```

By the definition of **APPEND** and the hypothesis that **A** is a **LISTP** we can rewrite the third **APPEND** expression above to produce

```
(EQUAL (CONS (CAR A)
             (APPEND (APPEND (CDR A) B)
                     C))
       (CONS (CAR A)
             (APPEND (CDR A)
                     (APPEND B C)))).
```

By our induction hypothesis we can replace

```
(APPEND (APPEND (CDR A) B)
        C)
```

above by

```
(APPEND (CDR A)
        (APPEND B C)).
```

Thus the conclusion becomes

```
(EQUAL (CONS (CAR A)
             (APPEND (CDR A)
                     (APPEND B C)))
       (CONS (CAR A)
             (APPEND (CDR A)
                     (APPEND B C))))
```

which is an identity. Thus the induction step holds. Q.E.D.

5.5. Simple Arithmetic

In the previous section we performed an induction in which we assumed the formula for **(CDR A)** and proved it for **A**, under the hypothesis **(LISTP A)**. This induction was justified by the observation that the **COUNT** of **(CDR A)** is smaller than that of **A** when **A** is a **LISTP**. In general, if **r** is the recognizer of a shell class with base object **(base)** and accessors ac_1, ..., ac_n, it is a theorem that

```
(IMPLIES (AND (r X)
              (NOT (EQUAL X (base))))
         (ORD-LESSP (COUNT (ac_i X)) (COUNT X)))
```

for each $1 \leq i \leq n$. This permits "structural" inductions on the shell class **r**.

In this section we prove the simple arithmetic theorems leading to this result. In the next section we prove the above metatheorem and explain what we mean by "structural inductions."

Theorem. **NUMBERP-SUB1:**
(NUMBERP (SUB1 X))

Proof. The proof is by cases. If **X** is not a **NUMBERP** or is 0, **(SUB1 X)** is 0 by **Axiom 12.7**, and 0 is a **NUMBERP** by **Axiom 12.3**. Thus, assume **X** is a non-0 **NUMBERP**. By **Axiom 12.5**, **X** is **(ADD1 (SUB1 X))**. If **(SUB1 X)** is a **NUMBERP** we are done. Thus assume the contrary. Then by **Axiom 12.7**, **(SUB1 (ADD1 (SUB1 X)))** is 0 and hence a **NUMBERP**. Q.E.D.

Theorem. **NUMBERP-PLUS:**
(NUMBERP (PLUS I J))

Proof. By the definition of **PLUS** (Axiom 18), **(PLUS I J)** is either **(FIX J)** or the result of an **ADD1**. If the former, it is a **NUMBERP** by the definition of **FIX** (Axiom 17). If the latter, it is a **NUMBERP** by **Axiom 12.2**. Q.E.D.

Theorem. ASSOCIATIVITY-OF-PLUS:
```
(EQUAL (PLUS (PLUS I J) K)
       (PLUS I (PLUS J K))).
```

Proof. We will induct on **I**. The case split is on **(NOT (ZEROP I))**. In the induction step we will assume the instance obtained by replacing **I** by **(SUB1 I)**. The measure we use is **(FIX I)**.

The formulas we must prove to justify the induction are

```
(ORDINALP (FIX I))
```
and
```
(IMPLIES (NOT (ZEROP I))
         (ORD-LESSP (FIX (SUB1 I)) (FIX I)))
```

The first theorem is trivial since **FIX** always returns a **NUMBERP** (by case analysis on **(NUMBERP I)**).

The second theorem is more interesting. By **NUMBERP-SUB1** we know that **(SUB1 I)** is a **NUMBERP**. Hence, **(FIX (SUB1 I))** is **(SUB1 I)**. By the hypothesis that **I** is non-**ZEROP** and the definition of **ZEROP** (**Axiom 16**) we know **I** is a **NUMBERP**. Hence, **(FIX I)** is **I**. Thus, the second theorem can be simplified to

```
(IMPLIES (NOT (ZEROP I))
         (ORD-LESSP (SUB1 I) I)).
```

By the definition of **ORD-LESSP** (**Axiom 24**), **ORD-LESSP** is **LESSP** on the arguments above, and thus the formula becomes

```
(IMPLIES (NOT (ZEROP I))
         (LESSP (SUB1 I) I))
```

But this is just **Axiom 23**.

In short, an induction in which we replace **I** by **(SUB1 I)** when **I** is a non-**ZEROP** is justified because **Axiom 23** says it is.

We now continue with the proof of the associativity of **PLUS**.

The base case for the associativity of **PLUS** is

```
(IMPLIES (NOT (NOT (ZEROP I)))
         (EQUAL (PLUS (PLUS I J) K)
                (PLUS I (PLUS J K)))).
```

By the definitions of **NOT** (**Axiom 8**) and **ZEROP** (**Axiom 16**) and propositional calculus, the hypothesis is equivalent to **(ZEROP I)**. Under that hypothesis, the conclusion is equal to

```
(EQUAL (PLUS (FIX J) K)
       (FIX (PLUS J K)))
```

by the definition of **PLUS** (Axiom 18). By case analysis on whether **J** is a **NUMBERP** and the definitions of **PLUS**, **ZEROP**, and **FIX**, both sides above are equal to **(PLUS J K)**.

The induction step for the associativity of **PLUS** is

```
(IMPLIES (AND (NOT (ZEROP I))
              (EQUAL (PLUS (PLUS (SUB1 I) J) K)
                     (PLUS (SUB1 I) (PLUS J K))))
         (EQUAL (PLUS (PLUS I J) K)
                (PLUS I (PLUS J K)))).
```

Under the hypothesis that **I** is non-**ZEROP**, the definition of **PLUS** can be used to rewrite the second and third calls of **PLUS** in the conclusion above to produce the new goal:

```
(EQUAL (PLUS (ADD1 (PLUS (SUB1 I) J)) K)
       (ADD1 (PLUS (SUB1 I) (PLUS J K)))).
```

By the definition of **ZEROP** and **Axioms 12.2** and **12.4** we can show that no **ADD1**-expression is **ZEROP**, and thus we can apply the definition of **PLUS** to the first call of **PLUS** above and produce

```
(EQUAL
 (ADD1 (PLUS (SUB1 (ADD1 (PLUS (SUB1 I) J))) K))
 (ADD1 (PLUS (SUB1 I) (PLUS J K)))).
```

We can use **Axiom 12.6** and **NUMBERP-PLUS** to simplify the **(SUB1 (ADD1 (PLUS ...)))** expression above and produce

```
(EQUAL (ADD1 (PLUS (PLUS (SUB1 I) J) K))
       (ADD1 (PLUS (SUB1 I) (PLUS J K)))).
```

Finally, substituting the right-hand side of the induction hypothesis for the left into the conclusion above we produce the identity

```
(EQUAL (ADD1 (PLUS (SUB1 I) (PLUS J K)))
       (ADD1 (PLUS (SUB1 I) (PLUS J K)))).
```

Q.E.D.

Using similar techniques we can prove the following theorems:

Theorem. PLUS-RIGHT-ID:
```
(IMPLIES (ZEROP J)
         (EQUAL (PLUS I J) (FIX I)))
```

Theorem. COMMUTATIVITY-OF-PLUS:
```
(EQUAL (PLUS I J) (PLUS J I))
```

More interesting is the proof of the transitivity of **LESSP**:

Theorem . TRANSITIVITY-OF-LESSP:
```
(IMPLIES (AND (LESSP I J)
              (LESSP J K))
         (LESSP I K)).
```

Proof. We will induct on **I**, using the case split

```
(AND (NOT (ZEROP I))
     (NOT (ZEROP J))
     (NOT (ZEROP K))).
```

In the induction step we will have one induction hypothesis obtained by replacing **I** by **(SUB1 I)**, **J** by **(SUB1 J)** and **K** by **(SUB1 K)**. This substitution decreases the **FIX** of **I** just as in the previous example.

The base case reduces, with propositional calculus, to three subcases, one for each of the assumptions that **I**, **J**, or **K** is **ZEROP**. In each subcase we must prove

```
(IMPLIES (AND (LESSP I J)
              (LESSP J K))
         (LESSP I K))
```

In the two cases when either **J** or **K** is **ZEROP**, the definition of **LESSP** (**Axiom 22**) can be used to reduce one of the two **LESSP** hypotheses to **F**, and propositional calculus immediately completes the proof of the subcases. If **I** is **ZEROP**, **(LESSP I J)** is equivalent (by the definitions of **LESSP** and **NOT**) to **(NOT (ZEROP J))**, and **(LESSP I K)** is **(NOT (ZEROP K))**. Thus we wish to prove

```
(IMPLIES (AND (NOT (ZEROP J))
              (LESSP J K))
         (NOT (ZEROP K))),
```

which, by propositional calculus, is equivalent to

```
(IMPLIES (AND (NOT (ZEROP J))
              (ZEROP K))
         (NOT (LESSP J K))).
```

But by the definition of **LESSP**, if **K** is **ZEROP**, **(LESSP J K)** is **F**, and propositional calculus finishes the subcase.

The induction step for the transitivity of **LESSP** is

```
(IMPLIES (AND (NOT (ZEROP I))
              (NOT (ZEROP J))
              (NOT (ZEROP K))
```

```
(IMPLIES (AND (LESSP (SUB1 I)
                     (SUB1 J))
              (LESSP (SUB1 J)
                     (SUB1 K)))
         (LESSP (SUB1 I)
                (SUB1 K))))
(IMPLIES (AND (LESSP I J)
              (LESSP J K))
         (LESSP I K)))
```

But under the three non-**ZEROP** assumptions, the conclusion

```
(IMPLIES (AND (LESSP I J)
              (LESSP J K))
         (LESSP I K))
```

can be rewritten, by expanding all three calls of **LESSP**, to

```
(IMPLIES (AND (LESSP (SUB1 I)
                     (SUB1 J))
              (LESSP (SUB1 J)
                     (SUB1 K)))
         (LESSP (SUB1 I)
                (SUB1 K)))
```

which is the induction hypothesis. Q.E.D.

We can also prove such results as

Theorem. LESSP-PLUS:
(NOT (LESSP (PLUS I J) I))

Theorem. MIXED-TRANSITIVITY-OF-LESSP:
(IMPLIES (AND (LESSP I J)
              (NOT (LESSP K J)))
         (LESSP I K))

Intuitively, **(NOT (LESSP x y))** is $y \le x$. The first theorem above is $I \le I+J$, where **+** is on the natural numbers only. The second theorem is $I < J \land J \le K \to I < K$.

5.6. Structural Induction

We wish to prove, for every shell recognizer **r** and its corresponding base function symbol **base** and each of its **n** accessor functions **ac$_i$**:

```
(IMPLIES (AND (r X)
              (NOT (EQUAL X (base))))
         (ORD-LESSP (COUNT (ac_i X)) (COUNT X)))
```

Suppose we had such a theorem. Then it would be possible to perform any induction on **X** in which the case split is on

```
(AND (r X)
     (NOT (EQUAL X (base))))
```

and **n** induction hypotheses are provided, each obtained by replacing **X** by **(ac$_i$ X)** for some $1 \leq i \leq n$. Such an induction would be justified by **COUNT** by appeal to the theorem schema above.

We call such an induction a *structural induction for the shell type* **r** because it inductively decomposes structures of type **r** into their substructures until "bottoming out" on non-**r** objects or **(base)**. Many beautiful examples of structural induction are given by Burstall, who coined the term, in [15]. Our proof of the associativity of **APPEND** is an example of a structural induction: The base case was when **(NOT (LISTP A))**. The induction step was when **(LISTP A)**, and we inductively assumed the conjecture for **A** replaced by **(CDR A)**. We could have also assumed the conjecture for **(CAR A)**. The familiar induction on **I** by **(SUB1 I)** is a structural induction of type **NUMBERP**.

We now prove the justifying theorem schema. Familiarity with the shell principle is required to follow the proof.

Metatheorem. *Structural Induction Justification*:
For every shell recognizer, **r**, with corresponding base function symbol **base**, and for each of the **n** accessor function symbols **ac$_i$**, $1 \leq i \leq n$

```
(IMPLIES (AND (r X)
              (NOT (EQUAL X (base))))
         (ORD-LESSP (COUNT (ac_i X)) (COUNT X))).
```

Proof. By **Axiom 13**, **COUNT** returns a **NUMBERP** and hence by the definition of **ORD-LESSP** (**Axiom 24**), the **ORD-LESSP** call above can be replaced by a **LESSP** call. By the eleventh shell axiom schema we know that when **X** is a non-**(base)** object of type **r**, the **COUNT** of **X** is one greater than the sum of the **COUNT**s of its components. Replacing **(COUNT X)** by the right-hand side of the eleventh shell axiom schema renders our conclusion:

```
(LESSP (COUNT (ac_i X))
       (ADD1 (PLUS (COUNT (ac_1 X))
                   . . .
                   (COUNT (ac_i X))
                   . . .
                   (COUNT (ac_n X)))))
```

By repeated applications of **ASSOCIATIVITY-OF-PLUS** and **COMMUTATIVITY-OF-PLUS** our goal becomes

```
(LESSP (COUNT (ac_i X))
       (ADD1 (PLUS (COUNT (ac_i X))
                   (PLUS (COUNT (ac_1 X))
                         . . .
                         (COUNT (ac_{i-1} X))
                         (COUNT (ac_{i+1} X))
                         . . .
                         (COUNT (ac_n X))))))
```

We now expand the definition of **LESSP** (**Axiom 22**) and consider the cases on whether the first argument above, (**COUNT** (ac_i **X**)), is **ZEROP**. If the first argument is **ZEROP** the goal is reduced to **T** since the second argument is not **ZEROP** by **Axioms 12.2** and **12.4**. If the first argument is not **ZEROP** the recursive case obtains and, using **Axiom 12.6** and **NUMBERP-PLUS**, the goal becomes

```
(LESSP (SUB1 (COUNT (ac_i X)))
       (PLUS (COUNT (ac_i X))
             (PLUS (COUNT (ac_1 X))
                   . . .
                   (COUNT (ac_n X)))))
```

Observe that this goal has the form (**LESSP** (**SUB1 i**) (**PLUS i j**)) where we know that **i** is not **ZEROP**. But by **Axiom 23** we have that (**LESSP** (**SUB1 i**) **i**), and by **LESSP-PLUS** we have that (**NOT** (**LESSP** (**PLUS i j**) **i**)). Hence, by **MIXED-TRANSITIVITY-OF-LESSP**, we have the goal (**LESSP** (**SUB1 i**) (**PLUS i j**)). Q.E.D.

We can strengthen our position somewhat more by observing

Metatheorem. **LESSP-COUNT-ac_i**:
(**NOT** (**LESSP** (**COUNT X**) (**COUNT** (ac_i **X**))))

Proof Sketch. If **X** is a non-base object of the correct type the **COUNT** of (ac$_i$ **X**) is smaller than that of **X**; otherwise, (ac$_i$ **X**) is the default value for the **i**th accessor, which is some base object, and hence has **COUNT** 0. Q.E.D.

By combining this result with **MIXED-TRANSITIVITY-OF-LESSP** we can conclude that

Metatheorem. *Generalized Structural Induction Justification*:
For every shell recognizer, **r**, with corresponding base function symbol **base**

```
(IMPLIES (AND (r X)
              (NOT (EQUAL X (base))))
         (ORD-LESSP (COUNT nest) (COUNT X)))
```

where **nest** is any nest of corresponding shell accessors around **X**.

For example if **I** is a non-0 **NUMBERP** then the **COUNT** of (SUB1 (SUB1 I)) is **ORD-LESSP** the **COUNT** of **I**. Similarly, (CADDAR X) has a smaller **COUNT** than **X** if **X** is a **LISTP** (whether or not **X** has as much **LISTP** substructure as suggested by **CADDAR**.)

Henceforth, we will call a *structural induction* any induction that splits on whether the induction variable is a non-base object of a given type and then provides as its inductive hypotheses instances of the conjecture obtained by replacing the induction variable by arbitrary nests of shell accessors applied to the induction variable.

Part II

Using the System

6 Mechanized Proofs in the Logic

In this chapter we discuss the mechanization of proofs in this logic. In particular, we describe at a very high level how our mechanical theorem prover works, and we show a proof produced by it.

6.1. The Organization of Our Theorem Prover

In the last chapter we saw that it is possible to derive new rules of inference from the axioms and rules given, e.g., structural induction. Any proof using structural induction can be converted into a proof within the given formal system. Logicians and mathematicians are very fond of derived rules of inference because they permit the formal logic to be relatively primitive while allowing the production of sophisticated proofs. A well-known and very useful derived rule of inference is the tautology theorem: a formula of propositional calculus has a proof if and only if it is valid under a truth table. More complicated derived rules are those that justify the use of equality decision procedures and certain arithmetic decision procedures.

Our mechanical theorem prover uses a variety of such high-level derived rules of inference to discover and describe its proofs. In particular it uses the following six proof techniques:

- **Simplification**: a combination of decision procedures (for propositional calculus, equality, and linear arithmetic), term rewriting, and "metafunctions," which are user-supplied simplifiers that have been mechanically proved correct;

- **Destructor Elimination**: the trading of "bad" terms for "good" by choosing an appropriate representation for the objects being manipulated;

- **Cross-fertilization**: the heuristic use and elimination of equality hypotheses;

- **Generalization**: the adoption of a more general goal obtained by replacing terms in the given goal by new variables;

- **Elimination of Irrelevance**: the discarding of apparently unimportant hypotheses; and

- **Induction**.

As implemented, each of these proof techniques is a computer program that takes a formula as input and yields a set of formulas as output; the input formula is provable if each of the output formulas is. We call each of these six programs a "process." From the logical point of view, each such process is a derived rule of inference that is "run backwards." From the problem solving point of view, each process "reduces" the input goal to a conjunction of subgoals.

Not every process is applicable to every formula. For example, it may not be possible to further simplify a formula. When a process is applied to an inappropriate formula, the process returns the singleton set containing the formula, i.e., it implements the trivial derived rule that p can be proved if p can be proved. For example, the simplifier returns the singleton set containing its input formula if that input formula is already in simplest form.

Sometimes a process recognizes that its input is a theorem. For example, tautologies are recognized by the simplifier. In this case the output set is the empty set.

The theorem prover is organized around a "pool" of goal formulas. Initially the user places an input conjecture into the pool. Formulas are drawn out of the pool one at a time for consideration. Each formula is passed in turn to the six processes in the order they are listed above until some process is applicable.[19]

---

[19]Roughly speaking, a formula is printed when its offspring are deposited into the pool. By waiting until that point, we can explain which process hit the formula, what was done to it, and how many new goals have been generated. Of course, special cases arise when a formula is proved without the generation of new goals, etc.

When an applicable process produces a new set of subgoals, each is added to the pool. The consideration of goals in the pool continues until either the pool is empty and no new subgoals are produced—in which case the system has "won"—or one of several termination conditions is met—in which case the system has "lost." The system may "run forever" (until the host system's resources are exhausted), though this happens only rarely.

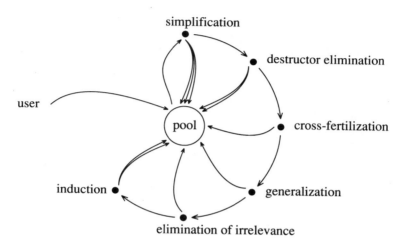

Organization of the Theorem Prover

In particular, when the user puts a formula into the pool, it is first drawn out by the simplifier. If the simplifier applies, it puts into the pool a set of new formulas whose conjunction is sufficient to prove the extracted formula. If the simplifier does not apply (i.e., the formula cannot be further simplified), the formula is passed to the destructor elimination process. If destructor elimination is applicable, it puts a new set of formulas into the pool; if not, it passes the formula to the cross-fertilization process, etc. This continues all the way around the circle of processes.

Roughly speaking, the first two processes in the circle preserve equivalence and are concerned primarily with simplifying formulas. The next three processes strengthen the formula in anticipation of the use of induction. By the time a formula arrives at the induction process it has been simplified and generalized as much as possible by our techniques.

When the system wins—i.e., the pool is finally emptied—the trace of the theorem prover is a proof of the input conjecture, provided each of the six processes is considered a derived rule of inference. When the system loses, the user should infer nothing about the validity of the original conjecture; the initial problem may or may not be a theorem. Even when the system quits on a subgoal that is manifestly invalid the original conjecture may be a theorem that was "lost" by overgeneralization in one of the processes.

Finally, the behavior of three of these processes, namely simplification, destructor elimination, and generalization, can be heavily influenced by rules derived from previously proved, user-supplied theorems. As we have mentioned, having an appropriate data base of rules is crucial to the machine's proof of deep theorems. We will deal at length with this issue later.

6.2. An Example Proof—Associativity of TIMES

Here is a proof produced by the theorem prover. We prove that multiplication is associative. All of the text in **typewriter font** was produced by the theorem prover. We have inserted the labels ✳1, ✳2, ..., in the proof so that we can discuss the proof in the next section. When the proof begins, the theorem prover is in the "Ground Zero" state: its data base of rules contains only those corresponding to the axioms and definitions in Chapter 4.

```
Theorem.
(EQUAL (TIMES (TIMES I J) K)
       (TIMES I (TIMES J K)))
```

```
Proof.

        Call the conjecture *1.                              ✳1


        Perhaps we can prove it by induction.  Three
inductions are suggested by terms in the conjecture.
They merge into two likely candidate inductions.
However, only one is unflawed.  We will induct
according to the following scheme:
        (AND                                                 ✳2
            (IMPLIES (ZEROP I) (p I J K))
            (IMPLIES (AND (NOT (ZEROP I))) (p (SUB1 I) J K))
            (p I J K))).

Linear arithmetic, the lemma COUNT-NUMBERP, and the
definition of ZEROP can be used to prove that the
measure (COUNT I) decreases according to the
well-founded relation LESSP in each induction step of
the scheme.  The above induction scheme leads to two
new goals:

Case 2. (IMPLIES (ZEROP I)                                   ✳3
                 (EQUAL (TIMES (TIMES I J) K)
                        (TIMES I J K))),
```

which simplifies, opening up the definitions of
ZEROP, EQUAL, and TIMES, to:

    T.

Case 1. (IMPLIES   *4
           (AND (NOT (ZEROP I))
                (EQUAL (TIMES (TIMES (SUB1 I) J) K)
                      (TIMES (SUB1 I) J K)))
            (EQUAL (TIMES (TIMES I J) K)
                (TIMES I J K))),

which simplifies, expanding ZEROP and TIMES, to:

    (IMPLIES   *5
       (AND (NOT (EQUAL I 0))
           (NUMBERP I)
           (EQUAL (TIMES (TIMES (SUB1 I) J) K)
                (TIMES (SUB1 I) J K)))
      (EQUAL (TIMES (PLUS J (TIMES (SUB1 I) J)) K)
           (PLUS (TIMES J K)
                (TIMES (SUB1 I) J K)))).

Appealing to the lemma SUB1-ELIM, we now replace I
by (ADD1 X) to eliminate (SUB1 I). We rely upon the
type restriction lemma noted when SUB1 was
introduced to constrain the new variable. This
generates:

    (IMPLIES   *6
           (AND (NUMBERP X)
                (NOT (EQUAL (ADD1 X) 0))
                (EQUAL (TIMES (TIMES X J) K)
                      (TIMES X J K)))
          (EQUAL (TIMES (PLUS J (TIMES X J)) K)
             (PLUS (TIMES J K) (TIMES X J K)))).

This further simplifies, trivially, to:

    (IMPLIES   *7
           (AND (NUMBERP X)
                (EQUAL (TIMES (TIMES X J) K)
                    (TIMES X J K)))
          (EQUAL (TIMES (PLUS J (TIMES X J)) K)
             (PLUS (TIMES J K) (TIMES X J K)))).

We use the above equality hypothesis by substituting
(TIMES (TIMES X J) K) for (TIMES X J K) and throwing
away the equality. This generates the goal:

```
        (IMPLIES (NUMBERP X)                                        *8
                (EQUAL (TIMES (PLUS J (TIMES X J)) K)
                       (PLUS (TIMES J K)
                             (TIMES (TIMES X J) K)))).
```

We will try to prove the above formula by
generalizing it, replacing (TIMES X J) by Y. We
restrict the new variable by recalling the type
restriction lemma noted when TIMES was introduced.
We thus obtain:

```
        (IMPLIES                                                    *9
                (AND (NUMBERP Y) (NUMBERP X))
                (EQUAL (TIMES (PLUS J Y) K)
                       (PLUS (TIMES J K) (TIMES Y K)))),
```

which has an irrelevant term in it. By eliminating
the term we get:

```
        (IMPLIES                                                    *10
                (NUMBERP Y)
                (EQUAL (TIMES (PLUS J Y) K)
                       (PLUS (TIMES J K) (TIMES Y K)))),
```

which we will finally name *1.1.   *11

     Perhaps we can prove it by induction. Three   *12
inductions are suggested by terms in the conjecture.
They merge into two likely candidate inductions.
However, only one is unflawed. We will induct
according to the following scheme:

```
    (AND
        (IMPLIES (ZEROP J) (p J Y K))
        (IMPLIES (AND (NOT (ZEROP J)) (p (SUB1 J) Y K))
                 (p J Y K))).
```
Linear arithmetic, the lemmas SUB1-LESSEQP and
SUB1-LESSP, and the definition of ZEROP establish that
the measure (COUNT J) decreases according to the
well-founded relation LESSP in each induction step of
the scheme. The above induction scheme leads to the
following two new formulas:


```
Case 2. (IMPLIES
                (AND (ZEROP J) (NUMBERP Y))
                (EQUAL (TIMES (PLUS J Y) K)
                       (PLUS (TIMES J K) (TIMES Y K)))).
```

This simplifies, unfolding ZEROP, EQUAL, PLUS, and
TIMES, to:

    T.

Case 1. (IMPLIES   *13
         (AND
          (NOT (ZEROP J))
          (EQUAL (TIMES (PLUS (SUB1 J) Y) K)
                 (PLUS (TIMES (SUB1 J) K) (TIMES Y K)))
          (NUMBERP Y))
         (EQUAL (TIMES (PLUS J Y) K)
                (PLUS (TIMES J K) (TIMES Y K))))).

This simplifies, applying SUB1-ADD1, and opening up
the functions ZEROP, PLUS, and TIMES, to the formula:

     (IMPLIES
      (AND
       (NOT (EQUAL J 0))
       (NUMBERP J)
       (EQUAL (TIMES (PLUS (SUB1 J) Y) K)
              (PLUS (TIMES (SUB1 J) K) (TIMES Y K)))
       (NUMBERP Y))
      (EQUAL (PLUS K (TIMES (PLUS (SUB1 J) Y) K))
             (PLUS (PLUS K (TIMES (SUB1 J) K))
                   (TIMES Y K)))).

This again simplifies, using linear arithmetic, to:

    T.

     That finishes the proof of *1.1, which finishes   *14
the proof of *1. Q.E.D.

6.3. An Explanation of the Proof

Between the time the conjecture was submitted and the time the system printed
the text at *1, each of the first five processes attempted to transform the formula
and none succeeded. At *1 the induction process got the formula and chose to
induct on **I**. The paragraph below *1 explains why this induction was chosen.
The implementation of our induction mechanism is described in detail in [4]
where we define such notions as the inductions "suggested" by a term, the
"merge" of two inductions, and when an induction is "flawed." The induction
schema chosen is given in *2, with **(p I J K)** used schematically to

represent the entire conjecture. Note that the induction is structural induction of type **NUMBERP** on **I**. The paragraph following ✳2 explains why this induction is permitted under our Principle of Induction. The induction process puts two new formulas into the pool, the base case and the induction step.

Formula ✳3 is the base case. The theorem prover labels the formula **Case 2**.[20] The base case is drawn out of the pool by the simplifier and is reduced to **T**.

Formula ✳4 is the induction step. It is drawn out of the pool next and is simplified to ✳5. Technically, ✳5 is put back into the pool, drawn out again by the simplifier, and cannot be further simplified. Formula ✳5 is thus handed off to the next process, destructor elimination.

Because the formula has **(SUB1 I)** in it, the destructor elimination process chooses to replace **I** by **(ADD1 X)**, where **X** is a new, numerically typed variable. This eliminates **(SUB1 I)**, which is now **X**. The output of the destructor elimination process is ✳6, which is put back into the pool and resimplified.

Formula ✳6 has a trivial hypothesis, namely the second, which says **(ADD1 X)** is not **0**, a remnant of the first hypothesis of ✳5 which said **I** was not **0** and which is now obviously true by the representation chosen for **I**. The simplifier removes this hypothesis without using any named rules. That is why it says formula ✳6 *trivially* simplifies to ✳7.

Formula ✳7 is put into the pool and is subjected to both simplification and destructor elimination without effect before it arrives at the cross-fertilization process. Here the equality hypothesis, which is actually the induction hypothesis, is substituted into the simplified induction conclusion. Furthermore, the induction hypothesis is then discarded on the heuristic grounds that it has been "used." Because a hypothesis is discarded, the output of the cross-fertilization process may not be a theorem even though the input is. All that is guaranteed is that if the output is a theorem, then the input can be proved from it. The output is ✳8, which is passed through all the preceding processes and eventually arrives at the generalization process.

The generalizer notes that **(TIMES X J)** occurs on both the left- and right-hand sides of the induction conclusion and decides to attack the more general conjecture obtained by replacing **(TIMES X J)** by the new variable **Y**. Because **(TIMES X J)** is known to be a number, the generalizer restricts **Y** to being a number. The output of the generalizer is ✳9. Like cross-fertilization, the generalizer may produce a non-theorem as its output even if its input is a

---

[20]In general the system numbers cases backwards. The reason for this is so that when you return to your terminal with your coffee and find it working on **Case 57** you know how far you have to go.

theorem.

Formula ✳9, after traversal through all of the preceding processes, arrives at the process that eliminates irrelevance. The hypothesis that **X** is a number is judged unnecessary and discarded because **X** does not occur elsewhere in the conjecture. The output is ✳10. In fact, the other hypothesis, **(NUMBERP Y)** is also unnecessary, but the theorem prover does not detect that.

Formula ✳10 is put in the pool and cycles through all of the first five processes untouched. The system will attack it by induction. However, rather than start on the induction immediately, we prefer to finish processing any remaining formulas in the pool. Thus, at ✳11 we generate a name for the formula, ***1.1**, and set it aside to be proved by induction.

It is worth noting that the formula ***1.1** is in fact the statement that multiplication distributes over addition. It was generated automatically by the combination of the foregoing heuristics and adopted as a subgoal to prove the associativity of multiplication.

After naming ***1.1** and setting the formula aside, the system continues processing formulas in the pool. However, there are none in this example. Thus, having finished with all the cases of the last induction, the system picks up the formula set aside and at ✳12 applies the induction process to it.

The induction process chooses the obvious induction on **J** and produces two new cases, each of which is proved by simplification. Note that the induction step, ✳13, requires two applications of simplification, the second using the linear arithmetic decision procedure.

Finally, at ✳14, the system notes that all formulas have been proved.

7 An Introduction to the System

Of course, it takes more to mechanize our logic than merely a mechanical theorem prover. The system widely known as the "Boyer-Moore theorem prover" includes the theorem proving program sketched above but also provides a large number of features having little to do with theorem proving, such as a mechanization of the shell and definition principles, dependency tracking, a compiler for the logic, a run-time environment for executing functions in the logic, and various facilities for keeping track of the evolving data base of rules.

This chapter is essentially a tutorial introduction to our system. We introduce the notion of the data base and its rules, the logical "events" that add new rules to the data base, the most commonly used commands, and various issues of general concern such as errors, aborting computations, etc.

7.1. The Data Base of Rules

The theorem proving system is, in essence, a mechanical tool for building theories. The user generally constructs his new theory from an old one by adding shell declarations and function definitions and proving theorems about the new concepts. The system is organized as an interactive command interpreter that performs operations on a global data base representing the evolving theory.

The data base contains the axioms, the user-defined shells, defined functions, and theorems proved by the system. Some commands add facts (e.g., definitions or proved theorems) to the data base. Other commands permit the user to inspect the data base. Still other commands remove facts from the data base. When facts are removed, logically dependent facts are also removed. Finally, commands are provided for writing the data base to a file and restoring it from a file so that work can be saved from one session to the next.

In a shallow sense, the theorem prover is fully automatic: the system requires no advice or directives from the user once a proof attempt has started. The only way the user can alter the behavior of the system during a proof attempt is to abort the proof attempt. However, in a deeper sense, the theorem prover is interactive: the data base—and hence the user's past actions—influences the behavior of the theorem prover. Five of the proof techniques—namely linear arithmetic, rewriting, metafunctions, destructor elimination, and generalization—use the data base as a source of *rules* to apply to the conjecture at hand.

From where do these rules come? They are generated from the theorems formulated by the user and previously proved by the system. When a theorem is submitted for proof, the user attaches to it one or more tokens that declare what classes of rules are to be generated from the theorem, if proved. The tokens are taken from the set {**REWRITE, META, ELIM, GENERALIZE**}. Given a class of rule to be generated, e.g., **REWRITE**, the precise form of the rule generated from a theorem is dependent upon the syntactic form of theorem.

For example, the theorem

```
(IMPLIES (NOT (MEMBER X A))
         (EQUAL (DELETE X A) A))
```

generates the **REWRITE** rule: Replace (instances of) **(DELETE X A)** by (the instance of) **A** provided (the instance of) **(MEMBER X A)** rewrites to **F**. The equivalent formula

```
(IMPLIES (NOT (EQUAL (DELETE X A) A))
         (MEMBER X A))
```

generates a radically different rule: Replace **(MEMBER X A)** by **T** provided **(EQUAL (DELETE X A) A)** rewrites to **F**.

Propositionally equivalent theorems may have radically different interpretations as rules. Even the order in which theorems are proved is important since it affects the order in which the corresponding rules are applied.

Each rule has an associated *status* indicating whether the rule is *enabled* or *disabled*. The status of a rule can be set by the user. When a rule is disabled it is never applied.[21]

---

[21]Well, almost never! For example, we do not check the status of rules stored as type prescriptions.

A data base is thus more than a logical theory: it is a set of rules for proving theorems in the given theory. The user leads the theorem prover to "difficult" proofs by "programming" its rule base. Given a goal theorem, the user generally discovers a proof himself, identifies the key steps in the proof, and then formulates them as lemmas, paying particular attention to their interpretation as rules.

The key role of the user of our system is guiding the theorem prover to proofs by the strategic selection of the sequence of theorems to prove and the proper formulation of those theorems. Successful users of the system must know how to prove theorems in the logic and must understand how the theorem prover interprets them as rules.

7.2. Logical Events

The act of adding a new rule to the data base or changing the status of a rule in the data base is called an *event*. Some events are associated with an extension of the logic itself, e.g., the addition of a new axiom (and its generated rules), the addition of a new shell (and its generated rules) or the addition of a new function definition (and its generated rules). Other events are associated merely with an extension of the syntax, namely the declaration of the arity of a new function symbol. The most common event is the certification of a formula as a theorem (and the addition of its generated rules).

Each event has a *name*, which is a word chosen by the user, and generally is either the name of a function introduced by the event or the name of the axiom or theorem introduced. Event names must satisfy the same restrictions we have on function and variable names in the logic.

The data base is actually an acyclic directed graph with events stored at the nodes. The nodes are named by the event name. In addition to a unique event, each node has several other items of data associated with it, such as, the time at which the event occurred and the names of auxiliary functions or axioms introduced.

The arcs connecting nodes represent "immediate dependency." The system automatically keeps track of most—but not all (see page 271)—logical dependencies among events. For example, if **SORT** is defined in terms of **INSERT**, then the node for **SORT** is connected to that for **INSERT** by an arc. If **INSERT** is removed from the data base, so is **SORT**.

We discuss the exact form of a node in the Reference Guide on page 269.

7.3. A Summary of the Commands

We here summarize the most commonly used commands.
   The commands that create events are

- **BOOT-STRAP**: creates the initial data base of axioms and definitions.

- **DEFN**: adds a function definition as a new axiom after checking its admissibility and adds the rules generated by the definition.

- **PROVE-LEMMA**: attempts to prove a conjecture and, if successful, adds to the data base the note that the conjecture is a theorem and adds the rules generated by the theorem.

- **ADD-SHELL**: adds the axioms obtained by instantiating the shell principle and adds the rules generated from those axioms.

- **DCL**: declares the arity of a ''new'' function symbol (making the symbol henceforth ''old'') thus permitting its use in formulas.

- **ADD-AXIOM**: adds a new axiom to the theory and adds the rules generated by it.

- **TOGGLE**: enables or disables rules already in the data base. **TOGGLE** commands are also invoked by the **DISABLE** and **ENABLE** commands.

- **TOGGLE-DEFINED-FUNCTIONS**: enables or disables the executable counterparts of defined functions, thus permitting or inhibiting the computation of explicit values on explicit values.

Each event has a name, which is a Lisp symbol. The name of the event associated with **BOOT-STRAP** is **GROUND-ZERO**. The name of a **DEFN** or **DCL** event is the name of the function introduced. The name of the **PROVE-LEMMA** or **ADD-AXIOM** event is the name of the formula, as supplied by the user. The name of an **ADD-SHELL** event is the user-supplied name of the constructor function. Both types of **TOGGLE**s include a user-supplied name among the arguments.
   The data base can be queried with the command

- **DATA-BASE**: returns the requested item associated with a given node in the data base.

The command

- **CH**: prints out the most recently executed events and so is useful in determining what rules and concepts have been introduced.

The following commands are of great help when trying to construct a useful data base of rewrite rules. The first command is frequently used when **PROVE-LEMMA** has failed to apply a rule that you expected would be applied; the command can help you determine why the rule was not used.

- **BREAK-LEMMA**: installs a monitor in the rewriter so that when the theorem prover considers the application of a given rule an interactive break occurs. From within this break you can watch the system's attempt to apply the rule.

- **ACCUMULATED-PERSISTENCE**: prints out a list of the most "expensive" rules in the data base, measured in terms of the number of rules tried during the last proof attempt.

The following command provides an execution environment in which terms in the logic can be run on concrete data ("explicit values"):

- **R-LOOP**: reads variable-free terms from the user's terminal and evaluates them in the logic.

The following commands remove nodes from the data base, removing all nodes which depend upon the given one. These commands take event names as arguments:

- **UNDO-NAME**: removes the named event and all of its dependents.

- **UNDO-BACK-THROUGH**: remove the named event and all events executed since the named event.

- **UBT**: a short version of **UNDO-BACK-THROUGH**.

Note. Because dependency tracking is not complete, we do not guarantee that **UNDO-NAME** actually produces a consistent state—it is possible that **UNDO-NAME** fails to find some results that logically depend upon those deleted. But **UNDO-NAME** is a quick and dirty way to experiment with alternative function definitions and theorems. We explain the situation in more detail on page 271.

The following commands process lists of events, performing each in turn:

- **PROVEALL**

- **DO-EVENTS**

The data base is saved and restored by

- **MAKE-LIB**: writes the current data base to the file system.

- **NOTE-LIB**: loads a data base from the file system.

7.4. Errors

The theorem prover has extensive error checking facilities. If we say a term is expected in the third argument of a command, we mean we cause an error if a term is not supplied. If we say a name has to be "new," we mean we cause an error if it is already known in the data base. Furthermore, all such errors are checked for before the system makes any changes to the data base. Thus, an error "in the middle" of a command like **ADD-SHELL** or **PROVE-LEMMA**, will not leave the data base in an inconsistent state.

See page 280 in the Reference Guide for a more complete description of error handling.

7.5. Aborting a Command

You will frequently wish to abort a proof attempt because you see that the theorem prover is going astray. We provide no special facility for aborting the execution of a command. However, this feature is provided in most host Lisp systems by typing some particular "control" character. We discuss the details on page 251 in the Reference Guide.

7.6. Syntax and the User Interface

The system is written in Lisp. The command interpreter for the system is actually just the top-level Lisp "read-eval-print" loop in which Lisp s-expressions are read and evaluated and the results are printed. The system's "commands" are actually just Lisp programs. To use the system, you must log onto a computer, enter Lisp, load the appropriate files to define the theorem prover primitives, and then call Lisp programs to axiomatize concepts, evaluate functions in the logic, submit conjectures to the theorem prover, etc. See the Installation Guide, chapter 14.

This arrangement has its pros and cons. On the pro side, the system's command interface immediately inherits the sophisticated interactive environment usually available in Lisp (e.g., command editing, histories, read-time abbreviations, output logs, or "dribble files"). In addition, you can mix Lisp and theorem prover commands to create new commands, process theorem prover output, etc. On the con side, you must be sufficiently familiar with Lisp to type, correct, and execute top-level Lisp forms. In addition, incorrect type-in can throw you into states (such as the debugger or an editor) that may be unfamiliar. Finally, and perhaps most seriously, if you are "malicious" you can "cheat" by using Lisp to modify the theorem prover's programs or state and thus produce the appearance that the theorem prover certifies a result when in fact it does not.

Nevertheless, the theorem prover's command interpreter *is* Lisp and henceforth we assume you are sufficiently familiar with Lisp to operate the theorem prover.

One subtle aspect of this decision is its effect on the syntax of terms in the logic. When you type a command, such as

```
(PROVE-LEMMA PROPERP-REVERSE (REWRITE)
    (PROPERP (REVERSE X)))
```

what actually happens is that the characters you type are read by the Lisp reader and converted into a Lisp s-expression. That s-expression is then evaluated. Thus, our program **PROVE-LEMMA** is actually applied to the s-expressions corresponding to what you typed, not to the character strings themselves. In particular what **PROVE-LEMMA** gets as the formula to be proved is not the character string " **(PROPERP (REVERSE X))** " but a Lisp list of length 2 whose car is the Lisp symbol **PROPERP**, etc.

It is actually the Lisp reader that implements the syntax we have described for terms. For example, it is the reader that provides the single-gritch **QUOTE** convention, dot notation, flexible use of white space, and the *;* comment convention. When read by the Lisp reader,

```
(APPEND '((A . 0) (B . 1))    ;initial segment
    ALIST)
```

produces exactly the same s-expression as

```
(APPEND (QUOTE ((A . 0) (B . 1))) ALIST).
```

We have carefully defined the syntax of terms so that if you type formulas in the indicated syntax they are read properly by Lisp.

However, our use of the Lisp reader means that the input syntax for terms is much more general than we have previously indicated: it permits all the read-time hacks available in Lisp. For example, Table 7.1 contains user type-in in the left-hand column and the term read in the right-hand column. In each case, the type-in produces a legitimate term. These examples were done under the Common Lisp reader on a Symbolics machine. The first example illustrates the fact that most Lisp readers automatically convert type-in into uppercase. The last example exploits the fact that prior to typing the expression, the user set the value of the Lisp variable **foo** to the list **(APPEND A B)**.

These examples are not meant to encourage the use of such syntax, merely to remind and warn you that you are typing to the Lisp reader, not some prissy parser for the logic.

One other aspect to the syntax is worth noting. Since all of our commands

Table 7.1

user type-in	term
(reverse x)	(REVERSE X)
(REVERSE X . NIL)	(REVERSE X)
(TIMES #O777 J)	(TIMES 511 J)
(APPEND #.foo C)	(APPEND (APPEND A B) C)

that take "terms" as arguments actually get Lisp s-expressions and the commands themselves are just Lisp programs, commands need not be *typed*. You may wish to write your own interface that simply applies our programs to the appropriate s-expressions. In such an application, the s-expressions can be produced by any Lisp procedure at all, not merely the reader.

7.7. Confusing Lisp and the Logic

A common mistake made by new users is to confuse Lisp and the logic. This confusion commonly takes on two different forms: (a) the meaning of terms in the logic is the same as their meaning in Lisp and (b) the interface to the theorem prover is the logic—i.e., your commands are "evaluated" as applications of logical functions not Lisp s-expressions.

The first misconception is contradicted by many simple examples. In the logic, **(CAR 0)** is **0**, while in Lisp it (usually) causes an error. In the logic, **(ADD1 T)** is **1**, while in Lisp it (usually) causes an error. In the logic, **(IF NIL 1 2)** is **1** because **IF** tests against **F** and **NIL** is not **F**, while in Lisp it is **2** because **IF** tests against **NIL** in Lisp. Finally, in the logic, the equation **(RUSSELL X) = (NOT (RUSSELL X))** is inadmissible as a function definition, while in Lisp that "recipe" for computing **RUSSELL** can be stored as the "definition" of **RUSSELL**. Of course, in Lisp, the attempt to compute **(RUSSELL 3)** "runs forever."

To illustrate the second misconception, consider

(DEFN SECOND (X) (CADR X))

First observe that our commands really mix both Lisp and the logic. The word **DEFN** is the name of a Lisp procedure. Its arguments are metalogical objects, namely a symbol, a list of symbols, and a term.

The command interpreter for our theorem proving system is Lisp, not the logic. The effect of the Lisp **DEFN** procedure is to define a function in the logic. It does not define a ''function''[22] or program in Lisp.

There is no *a priori* relation between the logical function named **fn** and the Lisp program, if any, named **fn**. A function symbol can be used in a term, e.g., to be evaluated by **R-LOOP** or proved by the theorem prover, only if the symbol has been introduced into the logic with **BOOT-STRAP**, **DEFN**, **DCL**, or **ADD-SHELL**. The Lisp definition, if any, of a symbol is irrelevant to the logic. Symmetrically, a symbol can be applied in Lisp only if it has been defined in Lisp with **DEFUN** or one of the myriad other ways to define function objects in Lisp. The logical definition, if any, of a symbol is irrelevant to Lisp.

---

[22]In common usage, Lisp programs are frequently called ''functions.'' We avoid use of the word ''function'' in that sense, preferring instead ''routine,'' ''procedure,'' ''command,'' or simply ''program.''

8 A Sample Session with the Theorem Prover

In this chapter we illustrate several aspects of the system: getting it started, "running" functions in the logic, defining new functions, proving several simple theorems to program the data base, and saving the data base to a file for future use.

Getting the system started is an installation-dependent operation. On some machines one merely types

    nqthm

to the operating system. On others, one might enter for example the locally available version of Common Lisp by typing

    kcl

to the operating system and then load some files that contain the theorem prover code. In Chapter 14 we describe how to obtain the sources for the theorem prover and install them at a new site. For the rest of this chapter we assume the theorem prover has been installed and "started up."

The theorem prover is nothing but a collection of Lisp programs. The user-interface to the theorem prover is just the read-eval-print loop of Lisp. To use the theorem prover, one must type Lisp expressions that invoke our various commands.

The first thing one must do is load an initial data base. This may be done either by executing the **BOOT-STRAP** command or the **NOTE-LIB** command.

Below we show the invocation of the **BOOT-STRAP** command and the response by the system:

```
(BOOT-STRAP NQTHM)
[ 8.5 11.8 0.0 ]
GROUND-ZERO
```

BOOT-STRAP initializes the system to the Ground Zero logic. It then prints out the "event time," [8.5 11.8 0.0], a triple of numbers indicating the preprocessing time, cpu time, and output time, in seconds, to carry out this command.[23]

The alternative way to initialize the data base is to execute a **NOTE-LIB** command, such as

```
(NOTE-LIB "doe:>nqthm>work")
```

This initializes the system's data base to that saved in the "library" files **"doe:>nqthm>work.lib"** and **"doe:>nqthm>work.lisp"**.[24] We show how to save a data base later in this section.

To run functions in the logic the command **R-LOOP** is provided. **R-LOOP** enters a "read-eval-print" loop in which the notion of "eval" used is "reduction." Reduction is the systematic application of the axioms and definitions to reduce a variable-free term to an equivalent explicit value using call-by-value order of evaluation. Every function symbol involved in the process must be defined, introduced by the shell principle, or axiomatized in the Ground Zero logic; applications of declared function symbols cannot be reduced.

Here is an invocation of **R-LOOP** and the subsequent interaction. The *****'s below are printed by **R-LOOP** to prompt the user for the next term to be evaluated. Following the ***** is a term typed by the user. On the next line is the explicit value term to which the input term is equal, or the message that the term was not reducible.

```
(R-LOOP)
Trace Mode: Off    Abbreviated Output Mode:   On
Type ? for help.

*(EQUAL T F)
 F
*(IF T X Y)
 (NOT REDUCIBLE)
```

---

[23]The times shown above are for the Austin Kyoto Common Lisp version running on an 8 megabyte Sun 3/60.

[24]The format of the file names shown here is that used in the Symbolics file system. The file name formats used by our system are those of its host operating system.

```
*(IF T 23 45)
 23
*(ADD1 23)
 24
*(MINUS 3)
 -3
*(CONS 1 2)
 '(1 . 2)
*(CAR '(1 . 2))
 1
*(LISTP '(1 . 2))
 T
*(PACK '(65 66 67 . 0))
 'ABC
*(LITATOM NIL)
 T
*(UNPACK NIL)
 '(78 73 76 . 0)
*(APPEND NIL '(E F G))
 '(E F G)
*(APPEND '(A B C D) '(E F G))
 '(A B C D E F G)
*(APPEND '(A B C D . 7) '(E F G))
 '(A B C D E F G)
*OK
Exiting R-LOOP.
NIL
```

The term **OK**, which is a variable symbol, is treated specially by **R-LOOP** as the signal that the user wishes to exit **R-LOOP** and return to the Lisp command interpreter. The value of **R-LOOP** is **NIL**.

The **DEFN** command submits to the system a new proposed definition. For example, the following command defines the function **REVERSE**:

```
(DEFN REVERSE (X)
   (IF (NLISTP X)
        NIL
        (APPEND (REVERSE (CDR X)) (LIST (CAR X)))))
```

The command is equivalent to the axiomatic act

Definition.
```
(REVERSE X)
   =
```

```
(IF (NLISTP X)
    NIL
    (APPEND (REVERSE (CDR X)) (LIST (CAR X)))).
```

The system's response to this command is

> **Linear arithmetic, the lemmas CDR-LESSEQP and CDR-LESSP, and the definition of NLISTP inform us that the measure (COUNT X) decreases according to the well-founded relation LESSP in each recursive call. Hence, REVERSE is accepted under the principle of definition. Observe that:**
>
> ```
>         (OR (LITATOM (REVERSE X))
>             (LISTP (REVERSE X)))
> ```
> **is a theorem.**
>
> ```
> [ 0.2 0.4 0.5 ]
> REVERSE
> ```

The paragraph printed concerns two topics. First, it explains why **REVERSE** is admissible. Second, it notes a theorem about the type of **REVERSE**. The theorem states that **REVERSE** returns either a **LITATOM** or a **LISTP**.

Having defined **REVERSE**, we can test it:

```
(R-LOOP)

*(REVERSE NIL)
 NIL
*(SETQ X '(A B C D E F G))      ; SETQ is an R-LOOP hack for
 '(A B C D E F G)               ; abbreviating constants
*(REVERSE X)
 '(G F E D C B A)
*(REVERSE (REVERSE X))
 '(A B C D E F G)
*(EQUAL (REVERSE (REVERSE X)) X)
 T
*OK
```

We now try to prove the conjecture that **(REVERSE (REVERSE X))** is **X**. The command below submits this conjecture to the theorem prover with the advice that it should be named **REVERSE-REVERSE** and should be built into the data base as a **REWRITE** rule, if it is proved.

```
(PROVE-LEMMA REVERSE-REVERSE (REWRITE)
    (EQUAL (REVERSE (REVERSE X)) X))
```

Give the conjecture the name *1.

We will try to prove it by induction. There is only one plausible induction. We will induct according to the following scheme:
```
(AND
 (IMPLIES (NLISTP X) (p X))
 (IMPLIES (AND (NOT (NLISTP X))
               (p (CDR X)))
          (p X))).
```
Linear arithmetic, the lemmas CDR-LESSEQP and CDR-LESSP, and the definition of NLISTP establish that the measure (COUNT X) decreases according to the well-founded relation LESSP in each induction step of the scheme. The above induction scheme leads to the following two new goals:

Case 2. (IMPLIES (NLISTP X)
                 (EQUAL (REVERSE (REVERSE X))
                        X)),

which simplifies, unfolding the definitions of NLISTP and REVERSE, to the new conjecture:

```
(IMPLIES (NOT (LISTP X))
         (EQUAL NIL X)),
```

which has two irrelevant terms in it. By eliminating these terms we get the formula:

F,

which means the proof attempt has

************* F A I L E D **************

[0.0 0.1 1.5]
NIL

The reader should be sufficiently familiar with the logic to follow the proof attempt, at least until the system eliminates irrelevant terms. The elimination of irrelevant atomic formulas is just a form of generalization: to prove **(IMPLIES (AND p q r) s)** it is sufficient to prove **(IMPLIES r s)**, a strategy one might adopt if **p** and **q** seem irrelevant. In the case above, everything seemed irrelevant and the theorem prover adopted the goal **F**—which, if proved, is indeed sufficient to prove the earlier subgoal.

When the system gives up, as above, its output should not be interpreted to mean "the input formula is not a theorem" but merely "the input formula was not proved." In this case, **PROVE-LEMMA** returns **NIL** and no changes are made to the system's data base.

Inspection of the proof attempt, namely the subgoal preceding **F**

```
(IMPLIES (NOT (LISTP X))
         (EQUAL NIL X))
```

leads to the observation that the input formula is not true if **X** is a non-**LISTP** other than **NIL**. For example, if **X** is **7** then both **(REVERSE X)** and **(REVERSE (REVERSE X))** are **NIL**, not **7**.

Returning to **R-LOOP**

```
(R-LOOP)

*(REVERSE 7)
 NIL

*(SETQ Y (APPEND X 7))
 '(A B C D E F G . 7)
*(REVERSE Y)
 '(G F E D C B A)

*(EQUAL (REVERSE (REVERSE Y)) Y)
 F

*OK
```

The desired property of **REVERSE** only holds if the list being reversed ends in a **NIL**. We therefore next define the predicate that checks whether a list ends in a **NIL**. We call such lists "proper."

```
(DEFN PROPERP (X)
  (IF (NLISTP X)
      (EQUAL X NIL)
      (PROPERP (CDR X))))
```


Linear arithmetic, the lemmas CDR-LESSEQP and CDR-LESSP, and the definition of NLISTP

```
establish that the measure (COUNT X) decreases
according to the well-founded relation LESSP in
each recursive call.  Hence, PROPERP is accepted
under the principle of definition.  Observe that:
      (OR (FALSEP (PROPERP X))
          (TRUEP (PROPERP X)))
is a theorem.


[ 0.1 0.4 0.5 ]
PROPERP
```

Having defined this concept, we can test it:

```
(R-LOOP)

*(PROPERP NIL)
 T

*(PROPERP '(A B C))
 T

*(PROPERP '(A B C . ATM))
 F

*(PROPERP X)
 T

*(PROPERP Y)
 F

*OK
```

The desired theorem about **REVERSE** is now proved without assistance. The system does an induction on **X**, generalizes the induction step after using and throwing away the induction hypothesis to produce a conjecture about **REVERSE** and **APPEND**, and then proves this subsidiary conjecture by induction.

```
(PROVE-LEMMA REVERSE-REVERSE (REWRITE)
  (IMPLIES (PROPERP X)
           (EQUAL (REVERSE (REVERSE X))
                  X)))


   Give the conjecture the name *1.
```

We will try to prove it by induction. Two
inductions are suggested by terms in the
conjecture. However, they merge into one likely
candidate induction. We will induct according to
the following scheme:

```
(AND
 (IMPLIES (NLISTP X) (p X))
 (IMPLIES (AND (NOT (NLISTP X))
               (p (CDR X)))
          (p X))).
```

Linear arithmetic, the lemmas CDR-LESSEQP and
CDR-LESSP, and the definition of NLISTP inform us
that the measure (COUNT X) decreases according to
the well-founded relation LESSP in each induction
step of the scheme. The above induction scheme
leads to the following three new goals:

Case 3. (IMPLIES (AND (NLISTP X) (PROPERP X))
                  (EQUAL (REVERSE (REVERSE X))
                         X)),

  which we simplify, expanding NLISTP, PROPERP,
  REVERSE, and EQUAL, to:

        T.

Case 2. (IMPLIES (AND (NOT (NLISTP X))
                       (NOT (PROPERP (CDR X)))
                       (PROPERP X))
                  (EQUAL (REVERSE (REVERSE X))
                         X)).

  This simplifies, expanding NLISTP and PROPERP,
  to:

        T.

Case 1. (IMPLIES
            (AND (NOT (NLISTP X))
                 (EQUAL
                   (REVERSE (REVERSE (CDR X)))

```
                    (CDR X))
                  (PROPERP X))
              (EQUAL (REVERSE (REVERSE X)) X)).
```

This simplifies, opening up the definitions of
NLISTP, PROPERP, and REVERSE, to:

```
        (IMPLIES
         (AND (LISTP X)
              (EQUAL (REVERSE (REVERSE (CDR X)))
                     (CDR X))
              (PROPERP (CDR X)))
         (EQUAL
           (REVERSE (APPEND (REVERSE (CDR X))
                            (LIST (CAR X))))
           X)).
```

Applying the lemma CAR-CDR-ELIM, we now replace
X by (CONS V Z) to eliminate (CDR X) and
(CAR X). We must thus prove:

```
        (IMPLIES
         (AND (EQUAL (REVERSE (REVERSE Z)) Z)
              (PROPERP Z))
         (EQUAL
           (REVERSE (APPEND (REVERSE Z) (LIST V)))
           (CONS V Z))).
```

We use the above equality hypothesis by
cross-fertilizing (REVERSE (REVERSE Z)) for Z
and throwing away the equality. We must thus
prove:

```
        (IMPLIES
         (PROPERP Z)
         (EQUAL
           (REVERSE (APPEND (REVERSE Z) (LIST V)))
           (CONS V (REVERSE (REVERSE Z))))).
```

We will try to prove the above conjecture by
generalizing it, replacing (REVERSE Z) by Y.

This generates:


```
(IMPLIES
  (PROPERP Z)
  (EQUAL (REVERSE (APPEND Y (LIST V)))
         (CONS V (REVERSE Y)))).
```

Eliminate the irrelevant term. This produces:


```
(EQUAL (REVERSE (APPEND Y (LIST V)))
       (CONS V (REVERSE Y))),
```

which we will finally name *1.1.

Let us appeal to the induction principle.
The recursive terms in the conjecture suggest two
inductions. However, they merge into one likely
candidate induction. We will induct according to
the following scheme:

```
(AND (IMPLIES (AND (LISTP Y) (p (CDR Y) V))
              (p Y V))
     (IMPLIES (NOT (LISTP Y)) (p Y V))).
```

Linear arithmetic and the lemma CDR-LESSP
establish that the measure (COUNT Y) decreases
according to the well-founded relation LESSP in
each induction step of the scheme. The above
induction scheme generates two new conjectures:

Case 2. (IMPLIES
           (AND
            (LISTP Y)
            (EQUAL
             (REVERSE (APPEND (CDR Y) (LIST V)))
             (CONS V (REVERSE (CDR Y)))))
           (EQUAL (REVERSE (APPEND Y (LIST V)))
                  (CONS V (REVERSE Y)))),

which we simplify, rewriting with CAR-CONS and
CDR-CONS, and unfolding the definitions of

```
APPEND and REVERSE, to:

    T.


Case 1. (IMPLIES
          (NOT (LISTP Y))
          (EQUAL (REVERSE (APPEND Y (LIST V)))
                 (CONS V (REVERSE Y)))).
```

This simplifies, applying CAR-CONS and CDR-CONS, and expanding the functions APPEND, LISTP, and REVERSE, to:

```
    T.
```

That finishes the proof of *1.1, which finishes the proof of *1. Q.E.D.

```
[ 0.4 5.6 6.0 ]
REVERSE-REVERSE
```

To review the most recent events we can type

```
(CH 2)
```

The output produced is

```
0    (PROVE-LEMMA REVERSE-REVERSE ...)
1    (DEFN PROPERP ...)
2    (DEFN REVERSE ...)
NIL
```

The events are enumerated backwards. The numbers assigned may be given to **UBT** to ''undo-back-through'' the indicated position, rolling the system's state back to that point. Event names may also be used. The final **NIL** is the value delivered by the **CH** program.

We might now try to prove a corollary of **REVERSE-REVERSE**:

```
(PROVE-LEMMA TRIPLE-REVERSE NIL
    (EQUAL (REVERSE (REVERSE (REVERSE A)))
           (REVERSE A)))
```

The first part of the attempt is shown below; however, we interrupt it in the middle of the description of an induction.

> `Call the conjecture *1.`
>
> `Perhaps we can prove it by induction.    There`
> `are two plausible inductions.    We [ABORT]`

We did not intend for this conjecture to be proved by induction. At first sight, **REVERSE-REVERSE** suffices to prove **TRIPLE-REVERSE** immediately. However, **REVERSE-REVERSE** says that `(REVERSE (REVERSE X))` is **X**, *if* `(PROPERP X)`. In the intended application, **X** is `(REVERSE A)`. The system tries to relieve the hypothesis that `(PROPERP (REVERSE A))` by recursively rewriting it. However, the fact that **REVERSE** always returns a proper list requires induction to prove. Put another way, the system cannot apply **REVERSE-REVERSE** because the simplifier does not "know" that **REVERSE** builds proper lists. We can remedy the situation by "educating" the simplifier, proving the **REWRITE** rule that `(PROPERP (REVERSE X))`.

This discussion, however, has glossed over a very important point: how, in more complicated settings, do you determine why a given rule was not used? When the "missing rule" is more complicated than **REVERSE-REVERSE** and hundreds of other rules are around to "mess up" the target term and hypotheses, the situation demands some kind of mechanical help. We illustrate that help here by using the **BREAK-LEMMA** facility to investigate the failure of the **TRIPLE-REVERSE** proof attempt.

First, we install a break on the rule in question by typing

> `(BREAK-LEMMA 'REVERSE-REVERSE)`

Then we invoke the theorem prover again on **TRIPLE-REVERSE**.

> `(PROVE-LEMMA TRIPLE-REVERSE NIL`
> `   (EQUAL (REVERSE (REVERSE (REVERSE A)))`
> `          (REVERSE A)))`

This time, when **REVERSE-REVERSE** is tried, we get an interactive break:

> `(Entering break on replacement rule`
> `REVERSE-REVERSE`

The "break package" prints a colon as the prompt character and waits for user input. We type a "?" which causes a brief summary of the available commands to be printed:

```
:  ?
You are in the BREAK-REWRITE command interpreter.
The commands specific to this break are:

   cmd                     effect
   OK            Attempt to relieve the hypotheses
                    and then break.

   GO            Proceed without further interaction.
   NAME          Print name of the broken rule.
   HYPS          List the hypotheses of the broken
                    rule.

   CONCL         Print the conclusion of the broken
                    rule.
   SUBST         Print the substitution being applied
                    to the broken rule.
   TARGET        Print the term to which the rule is
                    being applied.
   ??            General purpose commands.
```

We then type the commands to display the conclusion of the rule, the hypotheses of the rule, and the target term to which the rule is being applied:

```
: concl
(EQUAL (REVERSE (REVERSE X)) X)
: hyps
1.   (PROPERP X)
: target
(REVERSE (REVERSE A))
```

Observe that the rule is being applied to innermost nest of **REVERSE**s. To apply the rule we will have to establish that **A** is **PROPERP**. This is not possible since we know nothing about **A**. Nevertheless, we type the command **ok** to observe the attempt to relieve the hypothesis. Upon seeing the explanation of the failure, we type **go** which causes the system to complete the attempt to apply this rule and continue to simplify the goal formula.

```
: ok
Attempting to relieve the hypotheses of
   REVERSE-REVERSE...
Failed to establish the first hypothesis of
   REVERSE-REVERSE:
(PROPERP X)
under the substitution
```

```
X <- A
because the hypothesis rewrote to:
(PROPERP A)
: go
Application of REVERSE-REVERSE failed.
Exiting break on replacement rule
REVERSE-REVERSE.)
```

The rule is still being monitored and another break occurs. This time when we print the **target** term we see that it is the outer **REVERSE** nest, the one to which we expected to apply the rule. The **ok** command causes the system to try to relieve the hypothesis, and we see that it simplifies to **(PROPERP (REVERSE A))**, not **T**. Thus, we know why **REVERSE-REVERSE** was not applied.

```
(Entering break on replacement rule
 REVERSE-REVERSE
: target
(REVERSE (REVERSE (REVERSE A)))
: ok
Attempting to relieve the hypotheses of
    REVERSE-REVERSE...
Failed to establish the first hypothesis of
    REVERSE-REVERSE:
(PROPERP X)
under the substitution
X <- (REVERSE A)
because the hypothesis rewrote to:
(PROPERP (REVERSE A))
: go
Application of REVERSE-REVERSE failed.
Exiting break on replacement rule
REVERSE-REVERSE.)
```

Upon exiting the proof attempt continues and we abort it, as before:

```
Call the conjecture *1.

Perhaps we can prove it by induction.
There [ABORT]
```

Having discovered why **REVERSE-REVERSE** is not applied, we remove the break on it:

```
(UNBREAK-LEMMA 'REVERSE-REVERSE)
```

and proceed to "educate" the simplifier by proving the general theorem that
(REVERSE X) is PROPERP for all X.

```
(PROVE-LEMMA REVERSE-IS-PROPERP (REWRITE)
  (PROPERP (REVERSE X)))
```


Give the conjecture the name *1.

    Let us appeal to the induction principle.
There is only one suggested induction. We will
induct according to the following scheme:
```
      (AND
       (IMPLIES (NLISTP X) (p X))
       (IMPLIES (AND (NOT (NLISTP X))
                     (p (CDR X)))
                (p X))).
```
Linear arithmetic, the lemmas CDR-LESSEQP and
CDR-LESSP, and the definition of NLISTP inform us
that the measure (COUNT X) decreases according to
the well-founded relation LESSP in each induction
step of the scheme. The above induction scheme
generates two new conjectures:

Case 2. (IMPLIES (NLISTP X)
                 (PROPERP (REVERSE X))),

  which simplifies, opening up the definitions of
NLISTP, REVERSE, and PROPERP, to:

      T.

Case 1. (IMPLIES
           (AND (NOT (NLISTP X))
                (PROPERP (REVERSE (CDR X))))
           (PROPERP (REVERSE X))).

  This simplifies, expanding the functions NLISTP
and REVERSE, to:

```
(IMPLIES
   (AND (LISTP X)
        (PROPERP (REVERSE (CDR X))))
   (PROPERP (APPEND (REVERSE (CDR X))
                    (LIST (CAR X)))))).
```

Applying the lemma CAR-CDR-ELIM, we now replace X by (CONS V Z) to eliminate (CDR X) and (CAR X). We thus obtain:

```
(IMPLIES (PROPERP (REVERSE Z))
         (PROPERP (APPEND (REVERSE Z)
                          (LIST V)))),
```

which we generalize by replacing (REVERSE Z) by Y. We thus obtain:

```
(IMPLIES (PROPERP Y)
         (PROPERP (APPEND Y (LIST V)))),
```

which we will name *1.1.

We will appeal to induction. There are two plausible inductions. However, they merge into one likely candidate induction. We will induct according to the following scheme:

```
(AND
 (IMPLIES (NLISTP Y) (p Y V))
 (IMPLIES
        (AND (NOT (NLISTP Y))
             (p (CDR Y) V))
        (p Y V))).
```

Linear arithmetic, the lemmas CDR-LESSEQP and CDR-LESSP, and the definition of NLISTP inform us that the measure (COUNT Y) decreases according to the well-founded relation LESSP in each induction step of the scheme. The above induction scheme leads to the following three new formulas:

*(The proofs of the three cases
have been deleted for brevity.)*

**That finishes the proof of *1.1, which,
consequently, finishes the proof of *1.   Q.E.D.**

**[0.0 0.8 4.2]
REVERSE-IS-PROPERP**

At this point we reconsider the proof of **REVERSE-IS-PROPERP** and
decide that the proof is prettier if the relationship between **APPEND** and
PROPERP is proved first as a lemma.   Therefore, the just proved
REVERSE-IS-PROPERP is ''undone''—removed from the data base:

```
(UNDO-NAME 'REVERSE-IS-PROPERP)
((PROVE-LEMMA REVERSE-IS-PROPERP (REWRITE)
              (PROPERP (REVERSE X))))
```

The **UNDO-NAME** command returns a list of the commands that have been
removed from the data base.

Next we formulate the necessary relationship between **PROPERP** and
APPEND.

```
(PROVE-LEMMA APPEND-IS-PROPERP (REWRITE)
   (IMPLIES (PROPERP B) (PROPERP (APPEND A B))))
```

The proof is by induction on **A** but is omitted here. Actually, the future behavior
of the system would be more efficient if we had instead proved

```
(EQUAL (PROPERP (APPEND A B))
       (PROPERP B))
```

since, when used as a **REWRITE** rule, the equality eliminates **APPEND** without
backwards chaining.

Now, revisiting **REVERSE-IS-PROPERP**, we see the proof is much simpler:

```
(PROVE-LEMMA REVERSE-IS-PROPERP (REWRITE)
   (PROPERP (REVERSE X)))
```


Give the conjecture the name *1.

**Let us appeal to the induction principle.
There is only one suggested induction. We will
induct according to the following scheme:**

```
(AND
 (IMPLIES (NLISTP X) (p X))
 (IMPLIES (AND (NOT (NLISTP X))
               (p (CDR X)))
          (p X))).
```
Linear arithmetic, the lemmas CDR-LESSEQP and
CDR-LESSP, and the definition of NLISTP inform us
that the measure (COUNT X) decreases according to
the well-founded relation LESSP in each induction
step of the scheme. The above induction scheme
generates two new conjectures:

Case 2. (IMPLIES (NLISTP X)
                 (PROPERP (REVERSE X))),

   which simplifies, opening up the definitions of
   NLISTP, REVERSE, and PROPERP, to:

        T.

Case 1. (IMPLIES
          (AND (NOT (NLISTP X))
               (PROPERP (REVERSE (CDR X))))
          (PROPERP (REVERSE X))).

   This simplifies, applying CDR-CONS and
   APPEND-IS-PROPERP, and opening up the
   definitions of NLISTP, REVERSE, and PROPERP,
   to:

        T.

     That finishes the proof of *1.   Q.E.D.

[0.0 0.1 1.4]
REVERSE-IS-PROPERP
```

Our identification of **APPEND-IS-PROPERP** as a useful **REWRITE** rule is
typical of the way the informed user can cause the system to produce simple
proofs.

Finally,   having   laid   the   proper   groundwork,   we   return   to   the
```

TRIPLE-REVERSE conjecture:

```
(PROVE-LEMMA TRIPLE-REVERSE (REWRITE)
  (EQUAL (REVERSE (REVERSE (REVERSE A)))
         (REVERSE A)))
```

This simplifies, appealing to the lemmas
REVERSE-IS-PROPERP and REVERSE-REVERSE, to:

> T.

Q.E.D.

[0.1 0.1 0.1]
TRIPLE-REVERSE

To save the data base we can execute

(MAKE-LIB "demo")

which will write two files, one called **"demo.lib"** and the other called **"demo.lisp"**.[25] Having saved the data base, we could log out, reset the machine, boot, or otherwise destroy the current machine configuration and recover an equivalent state, as far as the theorem prover is able to determine, by starting up a fresh copy of the theorem prover and invoking

(NOTE-LIB "demo") .

---

[25] Actually, the unique, full names of the files created depends upon the setting of several variables and the defaults used by the host file system. See the discussion of File Names in the Reference Guide, page 285.

9 How to Use the Theorem Prover

This chapter might also be called **How To Use the Theorem Prover to Discover Proofs** or **How to Interact with the Theorem Prover** or **How to Read Theorem Prover Output**.

Recall the example proof of **REVERSE-REVERSE**: the theorem prover did an induction, simplified the induction step, eliminated a destructor, used an equality hypothesis in a heuristic way and threw it away, generalized a common subterm, discarded an irrelevant hypothesis, and did a second induction. This example is misleading in one respect: few users of the theorem prover let the system even try to produce such complicated proofs.

Successful users of the theorem prover tend to arrange things so that most proofs fall into one of two forms:

- induction followed by simplification of each case, or

- simplification alone.

Complicated proofs are broken down into lemmas or cases, and each case is proved in isolation and stored as a **REWRITE** rule. Thus, the theorem prover is kept "on a short leash." This is an attractive strategy for many reasons. First, the system is more predictable—less is expected of it and so it more often meets your expectations. Second, you'll spend less time analyzing unexpected subgoals to see if the system has a chance—when it deviates from the expected path, blow it out of the water with the **ABORT** key. Third, you'll spend less time trying to trick it into producing the entire proof "automatically." Fourth, once a subgoal has been enshrined as a rule in the data base you will not have to prove it again—seeing the system wind its way through a complicated proof of an early subgoal is impressive if the entire proof attempt succeeds, but it is maddening if a later subgoal makes the entire proof attempt fail. Finally, when you are all done, the resulting data base is useful for future problems in the same domain.

We call this style of use "cooperative" because the final proof structure is produced jointly by the user and the theorem prover. The key to using the theorem prover cooperatively is to *know when to scrutinize its output* and to know what to do when you want to change the structure of the emerging proof. The crucial "check points" are selection of the induction schema, transition from simplification to the other processes, attempted generalization, and the naming of a subgoal to be proved by induction.

The remainder of this chapter is organized as follows. First we illustrate a cooperative session with the theorem prover by redoing the proof of **REVERSE-REVERSE** in this style. Then we discuss how we use the traditional Lisp interface and text editor to carry out such a session. Finally, we give general guidelines for what to think about at each of the checkpoints.

9.1. REVERSE-REVERSE Revisited—Cooperatively

Suppose we are in the **GROUND-ZERO** state except that **REVERSE** and **PROPERP** have been defined. We wish to prove **REVERSE-REVERSE**:

```
(PROVE-LEMMA REVERSE-REVERSE (REWRITE)
   (IMPLIES (PROPERP X)
            (EQUAL (REVERSE (REVERSE X)) X))).
```

First, we execute the above command. The induction selected by the system, on the **CDR** of **X**, is appropriate. The proof of the induction step, **Case 1**, starts as follows:

```
Case 1.  (IMPLIES
            (AND (NOT (NLISTP X))
                 (EQUAL
                    (REVERSE (REVERSE (CDR X)))
                    (CDR X))
                 (PROPERP X))
            (EQUAL (REVERSE (REVERSE X)) X)).
```

This simplifies, opening up the definitions of NLISTP, PROPERP, and REVERSE, to:

```
(IMPLIES
 (AND (LISTP X)
      (EQUAL (REVERSE (REVERSE (CDR X)))
             (CDR X))
      (PROPERP (CDR X)))
 (EQUAL (REVERSE
         (APPEND (REVERSE (CDR X))
                 (LIST (CAR X))))
        X)).
```

Appealing to the lemma CAR-CDR-ELIM, we now ...

Note that the last formula printed was produced by simplification, put into the pool, drawn out by the simplifier, and *did not change*. It thus entered the destructor elimination process. The transition from simplification to any of the later processes is critical. We call this a "check point" and there are, in all, four of them.

At this particular check point you should ask yourself the question "Are there some facts about the combinations of functions in this subgoal that could be used to further simplify the formula?" In the case above, the answer is "yes, **REVERSE** distributes over **APPEND**, sort of."

In particular,

```
(PROVE-LEMMA REVERSE-APPEND (REWRITE)
  (EQUAL (REVERSE (APPEND A B))
         (APPEND (REVERSE B) (REVERSE A)))).
```

It happens that if this fact is used as a rewrite rule during the simplification above, the subgoal simplifies to **T** and the proof of **REVERSE-REVERSE** is complete. However, it is not necessary that you recognize the sufficiency of **REVERSE-APPEND** as long as you recognize its utility.

Having diagnosed the need for **REVERSE-APPEND**, you should abort the proof attempt of **REVERSE-REVERSE** and focus instead on proving **REVERSE-APPEND**. That is, issue the **PROVE-LEMMA** command for **REVERSE-APPEND**.

The system inducts on **A** by **CDR**, as appropriate. There is a base case and an induction step. The base case transits from simplification (all the way to generalization) on the formula

```
(IMPLIES (NOT (LISTP A))
         (EQUAL (REVERSE B)
                (APPEND (REVERSE B) NIL)))
```

Again, study the formula at the transition. Is there some fact we know that permits this to be simplified further? "Yes, **NIL** is a right-identity for **APPEND**, on **PROPERP** lists, and **REVERSE** produces a **PROPERP** list." We thus single out two facts:

```
(PROVE-LEMMA APPEND-RIGHT-ID (REWRITE)
   (IMPLIES (PROPERP X)
            (EQUAL (APPEND X NIL) X)))
```

and

```
(PROVE-LEMMA PROPERP-REVERSE (REWRITE)
   (PROPERP (REVERSE X))).
```

Again, abort the proof attempt of **REVERSE-APPEND** and try proving these two goals.

The first is proved without difficulty—that is, the system inducts, and simplification reduces each case to **T**.

Next, submit the command for the second goal, **PROPERP-REVERSE**. An induction on **X** is chosen. The base case simplifies to **T**. The induction step simplifies and transits to destructor elimination on the formula:

```
(IMPLIES (AND (LISTP X)
              (PROPERP (REVERSE (CDR X))))
         (PROPERP
           (APPEND (REVERSE (CDR X))
                   (LIST (CAR X))))).
```

Again we ask what we know about the function nests involved. The answer is "**APPEND** constructs a **PROPERP** list if its second argument is **PROPERP**." Formally, this relation is expressed

```
(IMPLIES (PROPERP Y)
         (PROPERP (APPEND X Y))).
```

However, it is good to write unconditional replacement rules when possible, and a stronger relationship comes to mind: "**APPEND** constructs a **PROPERP** list if and only if its second argument is **PROPERP**."

Thus, we submit

```
(PROVE-LEMMA PROPERP-APPEND (REWRITE)
   (EQUAL (PROPERP (APPEND X Y))
          (PROPERP Y))).
```

This is proved without difficulty.

We return to the proof of **PROPERP-REVERSE** by executing the **PROVE-LEMMA** command again:

```
(PROVE-LEMMA PROPERP-REVERSE (REWRITE)
  (PROPERP (REVERSE X))).
```

The proof is completed without difficulty now, since **PROPERP-APPEND** simplifies the induction step to **T**.

We thus return to **REVERSE-APPEND**, knowing that the base case will now simplify to **T** since we have that **NIL** is a right-identity for **APPEND** on **PROPERP** lists and **REVERSE** is **PROPERP**. Re-executing the **PROVE-LEMMA** command we see the same induction and the expected proof of the base case. However, the induction step transits from simplification to destructor elimination on

```
(IMPLIES
  (AND (LISTP A)
       (EQUAL (REVERSE (APPEND (CDR A) B))
              (APPEND (REVERSE B)
                      (REVERSE (CDR A)))))
  (EQUAL (APPEND (REVERSE (APPEND (CDR A) B))
                 (LIST (CAR A)))
         (APPEND (REVERSE B)
                 (APPEND (REVERSE (CDR A))
                         (LIST (CAR A)))))).
```

Is there anything we know about the function nests here? Facts about nests of **APPEND**s and **REVERSE**s are uninteresting since we are trying to prove the fundamental one. Nothing comes to mind and so we let the proof continue. The destructor elimination takes place, the equality hypothesis is used, and the following formula arrives at the generalization process:

```
(EQUAL (APPEND (APPEND (REVERSE B) (REVERSE X))
               (LIST Z))
       (APPEND (REVERSE B)
               (APPEND (REVERSE X) (LIST Z)))).
```

Always read carefully any formula to be generalized and look for relevant **REWRITE** rules for it.

Here an obvious rule suggests itself: "**APPEND** is associative."

```
(PROVE-LEMMA APPEND-IS-ASSOCIATIVE (REWRITE)
  (EQUAL (APPEND (APPEND A B) C)
         (APPEND A (APPEND B C)))).
```

This is proved without difficulty.

If we now reissue the **PROVE-LEMMA** command for **REVERSE-APPEND** the proof is straightforward.

To conclude, we give the command to prove **REVERSE-REVERSE** and the proof is done without difficulty.

The final list of commands in the order they were successfully processed is

```
(DEFN REVERSE (X)
  (IF (NLISTP X)
      NIL
      (APPEND (REVERSE (CDR X)) (LIST (CAR X)))))


(DEFN PROPERP (X)
  (IF (NLISTP X)
      (EQUAL X NIL)
      (PROPERP (CDR X))))


(PROVE-LEMMA APPEND-RIGHT-ID (REWRITE)
   (IMPLIES (PROPERP X)
            (EQUAL (APPEND X NIL) X)))


(PROVE-LEMMA PROPERP-APPEND (REWRITE)
   (EQUAL (PROPERP (APPEND X Y))
          (PROPERP Y)))


(PROVE-LEMMA PROPERP-REVERSE (REWRITE)
   (PROPERP (REVERSE X)))


(PROVE-LEMMA APPEND-IS-ASSOCIATIVE (REWRITE)
   (EQUAL (APPEND (APPEND A B) C)
          (APPEND A (APPEND B C))))


(PROVE-LEMMA REVERSE-APPEND (REWRITE)
   (EQUAL (REVERSE (APPEND A B))
          (APPEND (REVERSE B) (REVERSE A))))


(PROVE-LEMMA REVERSE-REVERSE (REWRITE)
   (IMPLIES (PROPERP X)
            (EQUAL (REVERSE (REVERSE X)) X)))
```

Below we list the commands submitted for execution and indicate whether the execution terminated with success. We indent to indicate the implicit subgoal structure of the session:

REVERSE	succeeded
PROPERP	succeeded
REVERSE-REVERSE	aborted
REVERSE-APPEND	aborted
APPEND-RIGHT-ID	succeeded
PROPERP-REVERSE	aborted
PROPERP-APPEND	succeeded
PROPERP-REVERSE	succeeded
REVERSE-APPEND	aborted
APPEND-IS-ASSOCIATIVE	succeeded
REVERSE-APPEND	succeeded
REVERSE-REVERSE	succeeded

Each successful proof produced above is of the form "induct and simplify each case" with the exception of the proof for **REVERSE-APPEND** which requires a destructor elimination and heuristic equality substitution to set up an application of the associativity of **APPEND**.[26] Note that when we finish we have a useful library of rules about **APPEND**, **REVERSE**, and **PROPERP**. For example, without further difficulty we can prove the **TRIPLE-REVERSE** theorem.

9.2. Using Lisp and a Text Editor as the Interface

The theorem proving session illustrated above is typical of the current use of the system. Of course, few sessions are so strict in their adherence to a particular methodology. In many sessions we might have let the system "have its head" and thus have let it stumble upon complicated proofs of some of our lemmas simply because we felt it could manage and we had other things to think about.

A question that immediately comes to mind, however, is how the cooperative user manages to remember what he was doing when he aborted a proof and set out on a subgoal. Clearly some kind of stacklike bookkeeping mechanism is called for. However, what the user community has evolved so far is not so much a bookkeeping mechanism as just a style of using the text editing environments usually provided by host systems. In most systems it is possible to type

---

[26]The elimination of the destructors here is strictly unnecessary: we could have immediately carried out the equality substitution setting up the conclusive application of the associativity of **APPEND**. Often you will see such unnecessary proof steps. The problem is that the system tries its heuristics in a certain order.

text into an "edit buffer," evaluate part of the buffer in the Lisp system—possibly while "in" the editor but otherwise by "grabbing" the text and carrying it to the Lisp environment—and shipping the output to both the terminal and another edit buffer (here called the "session log").

Using these standard features we illustrate our own bookkeeping style by describing how the above session could be carried out. Start with an empty edit buffer. Type into it the **PROVE-LEMMA** command for **REVERSE-REVERSE**. Execute that command. Diagnose the need for **REVERSE-APPEND** and abort the proof attempt. Type the **PROVE-LEMMA** command for **REVERSE-APPEND** into the edit buffer immediately before the command just tried. Execute it. Diagnose the need for **APPEND-RIGHT-ID** and **PROPERP-REVERSE** and abort the proof attempt. Type the **PROVE-LEMMA** commands for **APPEND-RIGHT-ID** and **PROPERP-REVERSE** into the buffer immediately before the command just tried. Execute the first command. It succeeds. Execute the next command in the buffer. Diagnose the need for **PROPERP-APPEND** and abort the proof attempt. Type the **PROVE-LEMMA** command for **PROPERP-APPEND** into the buffer immediately before the command just tried. Execute it. It succeeds. Execute the next command (**PROPERP-REVERSE**). It succeeds. Execute the next command (**REVERSE-APPEND**). Diagnose the need for **APPEND-IS-ASSOCIATIVE** and abort the proof attempt. Type the **PROVE-LEMMA** command for **APPEND-IS-ASSOCIATIVE** into the buffer immediately before the command just tried. Execute it. It succeeds. Execute the next command (**REVERSE-APPEND**). It succeeds. Execute the next command (**REVERSE-REVERSE**). It succeeds. The final state of the edit buffer is that it has, in order, the successful events starting with **APPEND-RIGHT-ID** and ending with **REVERSE-REVERSE**.

We have experimented with other bookkeeping mechanisms to support this subgoaling structure. However, nobody uses them; we prefer the text editor approach. The reason is that the evolving buffer of commands soon becomes heavily annotated and less structured than suggested above. For example, explanations and comments are interspersed between commands, alternative command sequences tried and abandoned are recorded for posterity, and temporary notes are tacked up in the buffer:

```
??? I am stuck here.  I made a LIB file and I'm going
    home for the night.  The next proof needs a lemma
    relating FETCH and LINK.  I don't see what it is.
```

Finally, the edit buffer can be written out as a file and read as a coherent description of the current state.

9.3. The Crucial Check Points in a Proof Attempt

There are four crucial "check points" in a proof attempt. You should learn to recognize these points and know what to look for when a proof attempt reaches one of them.

9.3.1. Induction Selection

The first check point is when the system chooses an induction argument for a formula. Is the induction argument appropriate for the formula? We cannot pose this question in a more concrete form because the system selects the best induction we know how to manufacture from the terms involved. Usually you will have a particular induction argument in mind—for better or for worse—and all that is required is to determine whether the system used that argument. To force the selection of your induction argument, use the **INDUCT** hint of **PROVE-LEMMA**. A strategy we often adopt is to let the system proceed with its chosen induction and wait until a later check point to think about it. If we are confronted with a goal we don't see how to prove—"I don't see why this hypothesis implies that conclusion."—we go back to the output log and consider the induction more carefully.

9.3.2. Transition Out of Simplification

The second check point is when the simplification of a formula is complete and the processing transits to destructor elimination or one of the later processes. This is the check point at which you will spend most of your time. Formulas at this point have an important property: they are stable under simplification. They would not have made the transition to the later process had they been subject to further simplification. Thus a **REWRITE** rule can be designed to match a subterm of such a formula without having to worry that some sub-expression of the target will undergo additional simplification before the rule is tried.[27]

Questions you should ask include the following: Are there additional facts about the function nests in the formula that could be used to further simplify the formula? Typically the appropriate response is to recognize the need for a **REWRITE** rule, abort the current proof, and prove the new rule before restarting.

---

[27]Unless, of course, the subexpression is rewritten by the new rule itself!

We initially look for "local" simplifications—ones that suggest themselves without detailed consideration of the hypotheses. For example, we consider simplifications of each functional composition **(f (g ...) ...)** in the formula. If no such "local" simplifications suggest themselves, we usually ask "why is this formula a theorem?" and often see "nonlocal" reasons: two hypotheses are contradictory, a chain of lemmas must be invoked, or additional processing (e.g., destructor elimination or use of an equality hypothesis) is necessary.

It is sometimes the case that the necessary lemma has already been proved but is not being applied by the simplifier. Ask the following questions: Was it proved as a **REWRITE** rule? Is it currently enabled? What is the form of the rule generated? Does it match with a term in the simplified conjecture? If so, which hypothesis of the rule is not being established? Remember: a rule will be applied only if (a) its left-hand side matches a term being rewritten and (b) its hypotheses are established. If you want a rule to be applied, you must arrange for both of those things to happen.

This check point is *the* place to consider whether your rules match the terms in the conjecture. Asking that question earlier or later is often pointless: terms you see in other conjectures are destined to be rewritten and will have changed by the time your new rule is applied.

If the rule matches but is not firing it is almost certainly because some hypothesis cannot be established. We illustrated this in the first proof attempt for **TRIPLE-REVERSE** (page 198). In general, when a hypothesis is not being relieved, the first course of action is to prove a rule that establishes it.

If you cannot arrange for a rule to fire automatically, consider using the **USE** hint to **PROVE-LEMMA**.

The other commonly arising problem is that a definition fails to expand. The most convenient response is to use the **EXPAND** hint in the **PROVE-LEMMA** command. That hint requires that you provide exactly the term to be expanded, and this check point is *the* place to determine it.

In addition to considering the state of your **REWRITE** rules, the transition out of simplification should cause you to consider other issues. It is at this point that we often recognize that an inappropriate induction was done, that the conjecture submitted is not strong enough to go through an inductive proof, or that the conjecture submitted is not a theorem.

If we are unable to see any additional simplifications and do not have reason to doubt the induction or the validity of the conjecture, we usually let the system continue until the next check point.

9.3.3. Generalization

The third check point is when a formula is generalized. We almost never permit the system to generalize a formula for us. Many times we automatically abort when we see the words "**which we generalize.**" The question we ask ourselves here is exactly the same as at the transition out of simplification: what additional facts would permit this formula to simplify? But assuming we thought about that question at the last transition, we can broaden the question to "why is this formula a theorem?" That is, we're not interested here in just further simplifying it but rather in proving it. Typical responses are to identify a more general theorem that subsumes the current conjecture—one that is at the heart of the proof of the main conjecture. Things to look for are contradictory hypotheses or, more generally, generalizations of fragments of the given conjecture. For example, the first and fifth hypotheses, slightly generalized, may imply the conclusion, slightly generalized.

9.3.4. Pushing a Subgoal for Induction

The fourth check point is when a formula is given a name (e.g., "***1.4**") and pushed into the stack of things to be proved by induction. At the very least, ask yourself "Is the subgoal a theorem?" We more often simply abort—assuming we've already done one induction—and consider more carefully the **REWRITE** rules necessary to prove the conjecture earlier in simplification.

If you permit the system to proceed, it will attack these named formulas by induction. Therefore, a subsidiary question is "Is the subgoal sufficiently general to be proved by induction?" Often this will force you to invent a formula that is more general than the ones you've been thinking about. The formula will be provable by induction and, as a **REWRITE** rule, will simplify the current subgoal to **T**.

10   How the Theorem Prover Works

In this chapter we describe how the theorem prover works, with particular attention to those aspects of its behavior under the control of the user through previously proved theorems. Recall that when theorems are proved by the system the user is responsible for declaring what classes of rules are to be generated from the theorem. The four classes of rules are **REWRITE**, **META**, **ELIM**, and **GENERALIZE**. We note in the discussion below where the various classes of rules are used. In the next chapter we discuss in detail the generation and interpretation of rules.

Recall that the theorem prover is built out of six processes: simplification, destructor elimination, cross-fertilization (heuristic equality use), generalization, elimination of irrelevance, and induction. Each takes a formula as input and returns a set of formulas as output. When one process does not change the input formula, the next process in the list above is tried. We now discuss each of the six processes in turn, emphasizing those that are sensitive to previously proved theorems. However, we first discuss two more general issues, the representation of formulas inside the processes and the use of type information.

10.1. The Representation of Formulas

The formulas manipulated by our processes are kept in "clausal" form. A *clause*, in our sense, is a list of terms $(\mathtt{lit_1}\ \mathtt{lit_2}\ \ldots\ \mathtt{lit_n})$ and represents the formula

$$\mathtt{lit_1}{\neq}\mathtt{F}\ \lor\ \mathtt{lit_2}{\neq}\mathtt{F}\ \lor\ \ldots\ \lor\ \mathtt{lit_n}{\neq}\mathtt{F}$$

Each $\mathtt{lit_i}$ is called a *literal*.[28]

For example, when the user submits the following conjecture

```
(IMPLIES (AND (PRIME P)
              (NOT (DIVIDES P M)))
         (EQUAL (REMAINDER (EXPT M (SUB1 P)) P)
                1))
```

it is actually a *term* that is submitted. The term is converted into the following clause:

```
((NOT (PRIME P))
 (DIVIDES P M)
 (EQUAL (REMAINDER (EXPT M (SUB1 P)) P) 1))
```

The simplifier and all other processes actually manipulate this clausal form of the conjecture. The advantage to clausal form is that it encourages symmetric treatment of hypotheses and conclusions.

The conversion to clausal form is usually invisible to the user because the theorem prover prints clauses by first applying the inverse conversion, mapping the clause back into the form **(IMPLIES (AND h_1 ... h_n) concl)** before printing it. However, understanding the clausal form underlying the printed representation of formulas helps the user who is designing rules. For example, since the **AND** in the hypothesis of the implication above is not actually in the clausal form, no **REWRITE** rule designed to hit **(AND h_1 ... h_n)** will touch it.

---

[28]Traditionally, a literal is either an atomic formula or the negation of an atomic formula, rather than a term. A clause is traditionally a set, rather than a list, of literals.

10.2. Type Sets

Type sets indicate the shell classes over which the value of an expression ranges and are used extensively throughout the theorem prover.

Without loss of generality, let us assume that all the shells that will ever be added have been added and that the resulting history contains **n** shell recognizers, r_1, ..., r_n, the first six of which are **FALSEP**, **TRUEP**, **NUMBERP**, **LITATOM**, **LISTP**, and **NEGATIVEP**. Let us also assume that

(OTHERS X)

=

(AND (NOT (r_1 X)) ... (NOT (r_n X)))

Let Ω be the set $\{r_1 \dots r_n \text{ OTHERS}\}$. Then a *type set* is any subset of Ω. To say that a term **t** *has* type set $\{s_1 \dots s_k\}$ means that **(OR (s_1 t) ... (s_k t))** is a theorem. For example, the term **(IF (LISTP X) (CONS a b) NIL)** has type set {**LISTP LITATOM**}. The term **(IF (NUMBERP X) T X)** has type set Ω-{**NUMBERP**}.

The most notable use of type sets in the theorem prover is to encode the assumptions under which the theorem prover is working. As the rewriter explores a term, it maintains a context that encodes the current assumptions as type sets. For example, consider the problem of exploring an expression of the form **(IF test left right)**. While working on **left** it is permitted to assume that **test** is non-**F**, and while working on **right** it is permitted to assume that **test** is **F**. How do we assume **test** is "non-**F**" when working on **left**? Suppose we knew initially that the type set of **test** was **ts**. Then when working on **left** we could assign **test** the type set **ts**-{**FALSE**}. When working on **right** we assign **test** the type set {**FALSE**}.

Some **test**s permit us finer-grained control of the type sets. Suppose **test** is **(NUMBERP x)** and that under the current assumptions the type set of **x** is ts_x. If ts_x is {**NUMBERP**}, then **test** is **T**; if ts_x does not include **NUMBERP**, then **test** is **F**. Otherwise, when working on **left** we may assume that the type set of **x** is {**NUMBERP**}, and while working on **right** we may assume that it is ts_x-{**NUMBERP**}.

In fact this type of processing is generalized for user-defined predicates about which certain kinds of formulas have been proved. By proving the appropriate "compound recognizer" rules (see the next chapter) it can be arranged, for example, for the assumption of **(BOOLEANP x)** to set the new type set of **x** to {**TRUEP FALSEP**} on the left branch and to everything but {**TRUEP FALSEP**} on the right.

Because type sets are a general purpose way of encoding assumptions, they are used in virtually every process of the theorem prover. Such fundamental questions as "Is this term non-**F**?" send the theorem prover off into type set computation.

When functions are defined by the user, the system computes a "type prescription rule" (see the next chapter) that describes how a type set can be computed for any application of the function. The definitional mechanism prints out a formula that describes the type prescription rule generated. The user can override the generated rule by proving certain forms of **REWRITE** rules that establish smaller type sets. For example, one might prove **(NUMBERP (GCD X Y))** as a **REWRITE** rule, with the effect that the type set for **GCD** expressions would henceforth be computed to be {**NUMBERP**}.

10.3. Simplification

The simplifier is the most complex process in the theorem prover. It is the only process that can return the empty set of formulas—i.e., it is the only process that can establish a goal instead of merely transforming it into subgoals. The simplifier combines many different proof techniques: decision procedures for propositional calculus and equality, a procedure for deciding many of the truths of linear arithmetic over the natural numbers, a term rewriting system, and the application of metafunctions.

Recall that the simplifier takes as input a formula and produces an equivalent set of formulas. Formulas are represented as clauses or lists of literals, implicitly disjoined.

The heart of the simplifier is a term rewrite system, here called "the rewriter." The rewriter takes as input a term and a set of assumptions and returns a term equivalent to the input one, under the assumptions. The rewriter relies primarily upon **REWRITE** rules derived from axioms, definitions, and previously proved lemmas. For example, the theorem

```
(IMPLIES (PROPERP X)
         (EQUAL (REVERSE (REVERSE X)) X))
```

is used to replace every term of the form **(REVERSE (REVERSE x))** by **x**, provided the rewriter can establish **(PROPERP x)**. To establish a hypothesis, the rewriter rewrites it under the current assumptions and asks whether the result is non-**F**. Of course, a term among the current assumptions will rewrite to non-**F**.

Similarly, the definitions

```
(NOT X) = (IF X F T)
```

and

```
(NLISTP X) = (NOT (LISTP X))
```

are used to rewrite every occurrence of **(NLISTP x)** to **(IF (LISTP x) F T)**.

The rewriter also uses **META** rules which are, in essence, user-defined simplifiers for the logic, coded as functions on s-expressions in the logic. It is possible to state, within the logic, a formula establishing the soundness of such a ''metafunction.'' Once a metafunction has been proved sound, the theorem prover can be made to apply it as part of the simplifier just as it would a hand-coded Lisp procedure. This provides what is known as *metatheoretic extensibility*.

For example, the user might define the function **CANCEL** so that when given a list structure representing an equation, such as

```
' (EQUAL (PLUS A (PLUS B (PLUS D E)))
         (PLUS B (PLUS C D))),
```

it returns the list structure representing an equivalent equation, such as

```
' (EQUAL (PLUS A E) (FIX C)).
```

After defining **CANCEL** the user may then prove it correct. The appropriate theorem is

```
(EQUAL (EVAL$ T X A)
       (EVAL$ T (CANCEL X) A)).
```

If this theorem is classified as a **META** rule for the function symbol **EQUAL** (see the next chapter), then the rewriter will apply the function **CANCEL** to every equation it encounters and use the output (if different from the input) as the rewritten term.

To simplify a clause the simplifier rewrites each literal under the assumption that the remaining literals are false. In a sense, the simplifier replaces each literal by its rewritten counterpart. However, there are three special cases. If the rewritten literal is **T**, the clause is a theorem since one of its disjuncts is true. If the rewritten literal is **F**, the literal can be dropped from the disjunction. Finally, if the rewritten literal contains an **IF**-expression, the answer clause is split into two clauses, according to the test of the **IF**.

Below we give an extended example of the clause-level activity of the simplifier. Suppose the simplifier is given the clause {**p q r**}. Attention is initially focussed on the first literal. Let us denote this state of affairs as {**p q r**}.

⇑

That is, **p** is rewritten under the assumption that both **q** and **r** are false. Suppose **p** rewrites to **p′** under these assumptions. Then the simplifier state becomes

{**p′ q r**},

⇑

and **q** is rewritten under the assumption that both **p′** and **r** are false. Suppose **q** rewrites to (**q′** (**IF t a b**)). The **IF** is split out and the simplifier state becomes

{**p′ ~t** (**q′ a**) **r**}

⇑

∧

{**p′ t** (**q′ b**) **r**}

⇑

That is, there are now two clauses and the simplification process continues in both. In the first, **r** is rewritten, say to **r′**, under the assumptions that **p′** and (**q′ a**) are false and that **t** is true. In the second, **r** is rewritten, say to **r′′**, under the assumptions that **p′**, **t**, and (**q′ b**) are false.

The final answer returned by the simplifier is

{**p′ ~t** (**q′ a**) **r′**}

∧

{**p′ t** (**q′ b**) **r′′**}

The simplifier and rewriter are vastly more complicated than indicated here. Before starting the scan through the literals, the simplifier determines whether the clause is a propositional tautology or is a consequence of linear arithmetic. During rewriting, the equality hypotheses among the assumptions are used in a way that will decide whether the formula is a consequence of equality reasoning alone. When the rewriter encounters a **LESSP**-expression, the rewriter uses the linear arithmetic procedure to attempt to decide whether the **LESSP** relation follows by linear arithmetic reasoning from the assumptions. Finally, the rewriter may actually add some assumptions to those supplied in the top-level call, and its answer is equivalent to the input only under the augmented assumptions. These additional assumptions must be accounted for when the answer clauses are formed after rewriting each literal. A more or less complete description of the simplifier can be found by reading Chapters VII through IX of [4], then reading how metafunctions were added in [5], and finally reading of the integration of linear arithmetic in [12].

10.4. Elimination of Destructors

The destructor elimination process attempts to trade "destructive" terms for "constructive" ones, using rules derived from axioms and previously proved lemmas.

For example, suppose we wish to prove a formula of the form **(p X (SUB1 X))**. Suppose **X** is known to be a positive integer. It can then be represented by **(ADD1 I)**, for some natural number **I**. But then **(SUB1 X)** is **I**. Thus we can transform **(p X (SUB1 X))** into **(p (ADD1 I) I)**, trading the "destructive" term **(SUB1 X)** for the "constructive" term **(ADD1 I)**.

If **X** is not known to be a positive integer we can split the goal formula into two subgoals on that condition. In the case where **X** is known not to be a positive integer the expression **(SUB1 X)** will simplify to **0**.

Such trading of **SUB1** for **ADD1** is actually carried out in two steps. First, we use the **ELIM** rule generated from the theorem (axiom)

```
(IMPLIES (NOT (ZEROP X))
         (EQUAL (ADD1 (SUB1 X)) X)),
```

to replace **X** by **(ADD1 (SUB1 X))**. Thus, we transform **(p X (SUB1 X))** into **(p (ADD1 (SUB1 X)) (SUB1 X))**. Second, we generalize **(SUB1 X)** to **I**, constraining **I** to be a **NUMBERP** since we know (from type set considerations) that **(SUB1 X)** is numeric.

Note that it is the **ELIM** rule that determines which terms are "destructive" and which are "constructive." The user could arrange to eliminate **ADD1**s in favor of **SUB1**s.

There are much more sophisticated uses of the destructor elimination technique. A very useful application in number theory appeals to the fact that any number **X** can be represented as **R + YQ**, where **R** and **Q** are the remainder and quotient, respectively, of **X** by some non-0 number **Y**. Thus, given

```
(p X (REMAINDER X Y) (QUOTIENT X Y)),
```

where **X** is known to be a **NUMBERP** and **Y** is a positive **NUMBERP**, the destructor eliminator process could produce the goal

```
(p R+YQ R Q)
```

where **R** and **Q** are **NUMBERP**s and **R** is less than **Y**.

The first step is carried out by the **ELIM** rule generated from the theorem

```
(IMPLIES (AND (NUMBERP X)
              (NOT (ZEROP Y)))
         (EQUAL (PLUS (REMAINDER X Y)
                      (TIMES Y (QUOTIENT X Y)))
                X)).
```

The second is carried out by the **GENERALIZE** rule generated from

```
(IMPLIES (NOT (ZEROP Y))
         (LESSP (REMAINDER X Y) Y))
```

together with the observation that **REMAINDER** and **QUOTIENT** are numerically valued.

The above mentioned **ELIM** lemma essentially declares **REMAINDER** and **QUOTIENT** to be "destructive" and **PLUS** and **TIMES** to be "constructive." Trading one set of symbols for the other is productive only if the data base contains a useful set of rules for manipulating the new symbols. It is certainly the case that the theorem prover finds it easier to cope with **ADD1**, **PLUS**, and **TIMES** than their destructive counterparts **SUB1**, **DIFFERENCE**, and **REMAINDER** and **QUOTIENT**. However, we offer no objective characterization of "destructive" nor do we explain why "constructive" functions better suit the theorem prover's heuristics.

10.5. Heuristic Use of Equalities

A common way to use an inductive hypothesis that is an equality is to substitute one side of it for selected occurrences of the other side elsewhere in the conjecture and then to throw away the hypothesis. We call this *cross-fertilization*. This heuristic is implemented in the cross-fertilization process.

Throwing away a hypothesis is a way of generalizing the conjecture being proved. It is thus possible for the cross-fertilization process to take a theorem as input and produce a non-theorem as output. That is, cross-fertilization can cause the system to adopt a non-theorem as its subgoal—a heuristic mistake since the subgoal cannot be established. We try to avoid this mistake by throwing away the equality hypothesis only if we have already done an induction as a prior step in the proof attempt. Most often, the equality hypothesis thus thrown away is actually an inductive hypothesis.

No user-supplied rules affect the cross-fertilization process.

There is an interaction between cross-fertilization and simplification that, when it occurs, confuses many users. We comment upon it here.

The fertilization process is not the only process in the theorem prover that uses equality hypotheses to rewrite formulas. The simplifier also uses those equalities to canonicalize the formula, replacing all occurrences of the "complicated" side by the "simpler" side. Sometimes the rewriting performed by the fertilization process undoes that done by the simplifier. This momentarily produces a formula that is no longer in canonical form. When, in addition, the equality hypothesis is not thrown away by fertilization, the next simplification will undo the effects of the fertilization and a loop threatens. The loop is avoided by an explicit check in fertilization.

However, it is sometimes the case that the user has anticipated the production of the emphemeral uncanonical formula and has provided a rewrite rule explicitly to handle it. Unfortunately, that rewrite rule will not be applied because the formula is canonicalized by the simplifier from the inside-out. The solution to this problem is to use what we call "bridge" lemmas (see page 327).

10.6. Generalization

The generalization process replaces certain non-variable terms by variables. For example, the system might generalize

```
(EQUAL (APPEND (REVERSE A) NIL)
       (REVERSE A))
```

by replacing **(REVERSE A)** by the new variable **L**:

```
(EQUAL (APPEND L NIL)
       L) .
```

Obviously, if the output formula is a theorem, then the input formula is also a theorem (by instantiation). It is sometimes necessary to so strengthen a conjecture before attempting an inductive proof. However, the resulting generalization may be "too strong" in that it may fail to be a theorem, even though the input formula is a theorem.

To help prevent this, the generalization process constrains the variables introduced by taking note of the **GENERALIZE** rules. For example, if a **GENERALIZE** rule has been produced from the theorem **(PROPERP (REVERSE X))** then the subsequent generalization of **(REVERSE A)** to **L** will include the hypothesis that **L** is **PROPERP**. That is, the generalization of

```
(EQUAL (APPEND (REVERSE A) NIL)
       (REVERSE A))
```

will be

```
(IMPLIES (PROPERP L)
         (EQUAL (APPEND L NIL)
                L)).
```

The generalization process also takes into account the type set of the term being replaced. If the type set is a singleton, {**r**}, then the new variable is restricted to the shell **r**.

Recall that the destructor elimination process is actually carried out in two steps, the second step being the introduction of new variables for the destructor terms. It is actually the generalization mechanism—including the use of **GENERALIZE** rules and type sets—that is used.

10.7. Elimination of Irrelevancy

Irrelevant hypotheses in a conjecture may make it difficult to prove the conjecture by induction. The system has some elementary heuristics for identifying irrelevant hypotheses. Roughly speaking, it partitions the literals of the input clause into cliques whose variable symbols do not overlap and then deletes those literals in cliques that can, apparently, be falsified by instantiation. We say "apparently" because it does not actually choose instantiations but rather uses type set reasoning and several heuristics.

10.8. Induction

The system attempts to find inductive arguments suitable for a conjecture by analyzing the recursive functions called in it. Each recursion "suggests" a corresponding induction if the "measured" argument positions are occupied by variable symbols. For example, the term **(APPEND A B)** suggests induction on **A** by successive **CDR**s with the base case **(NLISTP A)**, because **APPEND** recurses in that way on its first argument. The term does not suggest induction on **B**. The term **(APPEND (CAR A) B)** does not suggest any induction: the term in the first argument position, **(CAR A)**, is not a variable and so we cannot form an induction hypothesis by instantiating it as in the recursion; the term in the second argument position is irrelevant because **APPEND** does not recurse into it.

The analysis of which argument positions are important takes place when functions are defined. Recall admissibility requirement (d) of the principle of definition. It requires that some measure **m** of the arguments decrease according to **ORD-LESSP** in each recursive call. When a definition is admitted by the mechanized definitional principle, a suitable **m** is found (or provided by the user). It is frequently the case that **m** does not measure all of the arguments of the definition. For example, the measure term traditionally used to justify the definition of **(APPEND X Y)** is **(COUNT X)**. The arguments actually used in **m** are the ones considered measured for purposes of the inductive analysis. We call those arguments a *measured subset* of the formals of the defined function.

Many functions have more than one measured subset. For example, suppose **(LT I J)** is defined to decrement both **I** and **J** by **SUB1** until either is **ZEROP**. Then both the **COUNT** of **I** and the **COUNT** of **J** decrease in each recursion. Either is sufficient to admit **LT**. But if both are known to the theorem prover, then **(LT I J)** suggests both induction on **I** and induction on **J**. Furthermore, a term such as **(LESSP (CAR X) J)** suggests induction on **J** even though the first argument is "blocked" by a non-variable.

Thus, the system's heuristics for choosing an induction suitable for a conjecture are more powerful if the system has alternative measured subsets for each function involved. By proper use of the **DEFN** command, and in particular, use of the **hints** argument, the user can point out alternative justifications. This is the only way the user can influence the induction process—except to override it completely using the **hints** argument of **PROVE-LEMMA**.

Once a set of suggested induction principles is identified, the system merges them to try to accommodate the various functions involved. Finally, it chooses between the final candidates using a variety of heuristics. No user-supplied rules influence these latter moves.

A complete description of the induction mechanism can be found in [4] with the minor addition described in [10].

11 The Four Classes of Rules Generated from Lemmas

As previously explained, the data base contains rules which determine the behavior of the system. Each rule has a name, and whenever the rule is used by the system the name of the rule is printed.[29] Each rule has a *status* which is either **ENABLED** or **DISABLED**. When the status of a rule is **DISABLED** the rule is not used.

There are four different *classes* of rules[30]:

REWRITE,
META,
ELIM, and
GENERALIZE.

Each class of rule influences a different aspect of the theorem prover's behavior. For example, a **REWRITE** rule may direct the system to replace all instances of

---

[29]This is not strictly true. See the discussion of "immediate dependency" on page 269.

[30]Historical Note: In the version of the theorem prover described in *A Computational Logic* we had another class of rules, the so-called **INDUCTION** rules. In that version of our system, the **DEFN** command attempted to construct a suitable measure for each submitted definition. The **INDUCTION** rules were used to guide this construction. **DEFN** no longer tries to construct a measure; it uses **COUNT** unless told to do otherwise by the user. Thus, **INDUCTION** rules have been eliminated.

one term by corresponding instances of another, provided certain conditions are satisfied. To use the theorem prover effectively, it is necessary to understand how such rules influence the behavior of the system.

However, the user of the theorem prover does not deal explicitly with rules; instead, the user deals with formulas in the logic, and the rules themselves are generated from the formulas. The name of each generated rule is the name of the formula from which the rules were generated. For example, a rule to replace all occurrences of (instances of) **(REVERSE (REVERSE X))** by **X** is generated from the formula **(EQUAL (REVERSE (REVERSE X)) X)**. To use the theorem prover effectively it is thus also necessary to understand how rules are generated from formulas: once the need for a given rule is recognized, the user must find a formula that will generate it.

Finally, our system is a theorem prover, not just a formula manipulator. Thus the transformations effected by the rules are supposed to be valid inferences in the logic. It turns out that the rules generated from a formula are valid iff the formula is a theorem. For example, the rule that replaces **(REVERSE (REVERSE X))** by **X** is not valid since **(EQUAL (REVERSE (REVERSE X)) X)** is not a theorem. The effort to prove a formula so as to obtain a certain rule often reveals that the desired rule is invalid.

The whole rule-validation-and-generation process is brought together at the user interface in a deceptively simple way: when the user submits a formula to the theorem prover he tags the formula with a set of tokens taken from **{REWRITE META ELIM GENERALIZE}**; if the formula is proved the corresponding rules are generated and added.

This interface is in many ways *too* simple; the user is vitally concerned with the production of rules but can discuss only formulas. This has two bad side effects. First, elegant and often simple truths are obscured by the need to express them in a way that permits their transformation into rules.[31] Second, the absence of explicit discussion of rules often lulls the inexperienced user into an ill-considered disregard for the procedural interpretation of his lemmas. This almost always comes back to haunt him; halfway through the construction of his first big proof, the user finds the system acting as though it were programmed by a monkey: obvious inferences are missed, trivial proofs are unimaginably difficult to obtain, and the system frequently takes (literally) forever to respond. The problem is that the data base is a spaghetti bowl of conflicting rules. The common solution is to use **DISABLE** commands to turn off virtually every rule and then use the hint facility to tell the system every proof. A more fun and

---

[31]A good solution to this problem is to prove the elegant form of the theorem as a lemma with the empty set of rule classes. This will store the formula under its name but generate no rules. Then prove the obscure, rule-generating version by explicit appeal (via a **USE** hint, see page 295) to the elegant formulation.

productive long term solution is to understand how the system uses rules and how rules are generated and then construct a data base that gives coherent advice about how to prove theorems in the given domain.

In summary, we have identified three issues in connection with the use of rules:

- how rules are used by the system,

- how rules are generated from formulas, and

- how formulas are proved.

The third issue, of course, encompasses this whole handbook.

We discuss the other two issues at length in this chapter. We deal with each of the two issues separately for each of the four types of rules, **REWRITE**, **META**, **ELIM**, and **GENERALIZE**. Within each section we first describe how rules of the type are used by the system—without regard for the logical validity of the transformations effected. Then we discuss how such rules are derived from formulas.

11.1. REWRITE

REWRITE rules are by far the most common, the most useful, and the most complicated kind of rule used by the system.

There are four different forms of **REWRITE** rules:

- **Type Prescription Rules**: used throughout the theorem prover to quickly compute the possible shell types returned by an expression,

- **Compound Recognizer Rules**: used to forward chain from user-defined predicates to conjunctions and disjunctions of shell types,

- **Linear Arithmetic Rules**: used inside the simplifier by the linear arithmetic decision procedure and its heuristic extension, and

- **Replacement Rules**: used inside the simplifier by the term rewrite system, to replace "complicated" terms by "simpler" ones.

Which kind of **REWRITE** rule is generated from a given formula depends on the syntactic form of the formula. In fact, we treat the submitted formula as a conjunction and generate a rule for each of the conjuncts. (We make this more precise below.) Thus, several rules of each kind may be generated from a single submitted formula.

Given a conjunct, we generate a type prescription rule, if possible. If a given conjunct cannot be encoded as a type prescription, we try to generate a compound recognizer rule. If that fails, we try to generate a linear arithmetic rule. If that fails, we try to generate a replacement rule. Sometimes it is impossible to generate any rule for a conjunct and this is reported. Despite the priorities above, almost all **REWRITE** rules are replacement rules. We therefore describe the form and meaning of replacement rules first and discuss the other types of rules later.

When a formula is submitted for class **REWRITE** we first flatten its **AND** and **IMPLIES** structure, transforming the submitted formula into an equivalent conjunction over a set of formulas, each of the form

```
(IMPLIES (AND h₁ ... hₙ) concl)
```

where no h_i is a conjunction and **concl** is neither a conjunction nor an implication. For example, the formula

```
(AND (IMPLIES h₁
            (AND concl₁ (IMPLIES h₂ concl₂)))
     (IMPLIES (AND h₃ h₄)
            (IMPLIES h₅ concl₃)))
```

is transformed into a conjunction of the following three formulas:

```
(IMPLIES h₁ concl₁)

(IMPLIES (AND h₁ h₂) concl₂)

(IMPLIES (AND h₃ h₄ h₅) concl₃)
```

After so flattening the **AND** and **IMPLIES** structure of the formula, we generate a type prescription, a compound recognizer, a linear arithmetic, or a replacement rule from each of the resulting formulas.

We therefore consider how we generate one of the four kinds of rules from a formula of the form **(IMPLIES (AND h₁ ... hₙ) concl)**.

11.1.1. Replacement Rules

Replacement rules are the most common form of **REWRITE** rules. They permit the rewriter to simplify terms by replacing subterms with equivalent ones. For example, a replacement rule might direct the system to "replace terms of the form **(REVERSE (REVERSE x))** by **x**, provided **(PROPERP x)** can be established." Another is "In the tests of **IF**s and in other propositional occurrences, **(ASSOC x (PAIRLIST u v))** should be replaced by **(MEMBER x u)**." Note that in the second example the two terms are not **EQUAL**: the **ASSOC** returns a **CONS**-pair when the **MEMBER** returns **T**. But the two terms are propositionally equivalent—they return **F** or non-**F** in unison—and hence are interchangeable in contexts where they are being treated as propositions.

In general, a *replacement rule* is a rule of the form **Replace** or **Propositionally replace lhs by rhs after establishing hyp_1, ..., hyp_n**, where **lhs** (*left-hand side*), **rhs** (*right-hand side*) and hyp_1, ..., hyp_n (*hypotheses*) are all terms.

Replacement rules are applied by the rewriter in an inside-out fashion. That is, replacement rules are applied to (**fn** a_1 ... a_n) only after the a_i have been rewritten.

To apply replacement rules to the target term (**fn** a_1 ... a_n) the rewriter searches the enabled rules in reverse chronological order, i.e., starting with the most recently proved one, looking for the first applicable rule. A rule with left-hand side **lhs**, right-hand side **rhs** and hypotheses hyp_i, i=1, ..., n, is *applicable* to the target term iff all of the following conditions are met:

- the rule is of the "**Replace**" form or the rule is of the "**Propositionally replace**" form and the target occurs as the test of an **IF**, a literal in a clause, or a hypothesis of a rule;

- there is a substitution σ such that **lhs**/σ is syntactically identical to the target;

- the hypotheses of the rule can be relieved under σ; and

- certain heuristic conditions are met.

The heuristic conditions prevent certain implausible backchaining paths and some infinite loops. (We discuss the implications of some of these heuristics later.) The test for applicability yields a substitution, σ', which is usually just σ but is, in general, an extension of σ. (We discuss how the extension is constructed later.)

When the first applicable rule is found, with substitution σ', the rule is applied by replacing the target with **rhs**/σ' and recursively rewriting the result.

To *relieve the hypotheses* of a rule, under some substitution σ, the rewriter iteratively considers the hypotheses in the order in which they are presented in the rule, attempting to establish each in turn and possibly extending σ each iteration. Intuitively, a hypothesis hyp_i is established under σ iff either hyp_i/σ is among the current assumptions or recursively rewrites to **T**. However, it is possible that some hyp_i contains variables not bound by σ. Such variables are called *free variables*. To establish such a hypothesis under σ, the rewriter attempts to find an extension σ' of σ such that hyp_i/σ' is among the current assumptions (or the "ground units," i.e., variable-free unconditional replacement rules). One special case is recognized: if hyp_i/σ is of the form (**EQUAL v term**), where **v** is a variable not occurring in **term**, a suitable extension is to substitute the rewritten form of **term** for **v**. If any suitable extension can be found, the rewriter extends σ with the first extension found and moves on to the next hypothesis. It does not backtrack to try alternative extensions.

The heuristic conditions are present to prevent some forms of infinite looping and implausible backwards chaining. The most commonly felt restriction pertains to rules that express commutativity or, in general, rules that permit one to permute the arguments in a nest of functions. For example, were the rule "**Replace (PLUS X Y) by (PLUS Y X)**" applicable to all expressions matching the left-hand side, the rewriter would loop forever, rewriting **(PLUS A B)** to **(PLUS B A)** and then to **(PLUS A B)** and then to **(PLUS B A)**, etc. Such "permutative" rules are applied only if **rhs/σ** occurs earlier than **lhs/σ** in a lexicographically based enumeration of terms. Thus, using the commutativity of **PLUS** rule, **(PLUS B A)** rewrites to **(PLUS A B)** but not vice versa. Similarly, the rule "**Replace (DELETE X (DELETE Y L)) by (DELETE Y (DELETE X L))**" is applicable to **(DELETE B (DELETE A LST))** and rewrites it to **(DELETE A (DELETE B LST))**; but the rule is not applicable to **(DELETE A (DELETE B LST))**.

This completes our explanation of how replacement rules are used by the theorem prover. On page 317 we give some hints for the effective use of such rules. We next consider how replacement rules are generated from formulas.

Suppose a formula of the form **(IMPLIES (AND hyp$_1$ ... hyp$_n$) concl)** is submitted and proved in class **REWRITE**. If the formula generates either a type prescription or a linear arithmetic rule, no replacement rule is generated. We discuss these two forms of rules later. If **concl** is a variable symbol or **QUOTE**d constant, no replacement rule is generated. If **concl** is of the form **(EQUAL lhs rhs)**, we generate the replacement rule

> **Replace lhs by rhs**
> after establishing hyp$_1$, ..., hyp$_n$.

If **concl** is of the form **(IFF lhs rhs)** we generate

> **Propositionally replace lhs by rhs**
> after establishing hyp$_1$, ..., hyp$_n$.

If **concl** is of the form **(NOT lhs)**, it is treated as though it were **(EQUAL concl F)**. A conclusion of any other form is treated as though it were **(IFF concl T)**.

The function definition

Definition.
(fn x$_1$ ... x$_n$) = body

may be thought of as generating the replacement rule

> **Replace (fn x$_1$ ... x$_n$) by body,**

in the sense that definitions, when used, are used only to replace function calls by their instantiated bodies. We call this "opening up" or "expanding" the definition. *Definitions are never "folded" or used "backwards."*

However, the applicability heuristics are quite specialized for replacement rules generated from definitions. For definitions that are not explicitly recursive, that is, for those definitions in which **fn** is not used as a function symbol within **body**, the applicability heuristics are almost the same as for unconditional replacement rules, except that the theorem prover monitors the number of **IF** expressions introduced and the size of the arguments that are duplicated by the expansion. These constraints are manipulated so that the simplifier will eventually expand every nonrecursive function application in a formula, though they may not all expand in a single call of the rewriter.

For definitions that are explicitly recursive, the applicability conditions are quite different than for unconditional replacements. There are several conditions under which we will expand a recursive definition, but the most commonly occurring one is that all of the argument expressions in the recursive calls in the rewritten function body are subterms of the current conjecture. Thus **(APPEND X Y)** will expand and introduce **(APPEND (CDR X) Y)** provided **(CDR X)** and **Y** are already in the current conjecture. If **(CDDR X)** is in the conjecture, **APPEND** will expand again. If not, it will not. This heuristic works well with induction: the induction hypothesis is exactly the information the rewriter needs to know which functions should be expanded.

11.1.2. Type Prescription Rules

A type prescription rule allows the system to compute the "type set" of an expression. Because of the ubiquity of type sets it is important that they be implemented efficiently. In particular, we desire a fast way to compute a type set for a term under a set of type set assumptions about other terms. Of course, any given term has many type sets, namely, every extension of the smallest one. Determining the smallest type set of a term is an undecidable problem, since the term is a theorem iff **FALSEP** is not in its smallest type set. Thus, we must content ourselves with an algorithm for computing some type set. Type prescription rules are a way that the user of the theorem prover can influence the type set algorithm.

Suppose the following formula were a theorem:

```
(OR (LISTP (NORM X Y))
    (LITATOM (NORM X Y))
    (EQUAL (NORM X Y) Y)).
```

One way this theorem could be used to is determine a type set for **(NORM a b)**, namely the union of {**LISTP LITATOM**} and the type set of **b**. A type prescription rule is an encoding of the information in such formulas.

A *type prescription rule* associated with a function symbol **fn** of arity **n** is an **n+1**-tuple <**ts, flg₁, ..., flg_n**> where **ts** is a type set and each **flg_i** is either true or false. The effect of such a rule, when enabled, is that a type set of a term **(fn a₁ ... a_n)** is the union of **ts** together with the union of type sets of those **a_i** such that **flg_i** is true. The most recently proved enabled rule is used.

We say a term **t** is a *type set term* about a term **a** if **t** either has the form

```
(OR (r₁ a)
    . . .
    (r_n a))
```

or the form

```
(AND (NOT (r₁ a))
     . . .
     (NOT (r_n a)))
```

where each **r_i** is a recognizer.

The *type set described* by a type set term **t** is either {**r₁ ... r_n**} or Ω-{**r₁ ... r_n**}, depending on whether **t** is a type set term of the first or second form above.

A formula is a *type prescription formula* if it has the form

```
(OR tst
    (equal (fn v₁ ... v_n) var₁)
    . . .
    (equal (fn v₁ ... v_n) var_K)),
```

where the **v_i**'s are distinct variable symbols and each **var_m** is some **v_i** and **tst** is a type set term about **(fn v₁ ... v_n)**. The type prescription rule *generated* from such a formula is <**ts, flg₁, ..., flg_n**>, where **ts** is the type set described by **tst** and **flg_i** is true iff one of the disjuncts in the formula is the equation **(EQUAL (fn v₁ ... v_n) v_i)**. The rule is associated with the function symbol **fn**.

If a formula is submitted as class **REWRITE** and it satisfies the requirements of a type restriction formula, we store the generated type prescription rule in the data base.

We actually recognize a wider class of formulas than merely those having the syntactic forms described. In particular, a special-purpose program tries to put the submitted formula into type prescription form using

- the definitions of nonrecursively defined Ground Zero functions (e.g., **IMPLIES** and **NLISTP**);

- the fact that **(EQUAL X (const))** is equivalent to **(r X)** if **const** is a shell constructor of no arguments (or **TRUE** or **FALSE**) and **r** is the corresponding recognizer (or **TRUEP** or **FALSEP**, respectively);

- the fact that recognizers are all mutually exclusive; and

- propositional calculus with equality.

Table 11.1 contains some examples of formulas submitted as **REWRITE** formulas that are recognized as type prescription terms and their generated type prescription rules.

Table 11.1

formula	type prescription

`(OR (LISTP (FN X Y))`
`    (NUMBERP (FN X Y))`
`    (EQUAL (FN X Y) Y))`
	$<\{$`LISTP NUMBERP`$\}$, `F T`$>$

`(IMPLIES (LISTP (FN X Y))` `         (EQUAL (FN X Y) Y))`	$<\Omega$-$\{$`LISTP`$\}$, `F T`$>$

`(IMPLIES`
`  (NOT (EQUAL (FN X Y) T))`
`  (EQUAL (FN X Y) F))`
	$<\{$`TRUEP FALSEP`$\}$, `F F`$>$

`(IMPLIES`
`  (AND (LISTP (FN X Y))`
`       (NOT (NUMBERP (FN X Y))))`
`  (EQUAL (FN X Y) Y))`
	$<\Omega$-$\{$`LISTP`$\}$, `F T`$>$

11.1.3. Compound Recognizer Rules

A compound recognizer rule allows the system to "forward chain" from a user-defined predicate about a term to type set information about the term. For example, suppose we defined a recursive function, **FORMP**, that recognized s-expressions composed of literal atoms and proper lists of **FORMP**s beginning with literal atoms. Thus

    (FORMP ' (PLUS X (ADD1 Y))) = T

    (FORMP 'X) = T

    (FORMP 3) = F

    (FORMP ' (PLUS *1*TRUE X)) = F

Observe that if **x** is a **FORMP** then **x** is either a **LITATOM** or a **LISTP**. It is sometimes convenient to be able to make such observations. For example, if **x** is known to be a non-**LISTP** and to be a **FORMP**, then it is clear that **x** must be a **LITATOM**. Such observations could be made by expanding the definition of **FORMP** and simplifying. But that means that the relationship between **FORMP** and the type mechanism must be rediscovered every time it is to be used.

   FORMP is an example of what we call a "compound recognizer"—a predicate that, in a weak sense, acts as a recognizer for a type set. A theorem such as

    (IMPLIES (FORMP X)
             (OR (LITATOM X)
                 (LISTP X))).

can be used to forward chain from the hypothesis that **(FORMP x)** is true to the information that the type set of **x** is a subset of {**LITATOM LISTP**}.

   What can we infer from the hypothesis that **(FORMP x)** is false? Certainly, we do not know that **x** is neither a **LITATOM** nor a **LISTP**—**x** could be a **LISTP** that violates the rules of **FORMP** on some element. But we do know that **x** is not a **LITATOM**, because all **LITATOM**s are **FORMP**s. In general, the type information gleaned from the assumption that **(fn x)** is true is different from that gleaned from the assumption that **(fn x)** is false.

   A *compound recognizer rule* is a triple of the form <**parity, fn, ts**> where **parity** is either **TRUE** or **FALSE**, **fn** is a function symbol of arity 1 and **ts** is a type set. If we have such a rule, we say **fn** is a *compound recognizer of parity* **parity** *for type set* **ts**.

   The rewriter uses compound recognizer rules as follows. Recall that the assumptions made during rewriting are recorded by assigning type sets to terms. For example, assuming **(NUMBERP x)** true actually leads to the internal assumption that the argument term, **x**, has type set {**NUMBERP**}. More generally, if **r** is a recognizer, then assuming (**r x**) true sets the type set of **x** to {**r**}. Similarly, if **fn** is a compound recognizer of parity **TRUE** for type set **ts**, then when (**fn x**) is assumed true, the rewriter assigns to **x** the type set obtained by intersecting its current type set with **ts**. This assignment is *in addition to* the normal processing of the assumption. For example, if **fn** is a Boolean valued function, the assumption that (**fn x**) is true will also lead to the assignment of the type set {**TRUE**} to (**fn x**). The rules of parity **FALSE** are used exactly the same way, when (**fn x**) is assumed false.

A formula is a *compound recognizer formula of parity* **TRUE** if it has the form

> **(IMPLIES (fn x) tst)**

or the form

> **(EQUAL (fn x) tst)**

where **x** is a variable symbol and **tst** is a type set term about **x**. The compound recognizer rule *generated* from such a formula is <**TRUE**, **fn**, **ts**>, where **ts** is the type set described by **tst**.

A formula is a *compound recognizer formula of parity* **FALSE** if it has the form

> **(IMPLIES (NOT (fn x)) tst)**

or the form

> **(EQUAL (fn x) tst)**

where **x** is a variable symbol and **tst** is a type set term about **x**. If the formula has the first form, then the compound recognizer rule *generated* from the formula is <**FALSE**, **fn**, **ts**>, where **ts** is the type set described by **tst**. If the formula has the second form, then the compound recognizer rule *generated* from the formula is <**FALSE**, **fn**, Ω-**ts**>, where **ts** is the type set described by **tst**.

If a formula is submitted as class **REWRITE** and it satisfies the requirements of a compound recognizer formula, we store the generated compound recognizer rule(s) in the data base.

Observe that some formulas are compound recognizer formulas of both parities. Such formulas generate two rules. An example is the formula

> **(EQUAL (BOOLEANP X) (OR (TRUEP X) (FALSEP X)))** .

When (**BOOLEANP x**) is assumed true, the rewriter intersects the type set of **x** with {**TRUE FALSE**} to get the new type set of **x**. When (**BOOLEANP x**) is assumed false, the rewriter intersects the type set of **x** with Ω-{**TRUE FALSE**} to get the new type set of **x**.

The rule above is a very useful rule about **BOOLEANP** because it completely captures the properties of the predicate in the most efficient way possible.

11.1.4. Linear Arithmetic Rules

By *linear arithmetic* we mean that fragment of natural number arithmetic dealing only with sum and difference, equality, and inequality.

The rewriter has a special purpose procedure for deciding some facts of linear arithmetic. When called upon to rewrite an arithmetic relation, such as a **LESSP** expression, in the context of some assumptions, the rewriter uses the procedure to determine whether the relation is a consequence of the arithmetic relations among the assumptions. It does so by adding the negation of the given relation to the set of assumed relations and attempting to derive an inconsistent ground inequality by cross multiplying and adding inequalities so as to cancel out terms.

For example, suppose that the following two inequalities are among the current assumptions:

(1)   **(LESSP (PLUS 3 a) (PLUS b c))**

(2)   **(LESSP (PLUS a c) b)**

and suppose we are asked to rewrite **(LESSP a b)**. If a contradiction follows from the assumption **(NOT (LESSP a b))**, then **(LESSP a b)** is equal to **T** under the current assumptions. The system thus attempts to derive a contradiction from (1) and (2) and the negation of the relation we are rewriting. (Note that **(NOT (LESSP a b))** is equivalent to **(LESSP b (ADD1 a))** since **LESSP** is the less than relation over the naturals not the rationals.) The linear arithmetic procedure therefore is applied to the following set of inequalities, here written in conventional notation:

(1) $3 + a < b + c$

(2) $a + c < b$

(3) $b < 1 + a$

The decision procedure eliminates variables one at a time, starting with the lexicographically largest. Suppose that variable is **c**. Adding together (1) and (2) and cancelling **c** produces

(4) $3 + 2a < 2b$

Having eliminated **c** it then eliminates **b**: multiplying each side of (3) by 2 and adding the result to (4) we get

(5)   **1 < 0**

which is a contradiction. Thus, the original set of (1)-(3) is unsatisfiable.

Of course, the terms **a**, **b**, and **c** need not be variables. They are, in general, arbitrary (non-**PLUS**, non-**DIFFERENCE**) expressions. Suppose they are in fact

```
a = (LENGTH (CDR STR))
b = (LENGTH (PATTERN K TABLE))
c = (DELTA2 (CDR STR) (PATTERN K TABLE))
```

Nevertheless, the linear arithmetic procedure treats the three addends **a**, **b**, and **c** as though they were variables when cross multiplying and adding inequalities.

However, the fact that the addends are typically non-variable terms means that often there are interesting arithmetic relationships between them, derivable from previously proved lemmas. For example, assumption (2), above, which now reads

```
(2)   (LESSP (PLUS (LENGTH (CDR STR))
                   (DELTA2 (CDR STR)
                           (PATTERN K TABLE)))
             (LENGTH (PATTERN K TABLE))),
```

may be merely a consequence of the more general lemma

Theorem. DELTA2-BOUND:
```
(IMPLIES (AND (STRINGP S)
              (STRINGP PAT))
         (LESSP (PLUS (LENGTH S)
                      (DELTA2 S PAT))
                (LENGTH PAT))).
```

Assumption (2) can be derived from **DELTA2-BOUND** by instantiating **S** to be **(CDR STR)** and **PAT** to be **(PATTERN K TABLE)** and establishing the two **STRINGP** hypotheses. **DELTA2-BOUND** is an example of a **REWRITE** lemma stored as a linear arithmetic rule.

A *linear rule* is a 3-tuple <**hyps**, **concl**, **key**>, where **hyps** is a list of hypothesis terms implicitly conjoined, **concl** is a term of the form **(LESSP lhs rhs)** or **(NOT (LESSP lhs rhs))**, and **key** is a non-variable term with the following properties: first, it is one of the addends of **lhs** or **rhs**. Second, it contains all of the variables in **concl** except, possibly, those occurring in **hyps**—thus if every variable in **key** and **hyps** is instantiated, every variable in **concl** is also. Third, under some substitutions **key** is the syntactically largest addend in **concl** and thus will be a candidate for immediate elimination.

The linear rule generated from the **DELTA2-BOUND** lemma is

```
<((STRINGP S) (STRINGP PAT)),              ; hyps
  (LESSP (PLUS (LENGTH S) (DELTA2 S PAT))  ; concl
         (LENGTH PAT)),
  (DELTAT2 S PAT)>                          ; key
```

Note that the only key addend in the conclusion of **DELTA2-BOUND** is
(DELTA2 S PAT).

Roughly speaking, the linear arithmetic procedure uses such rules as follows.
When the process of cross multiplying and adding inequalities has terminated
and no inconsistency is found, the data base of enabled linear rules is searched.
If the key term in some rule can be instantiated to yield the syntactically largest
addend in some inequality under consideration, i.e., the addend that must be
eliminated next from that inequality, the conclusion of the rule is instantiated
and added to the set of inequalities, provided the hypotheses can be relieved by
recursive rewriting.

A **REWRITE** lemma of the form **(IMPLIES (AND h_1 ... h_n)**
concl) is stored as one or more linear rules, $<(h_1 \ldots h_n)$, **concl**, **key**>,
provided **concl** is a (possibly negated) **LESSP** expression and there exists at
least one key addend. A linear rule is generated for every key addend in
concl.

11.2. META

Recall the example metafunction discussed on page 223. **CANCEL** is defined as
a function that takes a list representing an equation, e.g.,

```
'(EQUAL (PLUS A (PLUS B (PLUS D E)))
        (PLUS B (PLUS C D))),
```

and returns a list representing an equivalent, simplified equation, such as

```
'(EQUAL (PLUS A E) (FIX C)).
```

In section **"proveall"** of the example file **basic.events** we define
CANCEL as described above and prove it correct. Readers interested in develop-
ing metatheoretic simplifiers of their own are invited to study that example first.

The **META** rule associated with **CANCEL** is "**CANCEL is a metatheoretic**
simplifier for EQUAL." If **CANCEL** were redefined so as to apply not only to
equations (i.e., lists that begin with **EQUAL**) but to inequalities represented by
LESSP expressions, it would be useful to generate the additional rule:
"**CANCEL is a metatheoretic simplifier for LESSP.**"

If **simp** and **fn-symb** are function symbols in the logic, then "**simp is a**
metatheoretic simplifier for fn-symb" is a **META** rule. We call **fn-symb**

the *target function symbol* of the rule. **META** rules are stored among the replacement rules and, like the replacement rules, are tried in reverse chronological order. Roughly speaking, when the rewriter is searching for an applicable **REWRITE** rule for (**fn** a_1 ... a_n) and finds an enabled metatheoretic simplifier, **simp**, for **fn**, it attempts to reduce

```
(simp '(fn a₁ ... aₙ))
```

to an explicit value, '**v**, by evaluating the definition of **simp**. If successful and **v** is different from (**fn** a_1 ... a_n) and all the variables of **v** are among those of (**fn** a_1 ... a_n), then the rewriter replaces (**fn** a_1 ... a_n) by **v**.

The description above is inaccurate in two ways. First, metatheoretic simplifiers are not applied to all terms but merely to "tame" ones. Second, the output **v** of the simplifier is used to replace (**fn** a_1 ... a_n) only if **v** is tame.

The notion of "tameness" is a purely syntactic one, defined below. The key property of tame terms is that if **v** is a tame term whose variable symbols are x_1, ..., x_n, then **v** is equal to the "evaluation of '**v**," that is, **v** is equal to

```
(EVAL$ T 'v
       (LIST (CONS 'x₁ x₁)
             ...
             (CONS 'xₙ xₙ))).
```

More succinctly, if **v** is tame it is equal to the evaluation of its quotation, under the standard alist on its variable symbols. This is not necessarily the case for non-tame terms.

In order to generate a **META** rule, a formula must have the form

```
(EQUAL (EVAL$ T v a)
       (EVAL$ T (simp v) a)),
```

where **simp** is a function symbol of one argument and **v** and **a** are distinct variable symbols.

To better understand the role of tameness in this process, suppose **v** is a term to which we wish to apply **simp**. If **v** is tame, then it is equal to the evaluation of '**v** under the standard alist. By the theorem justifying the **META** rule for **simp**, the evaluation of '**v** is equal to that of (**simp** '**v**). But (**simp** '**v**) can be reduced to an equivalent explicit value '**w**.[32] If **w** is itself tame, then the

---

[32]Possibly not. Metatheoretic simplifiers ought to be explicit value preserving. If they are not, and on some explicit value they "run forever" or involve undefined function calls, time is wasted but no harm results.

evaluation of **' w** is equal to **w**. Hence, we are justified in replacing **v** by **w**.

What do we mean by "tame?" We define it below, along with the mutually recursive concept "total." Tameness is a syntactic property of terms, while totality is a syntactic property of function symbols. Roughly speaking, a term is tame iff every function in it is total, and a function is total iff its body is tame. However, the presence of **V&C$** and recursion complicate matters.

A term is *tame* if it is a variable, a constant, the application of a "total" function to tame terms, a term of the form **(V&C$ T 't alist)** or **(EVAL$ T 't alist)** where **t** and **alist** are tame, or a term of the form **(FOR v r 'cond op 'body alist)** where each of **v**, **r**, **cond**, **op**, **body** and **alist** are tame.

We classify each function symbol as to whether it is total or not at the time it is introduced, as a function of its body and the previously determined totality of its subfunctions.

Intuitively, **fn** is total if its body is tame, which means, roughly, that every function called in the body is total. However, the body may involve recursive calls of **fn** itself. When we are trying to determine whether **fn** is total, do we assume it is while computing the tameness of its body? At first glance the answer seems to be "yes, because we have proved, during the admission of the function, that every recursive call of **fn** decreases a measure of the arguments in a well-founded sense." But consider calls of **fn** occurring inside of quoted expressions given to **EVAL$**. Those calls have not been checked. For example, assuming **fn** total and then asking if its body is tame would result in the following function being considered total:

Definition.
(RUSSELL) = (NOT (EVAL$ T '(RUSSELL) NIL)),

since, if **RUSSELL** is considered total then the **EVAL$** expression above is tame. Therefore, in the definition of "total" we do not use the notion of "tame" and instead use the notion of "super-tame" which means that **fn** is considered total outside of **EVAL$** expressions—where the definitional principle insures termination—but not inside. Here are the precise definitions of "total" and "super-tame."

All the primitives except **V&C$**, **V&C-APPLY$**, **EVAL$**, **APPLY$** and **FOR** are *total*. A function defined by **(fn x_1 ... x_n)**=**body** is *total* iff **body** is super-tame with respect to **fn**.

A term is *super-tame* with respect to **fn** iff it is a tame term (under the assumption that **fn** is not total) or it is a call of a total function or **fn** on super-tame terms.

Every function definable without use of **V&C$** and its dependents is total. In addition, functions that involve **V&C$**, **EVAL$** and **FOR** are total provided the interpreted arguments are the quotations of tame terms and the other functions in the definition are total.

We now return to the discussion of **META** rules. As noted, a **META** rule may be generated from formulas of the form

```
(EQUAL (EVAL$ T v a)
       (EVAL$ T (simp v) a)),
```

where **simp** is a function symbol of one argument and **v** and **a** are distinct variable symbols.

When the user tags such a formula to be in the **META** class, he also provides a list of target function symbols, fn_1, ..., fn_n. The form of the tag must be

```
(META fn₁ ... fnₙ)
```

where each fn_i is a function symbol. This is the only case in which the tag classifying the rule to be generated is not simply the Lisp atom naming the class. The system generates a **META** rule "**simp is a metatheoretic simplifier for** fn_i" for each **i**.

The selection of the fn_i is entirely up to the user and does not affect the validity of the rules generated. For example, had **CANCEL** been stored as a metatheoretic simplifier for **PLUS** or **PERM** it would not hurt anything but the efficiency of the system. The theorem establishing the correctness of the simplifier does so for all terms (indeed, even for non-terms). That is, the theorem proved about **(simp v)** is that its value is equal to that of **v**, for all **v**, not just for those with the "expected" function symbols. To define **simp** so that the correctness result can be proved in this form usually requires explicit inspection of the topmost function symbol of the argument term—even though the user knows that it will only be applied to terms beginning with an fn_i —and an explicit clause in the definition that returns the input term in the event that it was of an "unexpected" kind.

11.3. ELIM

An example **ELIM** rule is "**Eliminate the destructor terms (REMAINDER X Y) and (QUOTIENT X Y) by replacing X with the constructor term (PLUS (REMAINDER X Y) (TIMES Y (QUOTIENT X Y))) and generalizing, when (AND (NUMBERP X) (NOT (ZEROP Y)))**."

In general, an **ELIM** rule is a rule of the form "**Eliminate the destructor terms** d_1, ..., d_n **by replacing x with the constructor term c-term and generalizing, when hyps**," where the d_i, **c-term**, and **hyps** are terms, **x** is a variable, and the set of d_i's satisfy the "destructor term restriction" for **hyps**, **c-term**, and **x**. We call **x** the *elimination variable* of the rule.

A set of terms (henceforth called "destructor terms") satisfies the *destructor term restriction* for **x**, **c-term**, and **hyps** iff (a) every destructor term is a "first-level function application" (see below), (b) no two destructor terms have the same outermost function symbol, (c) each variable occurring in **x**, **c-term**, or **hyps** occurs in each destructor term, (d) each destructor term occurs in **c-term**, and (e) **x** does not occur in **c-term** except inside the destructor terms.

We say a term is a *first-level function application* if it is of the form (**fn** v_1 ... v_n), where **fn** is a function symbol and the v_i are all variables and all distinct.

The process of destructor elimination looks for subterms of the input formula that match with the destructor terms of some enabled **ELIM** rule, under some substitution σ that instantiates the elimination variable, **x**, of the rule with a variable symbol, **v**. If more than one set of function symbols can be eliminated, the process chooses the most "complicated" according to a heuristic. Once a rule and substitution have been chosen, the elimination proceeds in the two steps described earlier. First the elimination variable's image, **v**, is replaced by the image of the constructor term, **c-term**/σ, in all occurrences outside the destructor term images. Then the destructor term images are generalized to new variable symbols, taking account of type set information and the **GENERALIZE** rules available.

Unless further constrained, the destructor elimination process may loop indefinitely in concert with the simplifier. Heuristics are used to stop such loops by not eliminating on a variable introduced by elimination.

A formula can generate an **ELIM** rule only if the formula has the form

```
(IMPLIES hyps (EQUAL c-term x))
```

where **x** is a variable symbol and the proper subterms of **c-term** which are first-level function applications, d_1, ..., d_n, satisfy the destructor term restriction for **x**, **c-term**, and **hyps**. The **ELIM** rule generated is "**Eliminate the destructor terms d_1, ..., d_n by replacing x with the constructor term c-term and generalizing, when hyps**."

On page 333 we give some guidelines on using **ELIM** rules.

11.4. GENERALIZE

Any term can be a **GENERALIZE** rule.

Suppose a term **t** is to be generalized by replacing it with a variable **v** in some formula. The enabled **GENERALIZE** rules are used to restrict **v**. This is done by adding instances of the **GENERALIZE** rules as hypotheses to the formula being generalized, before **t** is replaced by **v**. Instances are found by considering each rule, **gen**, and determining whether some non-variable sub-term of **gen** matches, under some substitution σ, the term **t** being generalized. If such a subterm and σ are found, **gen**/σ is added as a hypothesis before **t** is replaced by **v**. After all such hypotheses are added, **t** is replaced by **v** in the modified formula.

12   Reference Guide

We now present an alphabetical listing of the commands to the theorem prover along with the definitions of concepts used in the command descriptions.

12.1. Aborting or Interrupting Commands

Means for aborting a computation or interrupting and resuming a computation are not specified in *Common Lisp The Language*, but there always seems to be an implementation dependent means for doing these things. Of course, even if it is possible to abort or interrupt a process, the exact point in the computation where the effect will occur is bound to be very time dependent, i.e., it's a random thing to do, in the vernacular.

In general, aborting a computation means that control is taken away from the ongoing computation and is given to the top-level read-eval-print loop of Common Lisp. To abort a computation:

- On a Symbolics, simultaneously press the **CONTROL**, **META**, and **ABORT** keys.

- In Lucid on a Sun, simultaneously press the **CONTROL** and **c** keys and then type **:A** to the resulting break prompt.

- In KCL on a Sun, simultaneously press the **CONTROL** and **c** keys and then type **:Q** to the resulting break prompt.

It is sometimes necessary to try several times to abort because certain Lisp programs (e.g., the garbage collector) may cause keystrokes to be ignored. In addition, if the theorem prover is printing to the terminal when you try to abort, you may get several pages of output before the requested action seems to occur. This is because terminal output lags behind the actual computation (e.g., because of buffering).

By "interrupting" a computation we mean that control is temporarily taken away from the ongoing computation and given to an inferior read-eval-print loop. From within this loop you can evaluate Lisp expressions, e.g., to inspect the state. See **BREAK-REWRITE** for example. When you are ready for the interrupted computation to resume, you communicate this to the inferior read-eval-print loop, which then terminates and returns control to the interrupted computation. To interrupt a computation

- On a Symbolics, simultaneously press the **CONTROL**, **META**, and **SUSPEND** keys. To resume, press the **RESUME** key.

- In Lucid on a Sun, simultaneously press the **CONTROL** and **c** keys. To resume, type **:C** to the break prompt.

- In KCL on a Sun, simultaneously press the **CONTROL** and **c** keys. To resume, type **:R** to the break prompt.

Warning: It is technically dangerous to abort any command that changes the data base, including the event commands such as **ADD-SHELL**, **DEFN**, and **PROVE-LEMMA**. Such aborts may leave the data base in an inconsistent state. The only proofs we endorse are those constructed by an uninterrupted sequence of event commands.

Having thus officially disavowed the practice, let us now make a few practical remarks about the effects of aborting event commands. All commands that change the data base adhere to the policy of first storing "undo" information and then making the change. The undo information allows us later to remove an event from the data base. Thus, if you do abort an event command that might have made changes to the data base, use **UNDO-NAME** to remove the aborted event.

What do we mean by "that might have made changes to the data base?" How can you tell? The answer is, technically, see if the new name has an **EVENT-FORM** in the data base (see **DATA-BASE**). However, it doesn't hurt anything to do an **UNDO-NAME**; the worst that will happen is that an error is reported because the "event" to be undone does not exist.

However, we personally behave in a somewhat less rigid way. Whenever we abort a **DEFN** or **ADD-SHELL** we do an **UNDO-NAME**. We don't bother to do an **UNDO-NAME** when we abort a **PROVE-LEMMA** because **PROVE-LEMMA** doesn't change the data base until after the proof has successfully completed. Because the theorem prover's output lags behind its actual computation, it is possible that we will someday abort a proof—thinking that it is doomed to fail—after it has in fact succeeded. But it has not happened yet. If it happens, the inconsistency will show up if the same event name is submitted later. In any case, we never feel like we have completed a proof project until an uninterrupted run of the events is performed by **PROVEALL**.

12.2. ACCUMULATED-PERSISTENCE

General and Example Form:
(ACCUMULATED-PERSISTENCE)

This routine prints a summary of the persistence totals accumulated against function and rule names for the most recently started proof attempt during which the rewrite path was maintained. See **BREAK-LEMMA** and **MAINTAIN-REWRITE-PATH** for an explanation of related features.

The rewrite path is a stack of "frames" maintained by the rewriter and encodes a complete description of the currently active calls to the rewrite routine. Most frames record a call of the rewriter; each such frame is associated with a non-variable term (the term being rewritten) or a rule (the rule being applied). When the rewriter has completed the processing of the term or rule, the frame is popped off the rewrite path. The number of frames built while a given frame is on the path is called the persistence of the frame and is an indication of the amount of work attributable to the term or rule associated with the frame. When we pop a frame, we compute its persistence and add it into an accumulating persistence table under the topmost function symbol of the term or the name of the rule. Thus, if a proof (successful or otherwise) has been run while the rewrite path was being maintained, the accumulated persistence table will indicate the "expense" of dealing with all of the function names and rules involved in the proof.

ACCUMULATED-PERSISTENCE prints to ***STANDARD-OUTPUT*** a summary of the accumulated persistence table. In particular, it says how many names have been seen by the rewriter and it lists the persistence totals of the 20 most persistent user-introduced names and the 5 most persistent primitive names. If names that are irrelevant to your proof appear in this listing, you could **DISABLE** them to speed up the proof.

12.3. ADD-AXIOM

General Form:
`(ADD-AXIOM name rule-classes term)`

Example Form:
`(ADD-AXIOM NUMBERP-LOC (REWRITE) (NUMBERP (LOC X M)))`

ADD-AXIOM is an event command for adding a new axiom to the logic and storing it and possibly some generated rules in the data base.   It does not evaluate its arguments. **name** must be a new name and will be made the name of the event in the data base, **rule-classes** must be a (possibly empty) list of rule classes and **term** must be a well-formed term (see **TRANSLATE**). **ADD-AXIOM** stores **term** in the data base as an axiom; in addition, rules of the classes specified by **rule-classes** are generated from **term** and stored. Each rule has the name **name** and is initially **ENABLED**.   An error is caused if **term** is unsuitable for some class in **rule-classes** and no change is made in the data base.   If successful, **ADD-AXIOM** prints a time triple for the event and returns the name of the new event, **name**.

When formulating input for **ADD-AXIOM** you must be cognizant of the rule interpretation of **term** in addition to its mathematical content. See Chapter 11 for a detailed explanation of the effect of each type of rule and how rules are generated from formulas and rule classes. See Chapter 13 for advice.

Note that if **rule-classes** is **NIL** then the term is stored as an axiom and will be available for **USE** hints but will generate no rules.

We strongly advise against the use of **ADD-AXIOM**. Moderate use of the theorem prover usually provides convincing evidence for the proposition that users frequently believe formulas to be valid when they are not.   Conferring upon an unproved formula the stamp **Axiom** in no way lessens the danger that it is inconsistent with the other axioms. If a concept or relation can be defined within the logic, we urge you to so define it. If a formula is in principle provable, we urge you to prove it.

12.4. ADD-SHELL

General Form:
`(ADD-SHELL const base r ac-descriptors)`

Example Form:
```
(ADD-SHELL PUSH EMPTY-STACK STACKP
           ((TOP (ONE-OF NUMBERP LITATOM) ZERO)
            (POP (ONE-OF STACKP) EMPTY-STACK)))
```

ADD-SHELL is an event command for adding a new shell to the logic. It does not evaluate its arguments. **ac-descriptors** must be a list of **n** elements. Each element must be a triple of the form $(\text{ac}_i \ \text{tr}_i \ \text{dv}_i)$. If **base** is non-**NIL**, the command has the theoretical effect of the axiomatic act

Shell Definition
Add the shell **const** of **n** arguments
with base function symbol **base**,
recognizer symbol **r**,
accessors $\text{ac}_1, ..., \text{ac}_n$,
type restrictions $\text{tr}_1, ..., \text{tr}_n$, and
default functions $\text{dv}_1, ..., \text{dv}_n$.

If **base** is **NIL** no base function symbol is supplied. Note that the **ADD-SHELL** command causes an error if the corresponding invocation of the shell principle is inadmissible in the current history. If admissible, the command adds a new event in the data base whose name is **const**. In addition, the command adds a large number of rules to the data base. The names of the rules are generated from the user-supplied names above. We do not describe the rules generated or their precise names here. The command prints a time triple and returns **const**.

It is with **ADD-SHELL** that **BOOT-STRAP** builds in the rules for the natural numbers, lists, and the other primitive shells. The only ways in which those primitive shells are ''more built-in'' than user declared shells are (a) because they are satellites of **GROUND-ZERO** they cannot be undone individually and we do not keep track of references to them, (b) the **QUOTE** notation provides succinct abbreviations for them, and (c) the linear arithmetic procedure is built specifically for the **NUMBERP**s.

12.5. BOOT-STRAP

General Form:
(BOOT-STRAP flg)

Example Form:
(BOOT-STRAP NQTHM)

BOOT-STRAP is an event command. It erases the current data base and initializes it to the Ground Zero logic. This command creates a very large number of rules corresponding to the primitive shells and the definitions of the functions in the Ground Zero logic. It prints a time triple and returns the event name **GROUND-ZERO**.[33]

---

[33]A quick and dirty sketch of the theory created by **BOOT-STRAP** is available by printing the value of the Lisp variable **BOOT-STRAP-INSTRS**.

The **flg** argument lets the user select which of two sets of Ground Zero axioms should be used. The argument is not evaluated by Lisp. If **flg** is **NQTHM** the theory used is that documented in this handbook. If no **flg** argument is supplied or if **NIL** is supplied or if **flg** is **THM**, the system is booted into a constructive logic very similar to the one we used before adopting the current one. We call the first logic "**NQTHM** logic" (for "New Quantified THM") and say the theorem prover is running in "**NQTHM** mode" when that logic is being used. We call the second logic "**THM** logic" and the associated mode "**THM** mode."

THM logic differs from **NQTHM** logic in the following respects:

- **THM** does not support the ordinals. **ORD-LESSP** and **ORDINALP** are not defined in **THM**. Two simple lexicographic relations, **LEX2** and **LEX3**, are defined. (**LEX2** (**LIST** i_1 j_1) (**LIST** i_2 j_2)) is **T** precisely if either (**LESSP** i_1 i_2) or (**EQUAL** i_1 i_2) and (**LESSP** j_1 j_2). **LEX3** is defined similarly. **LESSP**, **LEX2**, and **LEX3** are the only accepted well-founded relations in **THM**.

- **THM** does not support **V&C$** but does provide a more restricted sense of **EVAL$**. In particular, **ASSOC**, **PAIRLIST**, **FIX-COST**, **STRIP-CARS**, **SUM-CDRS**, **SUBRP**, **APPLY-SUBR**, **FORMALS**, **BODY**, **V&C$**, and **V&C-APPLY$** are defined in **NQTHM** but are not defined in **THM**. **EVAL$** and **APPLY$** are axiomatized in **THM** but they are not equivalent to their counterparts in **NQTHM**. (**EVAL$ T X A**) in **THM** is equivalent to (**MEANING X A**), as it is defined in [5]. (**EVAL$ 'LIST X A**) is equivalent to (**MEANING-LST X A**) of [5]. **APPLY$** in **THM** is axiomatized as is **APPLY** in [5]. Roughly speaking this means that **EVAL$** "does not know its own name." Additional restrictions are enforced in **THM**: no definition body may use **EVAL$** or **APPLY$**. The consequence of these restrictions is that mapping functions like **FOR** cannot be defined, but **EVAL$** of **'term** is always equal to **term** under the standard alist, provided **term** does not mention **EVAL$** or **APPLY$**. The only intended use for **EVAL$** in **THM** is in the statement of correctness for metafunctions.

- **THM** does not support **FOR**. Hence, the functions included in the **NQTHM** Ground Zero theory exclusively for the definition of **FOR** are not defined in **THM**: **ADD-TO-SET**, **APPEND**, **MAX**, **UNION**, **QUANTIFIER-INITIAL-VALUE**, **QUANTIFIER-OPERATION**, and **FOR**.

- **THM** contains definitions for the functions **LENGTH**, **SUBSETP**, and **LAST**, which are not defined in the Ground Zero logic of **NQTHM**.

THM logic differs somewhat from the logic supported by the previous release of our theorem prover. Let us call the previous version of the logic the "old" logic. The differences between **THM** logic and the old logic are as follows:

- **IFF** is included in **THM** but not in the old logic. This permits the implementation, in **THM** mode, of "propositional replacement" rules. If you have an old-style event list including a definition of **IFF**, you should delete it (if it is defined as is our **IFF**) or rename it and all its uses otherwise.

- **EVAL$** and **APPLY$** are included in **THM** but not in the old logic. In fact, they "replace" the functions **MEANING, MEANING-LST,** and **APPLY** of the old logic. The implementation of metalemmas in **THM** and **NQTHM** was simplified by changing the names of **MEANING** and **APPLY** to **EVAL$** and **APPLY$**. See the next note. If you have an old-style event list involving theorems about **MEANING** and **APPLY**, use **EVAL$** and **APPLY$** instead.

- The form of metalemmas in **THM** is as described here, not as described in [5]. The old style of metalemmas required proving that the metafunction returns a "**FORMP**". The new style does not. If you have an old-style event list containing a metalemma, reformulate it as described here. The new theorem will be simpler.

- In addition to **MEANING, MEANING-LST,** and **APPLY**, the following functions were defined in the old logic but are not defined in **THM**:   **FORMP,   FORM-LSTP,   ARITY,   SYMBOLP, LEGAL-CHAR-CODE-SEQ,   ILLEGAL-FIRST-CHAR-CODES,** and **LEGAL-CHAR-CODES**. These functions all participated in the definition of **FORMP** and hence were necessary for the old-style form of metalemma. Because they are no longer necessary for metalemmas, and because we imagine that no user relied upon them except for metalemmas, we simply omitted putting them into the **THM** logic.

12.6. BREAK-LEMMA

General Form:
(BREAK-LEMMA name)

Example Form:
(BREAK-LEMMA 'REVERSE-REVERSE)

The argument, **name**, is evaluated and should be the name of a replacement rule or linear arithmetic rule. **BREAK-LEMMA** alerts the rewriter to look out for all attempted applications of the named rule. Whenever the rule is tried, an interactive break occurs. To remove **name** from the list of monitored rules, use **UNBREAK-LEMMA**. Note that **BREAK-LEMMA** cannot be used to break on function definitions or on type-prescription, meta, elimination, or generalization rules. If **name** is not the name of a **PROVE-LEMMA** or **ADD-AXIOM** event with lemma type **REWRITE**, **BREAK-LEMMA** prints a warning message but alerts the rewriter anyway. It is most often the case that this warning message means you misspelled the name of the rule to be monitored, but it is sometimes useful to break on names that are satellites of other events (e.g., a rewrite rule introduced by an **ADD-SHELL**) so the simple test that **name** names an event is insufficient.

Warning. Because it is possible to execute an arbitrary Common Lisp form while in the interactive break under the theorem prover, it is possible to do arbitrary damage. For example, executing **(THROW 'PROVE T)** will immediately terminate the proof attempt successfully! We do not endorse proofs in which interactive breaks occur. We provide **BREAK-LEMMA** and **BREAK-REWRITE** simply as a means to help you diagnose what is going wrong with your rewrite rules.

Recall that to apply a replacement or linear arithmetic rule the first step is to find a substitution under which the left-hand side of the replacement rule or the key term of the linear arithmetic rule matches some target term being simplified. The substitution is computed by a simple pattern matcher that is complete: if a substitution exists to make the rule syntactically identical to the target, we find it (quickly). Subsequent steps in the application of a rule include relieving the hypotheses and rewriting the right-hand side of the conclusion. (See pages 235 and 242.)

When a matched rule's name appears on the list of monitored rules, an interactive break occurs immediately after the pattern matcher has succeeded. When the pattern matcher fails, no substitution exists and no break occurs even though the rule was actually considered briefly. Thus, if a rule is being monitored and no break for it occurs during a proof attempt, then either the rule is disabled or no instance of its left-hand side (or key term, as the case may be) was ever encountered by the rewriter. In this case it is probable that your expected target term got mangled somehow by other rules. We offer no mechanical help for tracking down the rules or identifying the mangled target. Our best advice is to think hard about what rules might have applied to your target.

If a substitution is found, then an interactive break occurs. By typing various commands you can inspect the state of the rewriter and step through the process of attempting to apply the rule. For replacement rules the steps are first relieve the hypotheses and then rewrite the right-hand side of the conclusion. For linear arithmetic rules there are more steps: relieve the hypotheses, rewrite the conclusion, convert the rewritten conclusion into polynomial form, and make heuristic checks on the resulting polynomials. Keep in mind that additional breaks may occur during the recursive processing done to relieve hypotheses and rewrite conclusions.

If at any step it is determined that the rule cannot be applied, the interactive break provides commands for displaying an explanation. However, the interactive break is not intended as a proof-checker: no facilities are provided for directing the theorem prover's strategy or affecting in any way the outcome of the attempt to apply the rule.

The interactive break is a Lisp read-eval-print loop where certain atoms are treated specially. The name of the Lisp function that implements the command interpreter is **BREAK-REWRITE** which, under certain conditions, can be invoked directly by the user during Lisp breaks to inspect the state of the rewriter (see page 264). The prompt character for the break is a colon. Your commands are read by the Lisp reader. The command **?** (i.e., the Lisp symbol obtained by reading a question mark followed by a carriage return) will cause a brief summary of the commands to be printed.

The available commands are divided into two categories: those that are specific to this particular step in the attempt to apply the rule and general commands for inspecting the state of the rewriter. The general commands are available all the time. The context-specific or "special" commands change with each step. For example, on entry to the break, the command **OK** means "try to relieve the hypotheses and break again when the attempt has finished." But immediately after the hypotheses have been relieved, **OK** means "proceed to rewrite the conclusion and break again when that has finished." In addition, the special commands at any particular time may include some that make sense only at that time. For example, one can ask to the see the **TARGET** term anytime, but one can ask for the **FAILED-HYP** only after a failed attempt to relieve the hypotheses.

Roughly speaking, the special command **OK** always means "go ahead with the next step and break when it is done" while the special command **GO** always means "go ahead with the next step and all subsequent steps of this application." **GO** is useful when you wish to shortcut the interactive processing of a rule because you have determined (say from the **TARGET** term) that the application at hand is not interesting.

Until you are familiar with the special commands you should type "**?**" often to see what your options are.

The general commands for inspecting the state of the rewriter are not summarized by the "**?**" command, since "**?**" is typed fairly often. A summary of the general commands may be obtained by typing "**??**". Using the general commands you can inspect the "rewrite path" from the current target term up to the top-level goal of the simplifier. The rewrite path is a stack of frames. Roughly speaking, each frame (except the first) represents a call of the theorem prover's rewrite routine. Commands permit you to see the entire list of frames sketchily or to focus attention on a particular frame and get more information. The frame on which attention is focused is called the "current frame" and is initially the frame in which the target term is being rewritten. You may use general purpose commands to move the current frame up or down the stack. Other commands display detailed information about the current frame. However, the position of the current frame in no way affects the simplifier or rewriter! That is, if you move the current frame up to a point where some other target is being rewritten, the theorem prover's attention does not shift to that target! The notion of the "current frame" is merely a convenient way to let you inspect the stack.

We now present an example of the use of general commands. Suppose we have the rules generated from the following two events:

```
(PROVE-LEMMA REVERSE-REVERSE (REWRITE)
  (IMPLIES (PROPERP X)
           (EQUAL (REVERSE (REVERSE X)) X)))
```

```
(PROVE-LEMMA PROPERP-APPEND (REWRITE)
  (IMPLIES (PROPERP B) (PROPERP (APPEND A B))))
```

Suppose also we have installed a break on **PROPERP-APPEND**:

```
(BREAK-LEMMA 'PROPERP-APPEND)
```

Finally, suppose we then execute the event

```
(PROVE-LEMMA LEMMA NIL
  (IMPLIES (AND (PROPERP B)
                (PROPERP A))
           (EQUAL
             (REVERSE (REVERSE (APPEND A B)))
             (APPEND A B))))
```

We show the resulting output below in **typewriter** font.

```
(Entering break on replacement rule PROPERP-APPEND

: ?
You are in the BREAK-REWRITE command interpreter.
The commands specific to this break are:

   cmd        effect
   OK         Attempt to relieve the hypotheses and
              then break.
```

GO	Proceed without further interaction.
NAME	Print name of the broken rule.
HYPS	List the hypotheses of the broken rule.
CONCL	Print the conclusion of the broken rule.
SUBST	Print the substitution being applied to the broken rule.
TARGET	Print the term to which the rule is being applied.
??	General purpose commands.

```
: TARGET
(PROPERP (APPEND A B))
```

Note that we are trying to use **PROPERP-APPEND** to prove that **(APPEND A B)** is **PROPERP**. We might wish to know how this subgoal has arisen. To find out, we use the general purpose commands. First we use **??** to get a summary of them.

```
: ??
You are in the BREAK-REWRITE command interpreter.
The general purpose commands are:
```

cmd	effect
PATH	Highlight the REWRITE path.
FRAME	Print the current frame, pruning deep terms.
PATH!	Print every frame in the path, pruning deep terms.
FRAME!	Print the current frame, with no pruning.
PATH!!	Print the path, with no pruning.
ASSUMPTIONS	Print the governing assumptions.
ANCESTORS	Print the negations of backchaining hypotheses.
ACCUMULATED-PERSISTENCE	
	Print the accumulated persistence totals.
BK	Move one frame towards the top-level SIMPLIFY.
NX	Move one frame away from the top-level SIMPLIFY.
TOP	Go to the top-level SIMPLIFY frame.
BTM	Go to the frame farthest from the top-level SIMPLIFY.

```
n (a natural number)
             Go to frame number n.
s-expr (a list expression)
             Evaluate Common Lisp s-expr
?            Special purpose commands.
```

The rewrite path will tell us how we got to the current target from the top-level goal of the simplifier. The sketchiest display of the rewrite path is given by the **PATH** command:

```
: PATH
  ( 90)    0. (top)
  ( 62)    1. Rewriting (EQUAL ...)
*( 61)    2. Rewriting (REVERSE ...)
  (  3)    3. Applying  REVERSE-REVERSE
*(  2)    4. Rewriting (PROPERP ...)
  (  0)    5. Applying  PROPERP-APPEND
```

There are six frames on the stack, numbered **0** through **5**. The topmost one, **0**, is the initial call of the simplifier. The bottommost one, **5**, is the frame in which we are working on the target term. From the above display we can see that we got to the target from the top by (a) rewriting an **EQUAL** expression in the topmost goal, (b) rewriting a **REVERSE** expression below that, (c) attempting to apply the rule **REVERSE-REVERSE** to that, (d) rewriting a **PROPERP** expression as part of the attempt, and (e) attempting to apply **PROPERP-APPEND** to that. However, in this sketch of the path we are not told the relation of one frame to the next.

Note also the parenthesized numbers on the left-hand edge of the display. Each number is the "persistence" of the corresponding frame. The persistence of a frame is the number of frames built since the given frame was built. The persistence of a frame is an indication of the amount of work expended so far on behalf of that frame. A frame is marked with a "*" if the persistence of the frame is at least twice the persistence of the frame immediately below it. In some sense, the frames marked with *'s contain terms or rewrite rules that have caused the rewriter a lot of work relative to the total amount of work so far.

From the fact that the persistence of frame **1** is **62** we know that 62 frames have been built since we began rewriting the **EQUAL** expression in frame **1**. Since only four of them are now active (frames **2-5**), we know the others have since been discarded. At first sight then, the **EQUAL** expression in frame **1** is relatively expensive to rewrite. But the persistence of frame **2** is **61**. Thus, except for the construction of frame **2** itself, all the work involved in frame **1** has been done under frame **2**. Now note the persistence of frame **3**. It is only **3**. Thus, 58 frames (61 minus 3) were built under frame **2** before we got around to trying **REVERSE-REVERSE** in frame **3**. We conclude that the **REVERSE** ex-

pression in frame **2** was relatively expensive to rewrite and frame **2** is marked
with a *. What work was done? After the frame was built we rewrote the
arguments to the **REVERSE** expression before looking for rules that match the
target. Thus, the 58 frames in question were used for the arguments and for any
REVERSE rules tried before **REVERSE-REVERSE**. See also
ACCUMULATED-PERSISTENCE.

The entire rewrite path is displayed in more detail by the following command:

```
: PATH!
---- Frame 0 -----                    (persistence 90)
Goal:
(IMPLIES (AND (PROPERP B) (PROPERP A))
         (EQUAL (REVERSE #) (APPEND A B)))


---- Frame 1 -----                    (persistence 62)
Rewriting the conclusion of the top-level goal:
(EQUAL (REVERSE (REVERSE #))
       (APPEND A B))
under the substitution:
NIL


---- Frame 2 -----                    (persistence 61)   <-***
Rewriting the first argument of the term in frame 1:
(REVERSE (REVERSE (APPEND A B)))
under the substitution:
NIL


---- Frame 3 -----                    (persistence 3)
Attempting to apply the replacement rule
REVERSE-REVERSE using the substitution:
X <- (APPEND A B)


---- Frame 4 -----                    (persistence 2)   <-***
Rewriting the first hypothesis of REVERSE-REVERSE:
(PROPERP X)
under the substitution:
X <- (APPEND A B)


---- Frame 5 -----                    (persistence 0)
```

```
Attempting to apply the replacement rule
PROPERP-APPEND using the substitution:
B <- B
A <- A
```

Observe that now we see more of each term being rewritten. However, we do not see each term in its entirety—note frame **1**. The symbol **#** is printed in place of deep subterms. This is what is meant by "pruning" in the **??** command summary. **PATH!** also gives an explanation relating the activity in each frame to the activity in the frame above. In particular, we see that the **REVERSE** expression being rewritten in frame **2** is in fact **(REVERSE (REVERSE (APPEND A B)))** and is the first argument of the **EQUAL** expression being worked on in frame **1**.

When the stack contains hundreds of frames, **PATH!** often provides too much information. That is why the notion of current frame exists. The commands **FRAME** and **FRAME!** print out the current frame. The command **n**, where **n** is a natural number, means "select frame **n** as the current frame." The commands **BK** (for "back") and **NX** (for "next") let you move the current frame back and forth and are useful for exploring an area of the path.

12.7. BREAK-REWRITE

General Form:
(BREAK-REWRITE)

This Lisp routine permits the user to inspect the rewrite path (see page 259) as though a **BREAK-LEMMA** rule monitor had caused an interactive break. **BREAK-REWRITE** is a user-level entry into the command interpreter and can be invoked directly by the user after forcing a Lisp break while the rewriter is operating.

The method used to force a Lisp break while a computation is in progress is implementation dependent. For example, in KCL the "control-C" key is pressed while on the Symbolics Lisp Machine the "Suspend" key is pressed. See page 252. Once a break has been caused, executing **(BREAK-REWRITE)** will enable you to inspect the rewrite path with the general purpose commands described in **BREAK-LEMMA** above. (The special purpose commands (e.g., **TARGET** or **CONCL**) do not make sense since there is in fact no rule associated with the break.) The command **OK** exits **BREAK-REWRITE** and returns to the Lisp break from which it was invoked.

For efficiency, the theorem prover does not maintain the rewrite path all the time. If **BREAK-REWRITE** is called when the path is not being maintained, or when the rewrite path is empty (so that there is no topmost frame), it prints a message and returns immediately. See **MAINTAIN-REWRITE-PATH**.

BREAK-REWRITE is useful when you are trying to find out why the theorem prover is spending an unusually long time silently simplifying a particular formula. (Of course, what is unusual depends on what is usual for you. There are successful proofs in which the system is silent for many minutes.) If you have previously enabled the maintenance of the rewrite path you might force a Lisp break. If you have not previously enabled the maintenance of the rewrite path you should abort the now silent proof attempt, use **(MAINTAIN-REWRITE-PATH T)** to turn on maintenance, restart the proof attempt and force a break as before when the silent simplification is in progress. Once you have forced a break while the simplifier is running, call **BREAK-REWRITE** and use the path and frame commands to see what is going on. Most likely you will be surprised at the depth of the path and perhaps at the names of some of the rules or functions on it. Typically in these situations the simplifier is backchaining through rules you have long since forgotten and has set itself subgoals that have little to do with the problem at hand; another common problem is that nonrecursive functions have been expanded and have introduced many cases or concepts needlessly. In any case, it is frequently the case that by inspecting the path you will find the names of rules and functions that can be **DISABLE**d to make the proof go faster.

In addition, **BREAK-REWRITE** is often useful in tracking down circularities in your rewrite rules. Circularities in the rewrite rules lead to stack overflows in the rewriter. Often when stack overflow occurs, there is no way to investigate it, because the Lisp stack is already as big as permitted. However, the rewrite path maintained by the rewriter is not part of the stack but is a separate data structure that persists even after an aborted computation. If the rewrite path was being maintained during a proof attempt that caused a stack overflow, you may abort out of the stack overflow error—thereby gaining all that stack space. Then, from the top-level Lisp read-eval-print loop invoke **(BREAK-REWRITE)**. If it reports that the theorem prover is not in the simplifier, it means "the theorem prover was not in the simplifier when the stack overflow occurred."[34] Otherwise, you will be able to use the **BREAK-REWRITE** commands to investigate the rewrite path as it stood at the time of the stack overflow. This will often make the loop manifest

This conjecture can be simplified, using the abbreviations ADDRP and IMPLIES, to:

---

[34]Some replacement rules are considered so simple that they are used as "abbreviations" and applied exhaustively *before* we begin normal simplification. These rules may contain loops, and at present we offer no aids in tracking down such loops.

```
Error: Bind stack overflow.
Error signalled by PROVE-LEMMA-FN.

Broken at PROVE-LEMMA-FN.  Type :H for Help.
>>:Q

Top level.

>(BREAK-REWRITE)
: PATH

  (3404)    0. (top)
  (3394)    1. Rewriting (GET ...)
  (3392)    2. Applying  GET-NORMALIZER
  (3382)    3. Rewriting (GET ...)
  (3359)    4. Applying  GET-NORMALIZER
    ...         ...
  (  92)  202. Applying  GET-NORMALIZER
  (  82)  203. Rewriting (GET ...)
  (  59)  204. Applying  GET-NORMALIZER
  (  49)  205. Rewriting (GET ...)
  (  26)  206. Applying  GET-NORMALIZER
  (  16)  207. Rewriting (GET ...)
  (  15)  208. Rewriting (ADD-ADDR ...)
  (  13)  209. Rewriting (CONS ...)
*(   8)  210. Rewriting (PLUS ...)
*(   2)  211. Rewriting (IF ...)
  (   0)  212. Rewriting (IF ...)
```

In using **BREAK-REWRITE** to look for circularities you must keep in mind that the path does not show everything that *has been used* to derive the current term, but what is being used right now. It might be that, in some sense, the "cause" of the loop is a rule not shown on the current path but which fires and completes, introducing a term which will permit it to fire again later during the rewriting.

12.8. CH

General Forms:
(CH n)
and
(CH m n)

Example Forms:
```
(CH 10)
(CH 'PROPERP-REVERSE)
(CH 12 20)
```

CH prints out the names of the events that have been created so far. **CH** takes one or two arguments which are used to specify an interval in the chronological sequence of events. The arguments are both evaluated and should be either event names or event numbers, where 0 is the most recent event, 1 the next most recent, etc. Events are printed in reverse chronological order, i.e., the youngest (most recently created) event is displayed first. If only one argument is supplied, it is taken as the rightmost end point, and 0 (the most recently created event) is used as the leftmost.

Here is an example. Suppose that we have just completed the proof described in the sample session starting on page 187. In particular, starting from **BOOT-STRAP** we defined **REVERSE** and **PROPERP** and then worked our way through the proofs of several lemmas about **PROPERP**, **APPEND**, and **REVERSE**, concluding with **REVERSE-REVERSE**. Then the following use of **CH** prints out a sketch of the entire session in reverse chronological order:

```
(CH 'GROUND-ZERO)

0    (PROVE-LEMMA REVERSE-REVERSE ...)
1    (PROVE-LEMMA REVERSE-APPEND ...)
2    (PROVE-LEMMA APPEND-IS-ASSOCIATIVE ...)
3    (PROVE-LEMMA PROPERP-REVERSE ...)
4    (PROVE-LEMMA PROPERP-APPEND ...)
5    (PROVE-LEMMA APPEND-RIGHT-ID ...)
6    (DEFN PROPERP ...)
7    (DEFN REVERSE ...)
8    (BOOT-STRAP NQTHM ...)
```

Equivalent **CH** commands are **(CH 8)**, **(CH 0 8)**, and **(CH 'REVERSE-REVERSE 'GROUND-ZERO)**.

CH prints a **D** after the number if the event is currently disabled. Thus, suppose we execute **(DISABLE PROPERP-REVERSE)** and **(DISABLE PROPERP-APPEND)**. If we print the events between **REVERSE-REVERSE** and **APPEND-RIGHT-ID** we get

```
2    (PROVE-LEMMA REVERSE-REVERSE ...)
3    (PROVE-LEMMA REVERSE-APPEND ...)
4    (PROVE-LEMMA APPEND-IS-ASSOCIATIVE ...)
5 D  (PROVE-LEMMA PROPERP-REVERSE ...)
```

```
6 D (PROVE-LEMMA PROPERP-APPEND ...)
7   (PROVE-LEMMA APPEND-RIGHT-ID ...)
```

Observe in the example above that the event numbers of the events shown have been increased by 2 because the two **DISABLE**s (actually **TOGGLE** events) have become events 0 and 1. In general, event numbers are so volatile that they are useful only in successive calls of **CH** as one scans through the chronology looking for a given interval. The only other command in our system that uses event numbers is **UBT**.

When the theorem prover is being used with a fast terminal and text editor it is often practical to print the entire chronology, as with **(CH 'GROUND-ZERO)** and then scan it at leisure with the editor. But with slow terminals or systems that discard text that has been scrolled off the top, the primitive interval handling of **CH** is useful.

12.9. CHRONOLOGY

General Form:
CHRONOLOGY

The Lisp variable **CHRONOLOGY** is set to the list of all event names in reverse chronological order. Thus, the first element of **CHRONOLOGY** is the name of the most recently processed event. The last element is always **GROUND-ZERO**, the name of the oldest event. Users typically print the value of **CHRONOLOGY** to refresh their memory of "where they are" or what names they have used. Printing **CHRONOLOGY** is a good way to see what is in a data base that has just been loaded. However, the value of **CHRONOLOGY** is often very long and the command **CH** is often more convenient.

Users should not bind or set **CHRONOLOGY**.

12.10. COMPILE-UNCOMPILED-DEFNS

General Form:
(COMPILE-UNCOMPILED-DEFNS filename)

Example Form:
(COMPILE-UNCOMPILED-DEFNS "/temp/foo")

The argument, **filename**, is evaluated and should be a file name. This routine creates a file of the specified name, containing the Common Lisp definitions of the currently uncompiled executable counterparts (see page 282) of all functions in the current data base; it then compiles that file, and loads it. Thus, after calling this routine all executable counterparts are defined with compiled code. This will significantly increase the speed with which **R-LOOP** computes the values of submitted expressions and may increase the speed of the theorem prover if your proofs involve computation with explicit values.

The name of the file created has as its extension the value of the variable **FILE-EXTENSION-LISP**. The directory on which the file resides is affected by the value of the variable ***DEFAULT-NQTHM-PATH***. The extension of the file loaded after the compilation is specified by the variable **FILE-EXTENSION-BIN** (see page 285).

We do not always automatically compile each executable counterpart as it is created because in some circumstances (e.g., when using Kyoto Common Lisp) invoking the function **COMPILE** involves significant overhead and the creation of weirdly named temporary files. In addition, because files are created there is the possibilities of protection violations and resource allocation errors, problems that the theorem prover is not able to gracefully report much less recover from. However, if you wish to have each executable counterpart **COMPILE**d as it is defined, you may set the flag ***COMPILE-FUNCTIONS-FLG*** to **T**. We advise against doing this except on Lisp machines.

12.11. DATA-BASE

General Form:
(DATA-BASE query name)

Example Forms:
(DATA-BASE 'IMMEDIATE-DEPENDENTS 'REVERSE)
and
(DATA-BASE 'IMMEDIATE-SUPPORTERS 'REVERSE)
and
(DATA-BASE 'EVENT-FORM 'REVERSE)

This is a low-level function for getting information about the data base. Before discussing the function we describe the data base in detail.

The data base is an acyclic directed graph. At each node is the following information:

- the name of the node,

- the event command which created the node,

- a number indicating the time at which the node was created (used to order event lists chronologically), and

- a list of satellites—the names of auxiliary axioms, functions, and executable counterparts introduced by the event command that created the node (see the discussion below).

A node has satellites if the creating event introduces a function symbol or introduces more than one axiom. For example, the **GROUND-ZERO** node has as its satellites the list of every primitive function symbol, every executable counterpart, and every rule added by **BOOT-STRAP**. **DCL** nodes have a single satellite that is the executable counterpart of the symbol introduced. **ADD-SHELL** nodes have many satellites: the base object, the recognizer, the accessors, the executable counterparts of all the new symbols, and all the rules generated by the shell axioms. No name is a satellite of more than one node.

We say a Lisp symbol is a *citizen* of the data base if it is either the name of a node or is a satellite of a node. The name of each axiom, theorem, function, and executable counterpart is a citizen. The only other citizens are the names of events such as **TOGGLE**s. Henceforth, whenever we refer to a citizen **x** as a node we mean either the node with name **x**, if such a node exists, or the node of which **x** is a satellite. Every citizen has a *status*, **ENABLED** or **DISABLED**, that is used as the status of the associated rule(s).

The *primary* of a citizen, **fn**, is defined as follows. If **fn** is a satellite of **p**, then **p** is the primary of **fn**. Otherwise, **fn** is a node and is its own primary.

The arcs in the data base graph represent "immediate dependency." The relation is defined below. It is *not* the obvious "logical dependency" relation.

We define *immediate dependency* as follows. Every node in the data base is immediately dependent on **GROUND-ZERO**. An **ADD-SHELL** event is immediately dependent upon the primary of every other shell function involved in its definition, i.e., the older recognizers in the type restrictions and the older base objects in the default values. Every node whose event contains a term (including the terms used in hints) is immediately dependent upon the primary of every function symbol in every such term. Every node whose admissibility requires theorem proving (i.e., **DEFN** and **PROVE-LEMMA** nodes) is immediately dependent upon the primary of every citizen reported used in the proofs. Furthermore, every such node is immediately dependent upon the primary of every prior event that generated a type prescription rule about any function used in the proofs.[35] **TOGGLE** events (including **DISABLE**s and **ENABLE**s) are dependent upon the primary of the event enabled or disabled. **TOGGLE-DEFINED-FUNCTIONS** events are dependent only upon

---

[35]The rewriter does not keep track of the use of type prescription rules because the type set mechanism is so heavily used. This clause in the definition of dependency is an attempt to compensate for this inadequacy by sweeping into the dependency relation some of the events that *might* have been used. Even this does not guarantee to get all of the rules used. See the warning below.

GROUND-ZERO.

The above definition establishes the meaning of the "immediate dependents" of every node. Note that the immediate dependents of a node include the reported uses of all of its satellites. We make the convention that the "immediate dependents" of a satellite are just those of its primary. For example, suppose **PUSH** is declared as a constructor with accessors **TOP** and **POP**. Then **PUSH** is the name of a node and **TOP** and **POP** are among its satellites. If **TOP** is used in some subsequent event, the event is recorded among the dependents of **TOP**'s primary, namely **PUSH**. Uses of **POP** and the other functions introduced in the shell declaration are similarly recorded against **PUSH**. We freely mix such dependencies because we do not provide a way to remove one accessor, say, from the data base without removing the entire shell declaration.

Warning: This notion of "immediate dependency" is flawed. Not every logical dependent is among the "immediate dependents." The problem is that not all facts *used* by the theorem prover are *reported* used. In particular, type prescription lemmas are not tracked and the executable counterparts for the metafunctions **SUBRP**, **APPLY-SUBRP**, **FORMALS**, **BODY**, **V&C$**, **V&C-APPLY$**, **EVAL$**, **APPLY$**, and **FOR** do not leave tracks when they operate on quoted constants, even though the values of those metafunctions depend not just on the constants but how certain functions are defined.

For example, suppose **FN** is a user-defined function. Then **(SUBRP 'FN)** reduces to **F**. Furthermore, no record is left that the computation depends on **FN**; indeed, in a way, it doesn't depend on the function **FN**, it depends on the atom **(PACK '(70 78 . 0))**. Thus, by using **UNDO-NAME** to remove an event and its dependents it is possible to get the data base into an inconsistent state: define **FN**, prove **'FN** is not a **SUBRP**, undo **FN**, add a shell with **FN** as the constructor, prove **'FN** is a **SUBRP**. Because we do not track the dependency of **(SUBRP 'FN)** on **FN**, undoing **FN** fails to undo the lemma that **'FN** is a non-**SUBRP**.

Moral: Do not rely upon the validity of any formula proved in a session in which **UNDO-NAME** was used. Think of **UNDO-NAME** as a quick and dirty way to approximate the logical theory obtained by removing the given event. When an interactive session has successfully led to the proof of the main theorem, replay the entire sequence of events from **GROUND-ZERO** or some trusted library without any undoing. See also the discussion of **UNDO-BACK-THROUGH**, a trusted way to remove events from the data base.

We now discuss the **DATA-BASE** procedure.

General Form:
(DATA-BASE query name)

The first argument is a Lisp symbol corresponding to one of the queries listed below. If the second argument, **name**, is not a citizen, the result is **NIL**. Otherwise, the result depends upon the **query** as described below.

query   **result**

PRIMARY   If **name** is the name of a node, **DATA-BASE** returns **name**. Otherwise, **name** is the name of a satellite and **DATA-BASE** returns the name of the node to which **name** is attached. Since **NIL** is not an event name, **(DATA-BASE 'PRIMARY x)** is non-**NIL** iff **x** is a citizen. If the result is different than **x**, **x** is a satellite of the result.

EVENT-FORM   Returns an event command equivalent to the one the user submitted to create **name**. **name** may be a satellite of the event returned. The command returned will be a list whose first element is the name of an event command, e.g., **PROVE-LEMMA**, **ADD-SHELL**, **TOGGLE**, etc. All list structures used as terms within the command are the result of translating (with **TRANSLATE**) the user type-in. The **EVENT-FORM** returned may differ in other respects from the one typed by the user. For example, the user may type a **DISABLE** command and the **EVENT-FORM** may be an equivalent **TOGGLE**, or the user may have omitted the **hints** argument to a **PROVE-LEMMA** command and the **EVENT-FORM** may supply the **hint NIL**.

STATUS   Returns the Lisp symbol **DISABLED** if **name** is currently disabled; otherwise returns the symbol **ENABLED**. Recall that if the name of a rule is **DISABLED** the rule is never applied.

SATELLITES   Returns a list of all the satellites of the primary of **name**.

FORMULA   Roughly speaking, **DATA-BASE** returns the formula named by **name**. However, this is not a well-defined concept since some names (e.g., the name of a **TOGGLE** event) do not have any associated formula, and other names (e.g., the name of a shell constructor) have many associated formulas. The precise specification is as follows: If **name** is the name of an **ADD-AXIOM** event, the axiom is returned. If **name** is the name of a **PROVE-LEMMA** event, the theorem is returned. If **name** is the name of a defined function—even a satellite—the defining equation is returned as a formula of the form **(EQUAL (name x_1 ... x_n) body)**. If **name** is anything else, **NIL** is returned.

IMMEDIATE-DEPENDENTS
                     Returns a list containing the names of the immediate depen-

dents of **name**, ordered chronologically.

ALL-DEPENDENTS

Returns the transitive closure of the immediate dependents relation starting at **name**, ordered chronologically. This is the list of all events that somehow depend upon **name**—in so far as we are able to determine given the incomplete usage reports. It is this list of events, plus **name** itself, that will be removed from the data base if **name** is removed.

IMMEDIATE-SUPPORTERS

Returns the list of all events claiming **name** among their immediate dependents, ordered chronologically.

ALL-SUPPORTERS

Returns the transitive closure of the immediate supporters relation starting at **name**, ordered chronologically. This is the list of all events upon which **name** somehow depends—in so far as we are able to determine given the incomplete usage reports.

12.12. DCL

General Form:
`(DCL fn args)`

Example Form:
`(DCL LOC (VAR MEM))`

DCL is an event command for introducing an undefined function symbol into the logic. It does not evaluate its arguments. **fn** must be a new function symbol and **args** must be a list of **n** distinct variable symbols. **DCL** declares **fn** to be a function symbol of arity **n**. **fn** is henceforth considered "old." **DCL** adds no axioms to the theory. Unless an error is caused because of improper arguments, **DCL** adds a new event to the data base, prints a time triple, and returns the new event name, **fn**.

If a function symbol has been introduced with **DCL** we say it is an *undefined* function symbol.

The example declaration above declares **LOC** to be a function of arity **2**, provided **LOC** has not been previously declared, defined, or axiomatized with the shell principle. After the declaration, it is permitted to use such expressions as `(LOC V M)` and `(LOC (CAAR X) (MEM ST))` as terms.

Undefined function symbols can be used in formulas, e.g., axioms, definitions, and theorems. However, they cannot subsequently be defined. Undefined functions are not explicit value preserving: calls of undefined functions on explicit values cannot be reduced to explicit values by the primitive axioms and definitions. Calls of functions defined in terms of undefined functions are usually not explicit value preserving—not if the undefined functions are necessarily involved in the computation. Since **DCL** adds no axioms, the primitive metafunctions **SUBRP**, **APPLY-SUBR**, etc., are undefined on **' fn** if they were undefined on **' fn** before the **DCL**. The user may add axioms to characterize **fn**.

12.13. DEFN

General Forms:
```
(DEFN fn args body)
```
and
```
(DEFN fn args body hints)
```

Example Forms:
```
(DEFN LEN (X)
      (IF (NLISTP X)
          0
          (ADD1 (LEN (CDR X))))))
```

and
```
(DEFN UP (I J)
      (IF (LESSP I J)
          (UP (ADD1 I) J)
          T)
      ((LESSP (DIFFERENCE J I))))
```

DEFN is an event command for defining a function symbol. It does not evaluate its arguments. **args** must be a list of n variable names $v_1, ..., v_n$. The command has the same theoretical effect as the axiomatic act:

Definition.
$$(fn\ v_1\ ...\ v_n) = body$$

with the following exception. Admissibility restriction (d) of the principle of definition is that "there is a term **m** ..." such that certain derived formulas are theorems. The *implemented* principle of definition further requires that the theorems be provable by the theorem prover's simplification process (see page 222)! If admissible, the theory is augmented by the axioms introduced by the above axiomatic act. In addition, the rules corresponding to those axioms are added to the data base. **DEFN** then computes the induction schemes suggested by the various measured subsets (see page 228). It also computes a type prescription rule for the function (see page 237) and preprocesses the body of the function to create a definitional replacement rule (named **fn**) for expanding calls of the function. To preprocess the body, **DEFN** expands the calls of all nonrecursive primitive functions in the body (e.g., **AND**, **FIX**) and then normalizes the resulting **IF**-expression so that no **IF** contains an **IF** in its test. This may exponentially increase the size of the body. Finally, **DEFN** creates a new event named **fn** and links it into the data base. Then **DEFN** prints a narrative describing the justification(s) of the definition and the type prescription computed, a time triple is printed, and **fn** is returned.

If the axiomatic act above is inadmissible (or the simplifier cannot prove the required formulas), an appropriate message is printed, an error is caused, and the data base is left as it was before the **DEFN** command was executed.

We have not yet discussed how the appropriate measure term is selected by **DEFN**. The answer is simple: unless otherwise instructed by the **hints** argument, **DEFN** tries **COUNT** on each argument changed in recursion. The optional **hints** argument permits the user-specification of a measure term to be used.

If non-**NIL**, **hints** must be a list of doublets as described below. Each doublet specifies a well-founded relation and a measure term. For each doublet, **DEFN** generates formulas which, if theorems, are sufficient to establish the theorems described in requirement (d). **DEFN** tries to prove each of the formulas for each doublet. If it is successful for any doublet, the definition is admissible. If it is unsuccessful on each, an error is caused. The **hints** argument allows multiple ''justifications'' of a definition; for example the first doublet might claim that the **COUNT** of the first argument gets smaller, while the second doublet claims that the second argument gets closer to **100**. Having alternative justifications makes the theorem prover more powerful when it is considering what induction should be used on a given conjecture. See the discussion of the induction process, page 228.

Each doublet must be of the form **(wfn m-term)**, where **wfn** is a ''known well-founded relation'' and **m-term** is a term all of whose variables are among those in **args**, namely x_1, ..., x_n. The known well-founded relations depend upon how **BOOT-STRAP** was called. If booted in **NQTHM** mode, the known well-founded relations are **ORD-LESSP** and **LESSP**.[36] In **THM** mode, the

---

[36]Technically, the logic requires use of **ORD-LESSP** to justify a definition or an induction. But it is easy to see, from the definition of **ORD-LESSP**, that if the analogous measure theorems are proved about **LESSP** then the required theorems could be proved for **ORD-LESSP**. When **LESSP** is used as the relation it is unnecessary to prove that the measure term satisfies **ORDINALP**: since **LESSP** coerces non-**NUMBERP**s to **0**, the measure term used in the required **ORD-LESSP** justification is just the **FIX** of the measure term used in the **LESSP** justification.

known well-founded relations are **LESSP**, **LEX2**, and **LEX3**.

When the system fails to prove the formulas justifying a submitted definition, it prints out an explanatory message that lists the measures tried and the simplified (but unproven) goals generated. If the measure you believe is the correct one was not tried, use the **hints** argument to specify the correct measure. If the measure you believe is the correct one was tried but could not be shown to decrease, prove **REWRITE** rules suitable to establish the printed goals and resubmit the definition.

12.14. DISABLE

General Form:
(DISABLE name)

Example Forms:
(DISABLE TIMES-2-REWRITE)
and
(DISABLE REVERSE)
and
(DISABLE *1*REMAINDER)

DISABLE is an event command that sets the status of a citizen to **DISABLED**. The command does not evaluate its argument. The argument, **name**, must be a citizen. The command creates a new event name, **new-name**, adds a new event to the data base with **new-name** as its name, and sets the status of **name** in the data base to **DISABLED**. Then **DISABLE** prints a time triple and returns **new-name**. **(DISABLE name)** is just an abbreviation for **(TOGGLE new-name name T)**. Indeed, even though we speak of "**DISABLE** events" the data base actually records all **DISABLE**, **ENABLE**, and **TOGGLE** commands as **TOGGLE** events.

Roughly speaking, the effect of **(DISABLE name)** is to prohibit the use of **name** in all subsequent proof attempts until the **DISABLE** is overridden with an **ENABLE** command or temporarily overridden with an **ENABLE** hint in **PROVE-LEMMA** or **new-name** is undone.

More precisely, suppose the status of **name** is **DISABLED** in the data base. Then if **name** is the name of a rule, the rule is never applied. If **name** is the name of a defined function, calls of the function are not expanded.[37] calls of the

---

[37]However, if all the arguments of a function call are explicit values, the executable counterpart of the function may be executed. Thus, **(REVERSE '(1 2 3))** will be replaced by **'(3 2 1)** even if **REVERSE** is disabled. To prevent this, disable the executable counterpart of the function as well.

If **name** is the name of the executable counterpart of a function, applications of the function to explicit values in formulas being proved are not reduced to explicit values.[38] Note that, while legal, there is no sense in disabling any name other than the name of a rule, a function, or an executable counterpart. For example, disabling the name of a **DISABLE** event has no effect.

The status of a name in the data base is either **ENABLED** or **DISABLED** according to the most recently executed **ENABLE** or **DISABLE** (or equivalent **TOGGLE**) event for that name still in the data base. If no such event is in the data base, the status is **ENABLED**.

A citizen can also be disabled "locally" (without affecting its status in the data base) via the **DISABLE** hint in **PROVE-LEMMA**.

Disabling is often important in trying to construct large proofs. Three situations requiring it arise so often we will discuss them explicitly here.

12.14.1. A Bolt from the Blue

Scenario: A proof that was supposed to work failed. Upon analysis of the output you see that a key **REWRITE** rule was not applied. Upon further analysis you see that it is because the target term to which it was supposed to apply was deformed by the prior application of another rule.

The most common solution to this is to disable the unwanted rule, either "globally" with the **DISABLE** command or "locally" with the **DISABLE** hint to **PROVE-LEMMA**. Depending on the nature of the unwanted rule it is sometimes more reasonable to re-express the desired rule so that its left-hand side anticipates the action of the other rule. This is particularly true if the "unwanted" rule is one of the fundamental rules of your evolving theory and having it disabled is disastrous. It should be noted that the "unwanted" rule might be a definition which is unexpectedly expanding.

---

[38]Applications of a **DISABLED** executable counterpart are reduced when they arise in the execution of some other executable counterpart. For example, suppose **REVERSE** is defined in terms of **APPEND** and the executable counterpart of **APPEND** is **DISABLED** as by **(DISABLE *1*APPEND)**. Then **(APPEND '(3 2) '(1))** will not be reduced to an explicit value when it appears in formulas being proved. But **(REVERSE '(1 2 3))** does reduce to **'(3 2 1)**, even though it requires the reduction of **APPEND** calls.

12.14.2. Nonrecursive Definitions

Scenario: A complicated nonrecursive function has been defined, and you have just finished proving a set of beautiful **REWRITE** rules that hide its complexity and let you manipulate calls of the function smoothly. However, none of your rules are ever applied!

The problem here is that nonrecursive functions are (almost) always expanded immediately. Thus, no rule about such a function will ever find a match in a simplified conjecture. This problem is discussed further on page 320. The solution, generally, is to disable the nonrecursive function as soon as you have characterized it with **REWRITE** rules. If you use nonrecursive functions extensively and do not want all proofs about them to proceed by simply expanding them into their cases, we advise the following approach: define the function, prove the fundamental properties as rewrite rules, disable the function, and base all subsequent proofs on the fundamental properties. You will frequently discover that you omitted a "fundamental property." **ENABLE** will be useful then.

12.14.3. Hierarchical Rule Development

Scenario: You have just finished proving a fundamental result in your evolving theory. You expect the result to be used widely in subsequent proofs. However, you find that it is not.

The problem here, often, is that the lemmas proved in order to derive the fundamental result are "getting in the way." Frequently, the proof of a major theorem requires the proofs of many minor ones that handle special cases. These "lemmas" are often formulated haphazardly simply to permit the derivation of the proof of the main theorem. However, because the lemmas necessarily deal with the same clique of function names as the main theorem, they will often find unanticipated applications outside the proof of the main theorem. In particular, they may well deform the very targets for which the main theorem was intended. The standard solution is to disable these intermediate or inconsequential lemmas once the main theorem has been proved.

12.15. DO-EVENTS

General Form:
```
(DO-EVENTS events)
```


Example Forms:

```
(DO-EVENTS '((DEFN LEN (X)
              (IF (NLISTP X)
                  0
                  (ADD1 (LEN (CDR X)))))
             (PROVE-LEMMA LEN-APPEND (REWRITE)
              (EQUAL (LEN (APPEND A B))
                     (PLUS (LEN A) (LEN B))))))
```

(DO-EVENTS XXX)

DO-EVENTS executes each event form in a list of such forms and is the most common way to replay an edited sequence of undone events or process an unproblematic sequence of newly created commands. The argument, **events**, is evaluated and should be a list of event forms.

DO-EVENTS iterates down **events**, considering each event form in turn. For each form it prettyprints the form, then evaluates the form (which causes additional printing, e.g., of proofs and time triples), prints the value of the form, and then prints a form feed.[39] **DO-EVENTS** terminates either when all events have been processed or some event either causes an **ERROR** or **FATAL ERROR** or some **PROVE-LEMMA** fails. **DO-EVENTS** returns **T** if all events were successfully processed and **NIL** otherwise.

Normally, the output of **DO-EVENTS**, and of the event commands it executes, is printed to the terminal. However, when used by **PROVEALL**, all output, including error messages, goes to the **proofs** and **err** extensions as noted on page 293. In this case, **DO-EVENTS** indicates its progress through **events** by printing out the name of each event form just before the form is executed. It prints out a comma upon completion of the execution of each form.

12.16. ELIM

ELIM is one of the rule class tokens that may be given to **ADD-AXIOM** or **PROVE-LEMMA** to indicate what kinds of rules should be generated from a formula. **ELIM** rules are used in the destructor elimination process, which is the second process tried (simplification being the first). We describe the destructor elimination process on page 225. On page 247 we describe how **ELIM** rules are generated and how they are used. On page 333 we give some hints regarding

---

[39]Actually, **DO-EVENTS** prints the value of the global Lisp variable **EVENT-SEPARATOR-STRING** to separate one event and its output from the next. The initial value of that variable is **#\Page**.

the use of **ELIM** rules.

12.17. ENABLE

General Form:
```
(ENABLE name)
```

Example Forms:
```
(ENABLE TIMES-2-REWRITE)
```
and
```
(ENABLE REVERSE)
```
and
```
(ENABLE *1*REMAINDER)
```

ENABLE is an event command that sets the status of a citizen to **ENABLED**. The command does not evaluate its argument. The argument, **name**, must be a citizen. The command creates a new event name, **new-name**, adds a new event to the data base with **new-name** as its name, and sets the status of **name** in the data base to **ENABLED**.   Then **ENABLE** prints a time triple and returns **new-name**. (ENABLE name) is just an abbreviation for (TOGGLE new-name name NIL).

See the discussion of **DISABLE** for details.

A citizen can also be enabled "locally" (without affecting its status in the data base) via the **ENABLE** hint in **PROVE-LEMMA**.

12.18. Errors

Each error condition checked and reported by the system is classified into one of three classes:

- **WARNING**: a cautionary message concerning a legal but perhaps unintended aspect of a command, e.g., that the body of a function definition makes no reference to one of the formal parameters.

- **ERROR**: a violation of the preconditions on a command, such as the submission of an ill-formed term, the submission of an inadmissible function definition, the attempted introduction of an event name already in the data base, etc. Generally **ERROR**s can be fixed by editing your type-in, though they sometimes indicate a deeper problem than mere syntax.

- **FATAL ERROR**: a violation of the internal invariants assumed by our code or the exhaustion of some resource (e.g., the variable symbols that may be introduced by destructor elimination). It is generally not possible to fix such an error. Except for resource errors or situations in which the user has entered our code via some route other than the documented commands, **FATAL ERROR**s should not arise.

The system may cause Lisp resource errors, such as stack overflow due to excessively deep function calling (usually an indication of circularities in the rewrite rules you have added) or the exhaustion of dynamic storage space (usually caused by circular rewriting that enlarges the term, excessive case splitting, or combinatoric explosion in the normalization of propositional expressions). The system should not cause any other kind of error, e.g., "Trap: Argument given to CAR was not a list, locative, or NIL," while it is being used entirely in accordance with this handbook. If such errors occur, please notify us.

All three types of errors print supposedly self-explanatory messages on the terminal. After **WARNING**s the computation proceeds as though nothing had happened. The other two kinds of errors cause interactive Lisp breaks.

It is not possible to fix an error from within the Lisp break and proceed. Proceeding from the break automatically aborts the computation that led to the error. The only reason we enter a break at all is to give you the opportunity to inspect the state of the computation before it is lost by the abort.

Getting out of the break is a system-dependent operation.

- On a Symbolics Lisp Machine, press the **ABORT** key.

- In Lucid on a Sun, type **:A** to the break prompt.

- In KCL on a Sun, type **:Q** to the break prompt.

These actions should return you to the top level of the Lisp system.

The data base is not disturbed by any command that halts with an **ERROR**. The same cannot be said if a **FATAL ERROR** occurs. See however the discussion of the data base integrity on page 252.

To fix an error you must edit (or retype) the command that caused it. Most Lisp systems support this, and since our code runs in many different implementations of Common Lisp and under many different kinds of host operating systems, we have not tried to implement a uniform error recovery mechanism.

12.19. Event Commands

The *event commands* are those that create nodes in the data base. The event commands are

- **ADD-AXIOM**
- **ADD-SHELL**
- **BOOT-STRAP**
- **DCL**
- **DEFN**
- **PROVE-LEMMA**
- **TOGGLE** (with its abbreviations **DISABLE** and **ENABLE**)
- **TOGGLE-DEFINED-FUNCTIONS**

12.20. EVENTS-SINCE

General Form:
(EVENTS-SINCE name)

Example Form:
(EVENTS-SINCE 'REVERSE)

The argument, **name**, is evaluated and must be the name of an event. **EVENTS-SINCE** returns the list of event forms for all events created since **name**. The list includes the event form for **name** itself and is ordered chronologically, starting with the event form for **name**.

12.21. Executable Counterparts

Corresponding to every function symbol in the logic is a Lisp procedure called the *executable counterpart* of the function. The name of the executable counterpart is obtained by concatenating the string, ''***1***'' onto the front of the function symbol. Thus, ***1*APPEND** is the executable counterpart of **APPEND**.

Executable counterparts are used to compute the value of functions on constants. Such computations are the essence of the execution facility provided by **R-LOOP** but also arise in the theorem prover proper. Whenever a term of the form **(fn 't$_1$ ... 't$_n$)**, e.g., the application of a function to explicit values, is produced, we use the executable counterpart of **fn** to compute the equivalent explicit value, if any.[40] To explain further we must first discuss the notion of explicit value.

Recall that an *explicit value* is a variable-free term involving only shell constructors and base objects with the property that each argument of each constructor satisfies the type restriction of the corresponding argument position. For example, **(CONS (ADD1 (ZERO)) (ZERO))** is an explicit value term.

Internally, each explicit value term, **t**, is represented by a Lisp data structure of the form **(QUOTE evg)**, where **evg** is called the *explicit value guts* of **t**. The explicit value guts is just the Lisp object corresponding to what we called the "explicit value descriptor" in section 4.7.4, page 118.[41]

The explicit value above is represented by **(QUOTE (1 . 0))**. The Lisp object **(1 . 0)** is the explicit value guts of **(CONS (ADD1 (ZERO)) (ZERO))**.

Suppose that **' e_1, ..., ' e_n** are n explicit value terms and that their respective explicit value guts are **e_1, ..., e_n**. Suppose **fn** is an n-ary function. Then **(fn ' e_1 ... ' e_n)** is a term which is likely to be equal to some explicit value. The executable counterpart of **fn**, ***1*fn**, can sometimes be used to compute the explicit value equivalent to **(fn ' e_1 ... ' e_n)** as follows: Apply the Lisp procedure ***1*fn** to the n Lisp objects **e_1, ..., e_n**. If a result, **e**, is returned then **' e** is the internal representation of an explicit value term equivalent to **(fn ' e_1 ... ' e_n)**. Otherwise, the execution of ***1*fn** will signal failure (by executing a Lisp **THROW**). Failure is signaled either because an undefined function is encountered on the execution path or, for functions involving **V&C$**, certain resource limits are exhausted. See **REDUCE-TERM-CLOCK**.

Note that we have not said that ***1*fn** computes an equivalent explicit *if there is one*, merely that *if *1*fn computes a value* it represents an equivalent explicit value. However, for a very large class of functions the equivalent explicit value always exists and the executable counterparts compute them.

We say a function **fn** is *explicit value preserving* if either (a) it is one of the

---

[40]More precisely, the executable counterpart of **fn** is so used, provided either **fn** is a shell constructor or base function symbol or it is enabled. Executable counterparts can be disabled individually with **DISABLE** or **TOGGLE**, as in **(DISABLE *1*APPEND)**. All executable counterparts can be disabled with **TOGGLE-DEFINED-FUNCTIONS**. Note that shell constructors and base function cannot be effectively disabled; they are used whether disabled or not. The theorem prover's internal form requires that explicit values be kept in a certain normal form.

[41]This is not quite true. A "dotted s-expression" in our formal presentation is a sequence whose next-to-last element is the dot character. In Lisp, the explicit value guts corresponding to a "dotted s-expression" is in fact a binary tree of Lisp list cells whose right-most cell contains an atom other than **NIL**. Such trees are printed by Lisp with a dot. Our dotted s-expressions are read by Lisp and converted into such trees. Thus, the user cannot tell whether the dot is "really there" as an element or just an artifact of printing unless he writes a Lisp program to inspect the data structure.

primitive functions other than the metafunctions **SUBRP**, **APPLY-SUBR**, **FORMALS**, **BODY**, **V&C\$**, **V&C-APPLY\$**, **EVAL\$**, **APPLY\$**, and **FOR** or (b) it is a defined function with the property that every function symbol used in the body, other than **fn** itself, is explicit value preserving. Explicit value preserving functions have the property that for every application to explicit values there exists an equivalent explicit value. Except for those functions which use the metafunctions excluded above and those which use functions introduced with **DCL**, every function in our system is explicit value preserving. It is in this sense we used the word "likely" above. For all explicit value preserving functions, the executable counterparts always compute the corresponding explicit values.

However, in addition to the syntactically defined class of explicit value preserving functions, there are defined functions which in fact reduce, or often reduce, to explicit values on explicit values even though metafunctions or undefined functions are used on some branches through their definitions. **V&C\$** itself is a good example: on many applications to explicit values, e.g., on applications to the quotations of terms composed of explicit value preserving functions, **V&C\$** can be reduced computationally to an explicit value.

Every function symbol in the logic has an executable counterpart whether the function is explicit value preserving or not. The **ADD-SHELL** command and the **DEFN** command create the executable counterparts for the symbols they introduce. The **DCL** command creates the trivial executable counterpart ("signal failure") for its function symbol. The command **TOGGLE-DEFINED-FUNCTIONS** can be used to disable all executable counterparts other than shell constructors and base objects. If ***1*fn** is disabled then **(fn 'e$_1$ ... 'e$_n$)** is not reduced to an explicit value by execution of ***1*fn**.

It is possible to compile executable counterparts. This generally makes **R-LOOP** evaluate your input much faster, and it will speed up your proofs if they involve explicit values. See **COMPILE-UNCOMPILED-DEFNS**.

12.22. Explicit Values

Explicit values are the canonical constants in the logic: terms composed entirely of shell constructors and bottom objects with the additional property that every subterm satisfies the type restriction for the constructor argument position occupied. See page 111, in Chapter 4 for a formal definition of explicit values. See page 118 for a formal description of the notation in which they are written. See the discussion of "executable counterparts," page 282, for a discussion of how we compute on explicit values.

12.23. Extensions

See the discussion of File Names on page 285.

12.24. FAILED-EVENTS

General Form:
FAILED-EVENTS

   FAILED-EVENTS is a Lisp variable that contains all of the event commands
submitted in the current session that did not terminate successfully.

12.25. File Names

Generally speaking it is not necessary to know anything about file names the
first few times you use the theorem prover: commands are typed to Lisp at the
terminal and their output is printed at the terminal. The first use of file names
usually occurs when you want to save the current data base to a file, with
MAKE-LIB, and subsequently restore the data base, with **NOTE-LIB**. The
other common use of file names is at the successful conclusion of a major phase
of a project when you will probably want to create an "endorsed data base" (see
page 312) and a coherent record of the event commands that construct it and the
proofs concerned. This is done by calling the function **PROVEALL**.
PROVEALL can be used to write the commands and their "normal" output to a
file, record error messages and warnings in separate file, and save the final data
base.
   To use these more sophisticated commands it is necessary to understand file
name formats and our file name conventions. The file name format used by the
theorem prover is that defined by the host operating system. *We assume you are
familiar with the file name formats on your machine.* We make two assumptions
about file name formats and then proceed to define our file name conventions.
Our assumptions are

   - File names are written as Lisp strings, i.e., ASCII character se-
     quences enclosed in double quotation marks, as in
     "doe:>nqthm>demo.lib".

   - A "full file name" is composed of two parts, the "root name" and
     the "extension." The root name is separated from the extension by
     the ASCII dot character, "**.**". The format of both the root name
     and the extension are dictated entirely by the host file system.

In the development of a given subject, e.g., the proof of correctness of the program **FSTRPOS**, the command file, the library files, the proof file, and the error message file all generally have the same root name, which on a Lisp machine might be `"doe:>smith>fstrpos"` and on a Unix system `"/usr/smith/fstrpos"`.

We use the extension of each file name to indicate the particular kind of data contained in the file. Commands that create or read files, such as **NOTE-LIB** and **PROVEALL**, take root names as their arguments and extend them by tacking on one of several fixed extension names according to the type of file to be read or written.

For example, proofs generated by **PROVEALL** are written into a file with the **proofs** extension while error messages are written to the **err** extension. There are, in all, six different extensions used by the system. The names used above, **proofs** and **err**, are just "generic" names used in this handbook. The actual strings used to form extensions may be specified by the user, by setting each of six global Lisp variables. Thus, the **proofs** extension of `"/usr/smith/fstrpos"` might be `"/usr/smith/fstrpos.proofs"` on one system and `"doe:>smith>fstrpos.prf"` on another. We make this precise in the definition below.

Given a root name, **file**, we speak of six different *extensions* of **file**, each known by a generic name. Each extension is formed by concatenating **file**, a dot, and then a character string (or Lisp symbol) associated with the generic name. To each generic name there corresponds a Lisp variable whose value is the associated character string. These variables may be set by the user. The generic names, the kind of data contained in such extensions, the Lisp variable concerned, and its initial setting are described below.

proofs	The **PROVEALL** program opens a file with the **proofs** extension to contain a transcript of the event sequence being executed. In particular, each event form is printed into the **proofs** extension, and then the form is executed with all of its output written to the **proofs** extension—error messages, comments on definitions, proofs, time triples, etc.—and then the value of the completed form is printed into the **proofs** extension. See **PROVEALL** for the details. The name used for the **proofs** extension is the value of the Lisp variable **FILE-EXTENSION-PROOFS**, which is initially `"proofs"`.
err	The **PROVEALL** program opens a file with the **err** extension to contain all **WARNING**, **ERROR** and **FATAL ERROR** messages generated during the **PROVEALL**. (These messages are also printed into the **proofs** extension as part of the transcript.) The **err** extension contains nothing but

such messages and is a convenient summary of the anomalies in the event sequence. The name used for the **err** extension is the value of the Lisp variable **FILE-EXTENSION-ERR**, which is initially **"err"**.

lib

The **lib** extension is one of two extensions in which the data base is saved by **MAKE-LIB** and restored by **NOTE-LIB**. The other is the **lisp** extension below. The data in the **lib** extension is written from and read into Lisp variables and property lists. The name used for the **lib** extension is the value of the variable **FILE-EXTENSION-LIB** and is initially **"lib"**.

lisp

The **lisp** extension is used in connection with files that contain Common Lisp code. **MAKE-LIB** and **NOTE-LIB** use the the **lisp** extension for a file containing the Common Lisp definitions of the executable counterparts of the functions in the saved data base. **COMPILE-UNCOMPILED-DEFNS** uses the **lisp** extension when it creates a file to be compiled. These uses of the **lisp** extension all concern files created by the system in connection with executable counterparts. But the source files of the theorem prover itself are also Common Lisp files and, as noted in the Installation Guide, Chapter 14, the programs **COMPILE-NQTHM** and **LOAD-NQTHM** also use the **lisp** extension. The name used for the **lisp** extension is the value of the Lisp variable **FILE-EXTENSION-LISP** and is initially **"lisp"**.

bin

A file with the **bin** extension should be the result of compiling the corresponding **lisp** extension. **COMPILE-UNCOMPILE-DEFNS** uses the **bin** extension to load the compiled file it creates. During installation of our system, **COMPILE-NQTHM** and **LOAD-NQTHM** (see Chapter 14) use the **bin** extension to load compiled files. The name used for the **bin** extension is the value of the Lisp variable **FILE-EXTENSION-BIN**. In general, **FILE-EXTENSION-BIN** should be set to the same extension used by the local compiler. That is, if your compiler puts the object code for file **foo** into **foo.o** then **FILE-EXTENSION-BIN** should be set to **"o"**; if your compiler puts the object code for file **foo** into **foo.bin** then **FILE-EXTENSION-BIN** should be set to **"bin"**. However, the only use we make of **FILE-EXTENSION-BIN** is when one of the programs mentioned above **LOAD**s the compiled code for a given root name. Many implementations of the Common Lisp **LOAD** program support the convention that, when no extension is used and a compiled file for the given root name exists, then the compiled file is **LOAD**ed. In such implementations it is not necessary to know the extension used by the compiler—which is to say, in such implementations one need not extend the root name to refer explicitly to the compiled file to be loaded. This convention is supported by the KCL, Symbolics, and Lucid Common Lisps. We take advantage of it by adopting the convention that when **FILE-EXTENSION-BIN** is **NIL** no extension is tacked on. This is the initial setting for **FILE-EXTENSION-BIN**. If your implementation of Common Lisp does not support the convention, you should set **FILE-EXTENSION-BIN** to the same string used by the local compiler.

fail   The **fail** extension is a file generated by **PROVEALL** when the event sequence causes an error or a proof fails. Thus, if a **PROVEALL** is started for a given root name and the execution has completed (as indicated, say, by the presence of a **lisp** file), the absence or presence of a **fail** file indicates the success or failure of the run. The name used for the **fail** extension is the value of the Lisp variable **FILE-EXTENSION-FAIL** and is initially **"fail"**.

We now raise a further complication in the use of file names: most Lisps—or the underlying operating systems—provide default mechanisms by which our "full file names" are further elaborated before a unique file identifier is generated. For example, on Unix the user who is "connected" to the directory **/usr/smith** may find that the **lisp** extension of the root name **"fstrpos"**, namely **"fstrpos.lisp"**, actually identifies the file **"/usr/smith/fstrpos.lisp"**. Similarly, by setting the appropriate "default path names," the user on the Lisp Machine can arrange for a simple root name such as **"fstrpos"** to identify files with much more elaborate unique names.

The Lisp variable ***DEFAULT-NQTHM-PATH*** may be used to determine the directory from which files are read and written while compiling, loading, or using the theorem prover. The initial value of ***DEFAULT-NQTHM-PATH*** is **NIL**, which means "do nothing." However, if the value is non-**NIL**, then we merge that value, using the Common Lisp function **MERGE-PATHNAMES**, whenever we **OPEN** a file for reading or writing and whenever we **LOAD** a file. If you specify a full pathname when using functions such as **NOTE-LIB**, **MAKE-LIB**, and **PROVEALL**, then the value of ***DEFAULT-NQTHM-PATH*** is irrelevant. However, if you specify a non-**NIL** value for

DEFAULT-NQTHM-PATH and you specify no directory in a file name passed to **NOTE-LIB**, **MAKE-LIB**, etc., then the file used will be on the directory specified by ***DEFAULT-NQTHM-PATH***. Example values of ***DEFAULT-NQTHM-PATH*** are **"/usr/smith"** and **"doe:>nqthm>"**.

12.26. GENERALIZE

GENERALIZE is one of the rule class tokens that may be given to **ADD-AXIOM** or **PROVE-LEMMA** to indicate what kinds of rules should be generated from a formula. **GENERALIZE** rules are used in the generalization process, which is the fourth process tried (after simplification, destructor elimination, and use of equalities). We describe the generalization process on page 227. On page 248 we describe how **GENERALIZE** rules are generated and how they are used.

12.27. MAINTAIN-REWRITE-PATH

General Form:
(MAINTAIN-REWRITE-PATH flg)

Example Form:
(MAINTAIN-REWRITE-PATH T)

This routine turns on and off the maintenance of the rewrite path (see page 259 for a discussion of rewrite paths and see the entries for **ACCUMULATED-PERSISTENCE**, **BREAK-LEMMA**, and **BREAK-REWRITE** for related features). The argument, **flg**, is evaluated and should be either **T** or **NIL**. If **T**, the rewrite path is henceforth maintained. If **NIL**, the rewrite path is not maintained. Maintenance of the stack involves storing into a data structure certain information about every call of the rewriter and degrades the performance to about 60% of its normal speed in proofs involving heavy use of replacement rules. Nevertheless, in deep proof developments we frequently maintain the rewrite path because of the information it provides us.

BREAK-LEMMA calls **MAINTAIN-REWRITE-PATH** the first time a rule is monitored since the path must be maintained in case an interactive break occurs. **UNBREAK-LEMMA** does *not* disable path maintenance when the last rule is removed from the list of monitored lemmas. It merely prints a message that path maintenance is still enabled. The reason is that you may still be planning to use **BREAK-REWRITE** or **ACCUMULATED-PERSISTENCE**. If not, you can regain the normal efficiency by turning off the maintenance of the rewrite path.

The rewrite path is not the Lisp control stack but a separate data structure. It persists even after an aborted computation. Therefore, if you are maintaining the rewrite path and abort some proof attempt (say, out of frustration over the time it is taking or because a stack overflow occurs) you can still inspect the path as it stood at the time of the abort. See **BREAK-REWRITE**.

12.28. MAKE-LIB

General Form:
(MAKE-LIB file)

Example Form:
(MAKE-LIB "demo")

    MAKE-LIB is the command-level routine for saving the data base so that it can be restored by **NOTE-LIB**. The argument, **file**, is evaluated and should be a valid file root name (see page 285). The data base is saved to a pair of files, namely the **lib** and **lisp** extensions of **file** (see page 285).

    Into the **lisp** extension of **file MAKE-LIB** writes the Lisp source code for the executable counterparts of all functions in the current data base. Into the **lib** extension it writes everything else in the data base. **MAKE-LIB** does not alter the data base. When the two files have been written, they are closed and **MAKE-LIB** returns a list containing the two file names created.

12.29. META

META is the first element in one of the rule class tokens that may be given to **ADD-AXIOM** or **PROVE-LEMMA** to indicate what kinds of rules should be generated from a formula. The general form of the token is **(META fn$_1$ $\cdots$ fn$_n$)**. **META** rules are used in the simplification process, which is the first process tried. We describe the simplification process starting on page 222. Starting on page 244 we describe how **META** rules are generated and how they are used.

12.30. Names—Events, Functions, and Variables

In the formal treatment of the logic in Chapter 4 we defined the variable and function symbols of our logic as follows:

Terminology. A sequence of characters, s, is a *symbol* if and only if (a) s is nonempty, (b) each character in s is a member of the set

```
{A  B  C  D  E  F  G  H  I  J  K  L  M
 N  O  P  Q  R  S  T  U  V  W  X  Y  Z
 0  1  2  3  4  5  6  7  8  9
 $  ^  &  *  _  -  +  =  ~  {  }  ?  <  >}
```

and, (c) the first character of s is a letter, i.e., in the set

```
{A  B  C  D  E  F  G  H  I  J  K  L  M
 N  O  P  Q  R  S  T  U  V  W  X  Y  Z}.
```

Terminology. The *variable symbols* and *function symbols* of our language are the symbols other than **T**, **F**, and **NIL**.

However, in the extended syntax we introduced the notion of "well-formed" s-expressions and their "translations" to formal terms. We then adopted the policy that all terms displayed thereafter (and used in the implementation) would in fact be well-formed s-expressions standing for their translations.

The result of this is that there is a discrepancy between the set of legal names in the formal syntax and the set of names you can actually use in formulas. For example, **QUOTE** is a legal function name, but there is no way in the implementation to write down an application of the function symbol **QUOTE**, and an error is caused if you try to define **QUOTE**.

We therefore give here the definitions of the *legal names* as that concept is practically defined by the extended syntax.

The variable names permitted in the implementation are the symbols, excluding **T**, **F**, and **NIL** as above.

The function names and event names permitted in the implementation are the symbols, as defined above, excluding the following:

- **T**, **F**, **NIL**, **QUOTE**, **LIST**, and

- any symbol, such as **CADDR**, which starts with a **C**, ends with an **R** and contains only **A**s and **D**s in between.

A function or event name is *old* (or *new*) iff it is (or is not) a citizen of the data base (see page 269).

12.31. NOTE-LIB

General Form:
(NOTE-LIB file)

Example Form:

```
(MAKE-LIB "demo")
```

NOTE-LIB is the routine for restoring a data base saved by **MAKE-LIB**. The argument to **NOTE-LIB**, **file**, is evaluated and should be a valid file root name; the **lib** and **lisp** extensions of **file** must exist and should have been created by **MAKE-LIB** (see the discussion of File Names, page 285).

NOTE-LIB destroys the data base extant when it is executed and configures the data base to be that which was extant when the corresponding **MAKE-LIB** for **file** was executed.

NOTE-LIB returns a list containing the names of the two files read.

12.32. NQTHM Mode

NQTHM mode refers to the set of axioms added to the data base by **BOOT-STRAP**. See the discussion of **BOOT-STRAP** on page 256.

12.33. PPE

General Form:
```
(PPE name)
```

Example Form:
```
(PPE 'REVERSE)
```

PPE stands for "PrettyPrint Event." The argument, **name**, is evaluated and should be a citizen of the data base. The command prints out the **EVENT-FORM** of **name**.

12.34. PROVE

General Form:
```
(PROVE term)
```

Example Form:
```
(PROVE '(PROPERP (REVERSE X)))
```

PROVE *is* the theorem prover. The argument, **term**, is evaluated by Lisp and should be a term. **PROVE** attempts to prove **term**; it returns **T** if the proof succeeds and **NIL** if the proof fails. The output is written to the terminal. There is no provision for hints. **PROVE** does not alter the data base.

12.35. PROVEALL

General Form:
```
(PROVEALL file events)
```

Example Form:
```
(PROVEALL "demo"
  '((DEFN REV1 (X A)
      (IF (NLISTP X)
          A
          (REV1 (CDR X)
                (CONS (CAR X) A))))
    (PROVE-LEMMA REV1-IS-REV (REWRITE)
                 (EQUAL (REV1 X A)
                        (APPEND (REVERSE X) A)))))
```

PROVEALL is the standard way to execute a sequence of event commands and collect the output into a file. The arguments are evaluated. The first argument, **file**, should be a file root name (see page 285). Four or five extensions of **file** will be created, namely the **proofs**, **err**, **lib**, **lisp**, and, possibly, the **fail** extensions. The second argument, **events**, should be a list of event forms to be executed.

PROVEALL first opens the **proofs** and **err** extensions of **file** and arranges for the event commands and **DO-EVENTS** to print all their "normal" output to the **proofs** extension and all error messages to the **err** extension. **PROVEALL** then prints a header into the **proofs** extension, giving the current time and date.

PROVEALL next uses **DO-EVENTS** to execute the event forms in **events**. **DO-EVENTS** executes each event form in turn until either they have all been executed or some form either causes an **ERROR** or **FATAL ERROR** or some **PROVE-LEMMA** fails. **DO-EVENTS** creates a complete transcript of the session in the **proofs** extension of **file**. In particular, the **proofs** extension will contain each event form executed, any **WARNING** or error messages caused, the justifications of each definition, the proof attempt for each **PROVE-LEMMA**, the time triple for each event, and the value of each event. The **err** extension will contain every **WARNING**, **ERROR**, and **FATAL ERROR** message printed in the **proofs** extension. Because the normal output of the event commands is being written to files, **DO-EVENTS** indicates its progress through **events** by printing just the event names to the terminal, each name being printed upon the commencement of the execution of the corresponding event.

Upon termination of **DO-EVENTS**, **PROVEALL** prints a "system description" into the **proofs** extension. This description gives the names of the files that were loaded to produce the version of the theorem prover used in the proveall. The format used differs from one host system to the next. **PROVEALL** also prints to the **proofs** extension the total amount of time consumed by the run, by summing (componentwise) the time triples printed.

PROVEALL then uses **MAKE-LIB** to save the data base. This creates both the **lib** and **lisp** extensions of **file**. Note that if **DO-EVENTS** terminates prematurely because of an error or unsuccessful proof, the data base saved will be the one in which the terminal event was executed. The output from that event will be in the **proofs** extension. The failure can be reproduced by using **NOTE-LIB** to restore the data base created by **PROVEALL** and then executing the terminal event.

Finally, if **DO-EVENTS** terminated prematurely, **PROVEALL** creates the **fail** extension of **file** and writes into it (and into the **err** extension) an **ERROR** message containing the event form that caused the failure.

As noted on page 271 and in the discussion of **UNDO-NAME** on page 311 we generally use **PROVEALL** to certify the correctness of a sequence of events constructed interactively with **UNDO-NAME**. In addition, it is useful as a way to create a file that has an unbroken listing of each of the definitions, theorems, and proofs in a given data base.

12.36. PROVE-LEMMA

General Forms:
```
(PROVE-LEMMA name rule-classes term)
```
and
```
(PROVE-LEMMA name rule-classes term hints)
```

Example Form:
```
(PROVE-LEMMA REVERSE-REVERSE (REWRITE)
    (IMPLIES (PROPER X)
             (EQUAL (REVERSE (REVERSE X)) X)))
```
and
```
(PROVE-LEMMA TIMES-LIST-EQUAL-FACT (REWRITE)
    (IMPLIES (PERM (POSITIVES N) L)
             (EQUAL (TIMES-LIST L) (FACT N))))

;Hints:
((USE (PERM-TIMES-LIST (L1 (POSITIVES N))
                       (L2 L)))
   (DISABLE PERM-TIMES-LIST)))
```

PROVE-LEMMA is an event command for proving a theorem and storing it and possibly some generated rules in the data base. It does not evaluate its arguments. **name** must be a new name and will be made the name of the event in the data base, **rule-classes** must be a (possibly empty) list of rule classes and **term** must be a well-formed term (see **TRANSLATE**). **PROVE-LEMMA** applies the theorem prover to **term**, printing commentary as the proof attempt proceeds. If the proof attempt is successful, **term** is stored in the data base as a theorem; in addition, rules of the classes specified by **rule-classes** are generated from **term** and stored. The name of each rule is **name**. An error is caused if **term** is unsuitable for some class in **rule-classes** and no change is made in the data base.

When formulating input for **PROVE-LEMMA** you must be cognizant of the rule interpretation of **term** in addition to its mathematical content. See Chapter 11 for a detailed explanation of the effect of each type of rule and how rules are generated from formulas and rule classes. See Chapter 13 for advice about how to use rules.

Note that if **rule-classes** is **NIL** then the term is stored as a theorem and will be available for **USE** hints (see below) but will generate no rules.

If the proof attempt succeeds, **PROVE-LEMMA** prints "**Q.E.D.**" and a time triple for the event and returns the name of the new event, **name**.

If the proof attempt fails, **PROVE-LEMMA** prints a "failure banner"

************** F A I L E D *************

and then a time triple. Then it returns **NIL**.

When the theorem prover fails the only claim made is the trivial one that our heuristics did not lead to a proof. The system's remarks should not be interpreted to mean that the input formula is not a theorem, even if the last formula printed is **F**: the heuristics might have generalized the input formula before failing. That said, however, two caveats are in order.

First, conjectures submitted for proof are frequently not theorems. Do not be too quick to dismiss a failed proof simply because the theorem prover is so weak. It is indeed weak, but you can't fool it either. If a point were awarded the opposition each time a player asserted an inconsistent belief, the theorem prover would never lose and would, in fact, win almost every session.

Second, when it fails on *theorems* it is frequently because the proof you had in mind involves some step that has not been made explicit by your previously proved lemmas—or at least by their interpretation as rules. See Chapter 9 where we discussed the notion of the crucial "check points" in a proof attempt and what you should do at each. If worse comes to worse, you can essentially tell the system your proof via the **hint** argument to **PROVE-LEMMA**, which we describe at length below.

The **hints** argument permits the user to give the theorem prover some guidance in its proof attempt. If nonempty, **hints** must be a list of tuples. The **CAR** of each tuple must be one of the symbols listed below, where we describe the form and effect of each acceptable tuple. An error is caused if any element of **hints** fails to have the correct form.

12.36.1. USE Hints

General Form:
```
(USE (name₁ (v₁,₁ t₁,₁) ... (v₁,ₙ₁ t₁,ₙ₁))
     ...
     (nameₖ (vₖ,₁ tₖ,₁) ... (vₖ,ₙₖ tₖ,ₙₖ)))
```

Example Form:
```
(USE (LEMMA1 (X (CAR A)) (Y 0))
     (LEMMA2 (X (SUB1 X)) (I X) (K (FACT X))))
```

A **USE** hint essentially forces the use of one or more instances of one or more previously proved theorems, definitions, or axioms. Each pair following the symbol **USE** specifies the name of a formula and a substitution. The **USE** hint creates the indicated instantiation of each formula and adds it as an explicit hypothesis to the conjecture, **term**, submitted to the theorem prover.

More precisely, the conditions on **USE** hints are as follows. Each **name$_i$** must be a citizen of the data base with a non-**NIL** associated **FORMULA** in **DATA-BASE**. It does not matter if **name$_i$** is enabled or disabled or if any rules were generated for **name$_i$**. Each **v$_{i,j}$** must be a variable symbol, each **t$_{i,j}$** must be a term, and **v$_{i,j}$** must be distinct from **v$_{i,k}$** if **j≠k**.

Provided the above conditions are met, the effect of such a **USE** hint on the behavior of **PROVE-LEMMA** is to cause a modified (but provably equivalent) conjecture to be submitted to the theorem prover. Rather than submitting **term**, **PROVE-LEMMA** submits

$$\text{(IMPLIES (AND thm}_1 \text{ ... thm}_k\text{) term)}$$

where **thm$_i$** is obtained by instantiating the **FORMULA** for **name$_i$**, replacing **v$_{i,j}$** by **t$_{i,j}$**.

Observe that each **thm$_i$** is provably non-**F**—each is an instance of a theorem, definition, or axiom. Hence, the submitted formula is equivalent to the input one.

However, the careful reader might also note that if **name$_i$** is enabled and is a well-constructed replacement rule, there is a very high likelihood that it will be used to eliminate **thm$_i$** from the modified conjecture. This renders the hint useless. It is generally a good idea to **DISABLE** any **REWRITE** rules instantiated with a **USE** hint.

The modified conjecture is often easier to prove because the necessary instances of the necessary theorems are explicitly present. Indeed, it is possible to reduce any noninductive proof in the logic to propositional calculus and equality reasoning after supplying all the necessary instances of lemmas.[42]

12.36.2. EXPAND Hints

General Form:
(EXPAND t_1 ... t_n)

Example Form:
(EXPAND (PRIME1 X (SUB1 X)))

Each t_i must be a term of the form **(fn x_1 ... x_k)** where **fn** is a defined function. That is, each t_i must be a call of a defined function. Variable symbols, calls of shell functions, and calls of undefined functions are prohibited. The **EXPAND** hint forces the expansion of each t_i whenever it is encountered by the rewriter.

The **EXPAND** hint is implemented simply by putting the (translated) t_i on a list that is known to the rewriter. Whenever a function call is considered for expansion the list is checked. Thus, it is not necessary that the t_i occur in the input conjecture. However, it is crucial that the *exact* form of the intended term be written in the hint. We give an example below.

Suppose **(SECOND X)** is defined to be **(CADR X)**. Suppose also that **(TIMES I (SECOND X))** occurs in the input conjecture and the intended proof requires its expansion but the system does not expand it automatically. An **EXPAND** hint is called for. The hint **(EXPAND (TIMES I (SECOND X)))** will *not* work. By the time the rewriter considers expanding the **TIMES** expression, it will have become **(TIMES I (CADR X))**. Thus, to force the expansion of **(TIMES I (SECOND X))** it is necessary to give the hint **(EXPAND (TIMES I (CADR X)))**! This is not generally a problem. The reason is that you will generally add **EXPAND** hints only in response to the failure of an earlier proof attempt. In that earlier attempt the term **(TIMES I (CADR X))** will have appeared at the checkpoint where you expected its expansion to appear and you will have realized "the theorem prover needs to expand *that* term."

---

[42]We do not recommend such a wholesale use of **USE** simply because the number of lemmas and instances needed would often produce a modified conjecture that was too large for the combinatorial processing done by all known propositional decision engines.

12.36.3. DISABLE and ENABLE Hints

General Forms:
(DISABLE name$_1$ ... name$_n$)
and
(ENABLE name$_1$ ... name$_n$)

Example Form:
(DISABLE LEMMA1 TIMES-2-REWRITE)

Effectively, the **DISABLE** and **ENABLE** hints temporarily set the status of the named citizens appropriately for the duration of the proof attempt in **PROVE-LEMMA**. The status of the citizens in the data base is not altered. The effect of **DISABLE** is thus to prevent the theorem prover from using any of the named rules during the proof attempt. **ENABLE** permits the named rules to be used even though they might have been **DISABLE**d in the current data base.

Each of the **name$_i$** must be a citizen of the data base. See the discussion of the **ENABLE** and **DISABLE** event commands for more information.

12.36.4. HANDS-OFF Hints

General Form:
(HANDS-OFF t$_1$ ... t$_n$)

Example Form:
(HANDS-OFF (TIMES N (FACT (SUB1 N))))

The **HANDS-OFF** hint prevents the rewriter from changing any of the terms listed in the hint. Each **t$_i$** must be a term. Each such term is added to a list known to the rewriter and each time the rewriter is entered it asks whether the term to which it has been applied is on the list. If so, it returns the term untouched.

12.36.5. INDUCT Hints

General Form:
(INDUCT (fn v$_1$ ... v$_n$))

Example Form:
(INDUCT (PRIME1 X Y))

The **INDUCT** hint forces the theorem prover immediately into the induction process. Furthermore, rather than select an induction using its heuristics, the induction used is that suggested by $(\text{fn } v_1 \ \ldots \ v_n)$. fn must be a recursively defined function, and the v_i must be distinct variables. The induction suggested has exactly the same case analysis as in the body of the definition of fn. Those branches not leading to recursive calls are base cases. Those branches leading to $k>0$ recursive calls $(\text{fn } t_{1,1} \ \ldots \ t_{1,n})$, ..., $(\text{fn } t_{k,1} \ \ldots \ t_{k,n})$ have k induction hypotheses. The ith induction hypothesis is obtained by instantiating each v_j by the corresponding term $t_{i,j}$ from the ith recursive call.

The output produced by the theorem prover in response to an **INDUCT** hint is very unenlightening: it prints nothing at all but simply produces the various cases as described above and proceeds to simplify each.

12.36.6. DO-NOT-INDUCT

General Form and Example Form:
`(DO-NOT-INDUCT T)`

If present, the **DO-NOT-INDUCT** **T** hint causes the theorem prover to abort with failure as soon as it encounters a goal for which it would otherwise enter the induction process. (The second element of the hint can, in fact, be any Lisp object and is used as the value of an internal flag. If the flag setting is **NIL** the hint has no effect at all. Thus, the "General Form" is also the "Example Form.")

12.36.7. DO-NOT-GENERALIZE

General Form and Example Form:
`(DO-NOT-GENERALIZE T)`

If present, the **DO-NOT-GENERALIZE** **T** hint disables the entire generalization process. (The second element of the hint can, in fact, be any Lisp object and is used as the value of an internal flag. If the flag setting is **NIL** the hint has no effect at all. Thus, the "General Form" is also the "Example Form.")

12.36.8. NO-BUILT-IN-ARITH

General Form and Example Form:
(NO-BUILT-IN-ARITH T)

If present, the **(NO-BUILT-IN-ARITH T)** hint prevents the built-in linear arithmetic procedure from being used. We use this hint only to demonstrate the ability (or inability) of the system to prove by heuristic means the elementary theorems about **LESSP** and **PLUS**. (The second element of the hint can, in fact, be any Lisp object and is used as the value of an internal flag. If the flag setting is **NIL** the hint has no effect at all. Thus, the "General Form" is also the "Example Form.")

12.37. R-LOOP

General and Example Form:
(R-LOOP)

R-LOOP permits the evaluation of terms in the logic. It is a Lisp style "read-eval-print loop" providing certain convenient nonlogical features through so-called "special forms." (Noninteractive entrances to **R-LOOP** are provided via the functions **R** and **S** described at the end of this section.)

Upon entry to **R-LOOP** the system prints a header indicating the values of certain "switch settings" explained below. Then **R-LOOP** prompts the user for type-in by printing a "*****" and then waiting until an s-expression, **t**, has been typed. As usual in our system, one is actually typing to the standard Lisp reader. Line editing, redisplay of previously typed input, etc., are all available as however provided by the host Lisp system. In some Lisp systems, the user must type a carriage return after the s-expression before the system actually reads it; in other systems, the final balancing close parenthesis initiates the read.

Once **t** has been read it is evaluated under the axioms and definitions as described below, unless **t** is one of the special forms also noted below. The process of evaluation will yield one of three possible outcomes: an error message indicating that **t** is not well-formed, a message indicating that **t** cannot be reduced to an explicit value, or an explicit value equivalent to **t**. In the latter case the value is printed. In all cases, **R-LOOP** then iterates by prompting for another s-expression.

Here is a sample exchange:

```
*(APPEND '(1 2 3) '(4 5 6))        ; user type-in
 '(1 2 3 4 5 6)                     ; R-LOOP's response
```

Users familiar with the Lisp "read-eval-print" loop will notice a slight but disconcerting difference: in Lisp the exchange would have been

```
*(APPEND '(1 2 3) '(4 5 6))    ; user type-in
 (1 2 3 4 5 6)                  ; Lisp's response
```

Note the absence of the ' in Lisp's response. **R-LOOP** deals exclusively with *terms*—the "values" printed are terms, they just happen to all be explicit values and thus, when printed in our syntax, usually are preceded by the ' mark. (Numbers, **T**, **F**, and **NIL** are the only explicit values displayed without use of **QUOTE** notation.)

By "evaluation" we mean the reduction of a term to an explicit value by a call-by-value style interpretation of the axioms and definitions. For example, to evaluate a term of the form **(PERM x y)**, **R-LOOP** recursively reduces **x** and **y** to explicit values and then (effectively) instantiates the body of **PERM** with those values and reduces the result.[43]

The evaluation performed by **R-LOOP** takes place under an assignment of explicit values to variable symbols. **R-LOOP** permits the user to set this assignment with the **SETQ** special form. This feature is provided so that the user can save the value of one evaluation for possible input to another. Thus, if **X** has the value **7** and **Y** has the value **8** then the evaluation of **(TIMES X Y)** is **56**.

If the term **t** is submitted for evaluation and produces the explicit value **v**, then it is a theorem that **(EQUAL t v)**, under the equality hypotheses implicit in the current asignment of values to variables.

Not all terms can be reduced to explicit values. Examples are variables not assigned values in the current **R-LOOP** assignment (i.e., "unbound variables" in the programmer's sense, "undefined abbreviations" in the mathematician's) and calls of undefined functions. Some terms which are provably equal to explicit values cannot be reduced to that explicit value by evaluation. For example, **(IF V 3 3)** is provably equal to **3** but does not reduce to **3** if **V** is "unbound." Similarly, **(V&C$ T '(RUSSELL) NIL)** is provably equal to **F**, if **RUSSELL** is defined as on page 79, but will not reduce to **F**. When a term submitted for evaluation cannot be reduced to an explicit value by **R-LOOP**, the answer " **(NOT REDUCIBLE)** " is printed.

R-LOOP has two mode switches that can be set by several special forms. One of the switches determines whether evaluation is "traced" and, if so, how. The other determines whether abbreviations are used when values are printed out.

The *trace mode* may be *full*, *partial*, or *off*. When trace mode is off, no printing occurs during the evaluation of terms. The value is printed when the evaluation has completed successfully. When trace mode is not off, printing

---

[43]The "**R**" in "**R-LOOP**" in fact stands for "reduce" as we defined it in [5].

occurs during the evaluation of each term. Trace mode prints a step-by-step proof of the equivalence of the input term and the derived value. The difference between full and partial trace mode is only how large the printed steps are. In full trace mode, every application of substitutions of equals for equals into the input term is printed. In partial trace mode, we print only the "major" steps associated with function expansion.

Suppose we define **APP** as **APPEND**:

Definition .
```
(APP X Y)
  =
(IF (NLISTP X)
    Y
    (CONS (CAR X)
          (APP (CDR X) Y)))
```

Below we illustrate the evaluation of **(APP ′(A) ′(1 2 3))**, first with trace mode off, then in full trace mode, and then in partial trace mode. Then, we illustrate **(APP ′(A B C) ′(1 2 3))** in partial trace mode.

```
(R-LOOP)
Trace Mode: Off    Abbreviated Output Mode:   On
Type ? for help.

*(APP ′(A) ′(1 2 3))
 ′(A 1 2 3)


*FULL-TRACE
Trace Mode:  Full

*(APP ′(A) ′(1 2 3))
=(IF (NLISTP ′(A))
     ′(1 2 3)
     (CONS (CAR ′(A))
           (APP (CDR ′(A)) ′(1 2 3))))
=(IF F
     ′(1 2 3)
     (CONS (CAR ′(A))
           (APP (CDR ′(A)) ′(1 2 3))))
=(CONS (CAR ′(A))
       (APP (CDR ′(A)) ′(1 2 3)))
=(CONS ′A (APP (CDR ′(A)) ′(1 2 3)))
=(CONS ′A (APP NIL ′(1 2 3)))
=(CONS ′A
```

```
              (IF  (NLISTP NIL)
                   '(1 2 3)
                   (CONS (CAR NIL)
                         (APP (CDR NIL) '(1 2 3)))))
    =(CONS 'A
           (IF T
               '(1 2 3)
               (CONS (CAR NIL)
                     (APP (CDR NIL) '(1 2 3)))))
    ='(A 1 2 3)


    *TRACE
    Trace Mode:  Partial

    *(APP '(A) '(1 2 3))
    =(CONS 'A (APP NIL '(1 2 3)))
    ='(A 1 2 3)


    *(APP '(A B C) '(1 2 3))
    =(CONS 'A (APP '(B C) '(1 2 3)))
    =(CONS 'A
           (CONS 'B (APP '(C) '(1 2 3))))
    =(CONS 'A
           (CONS 'B
                 (CONS 'C (APP NIL '(1 2 3)))))
    ='(A B C 1 2 3)


    *OK
    Exiting R-LOOP.
    NIL
```

The *output abbreviation mode* may be either *on* or *off*. The mode determines how the final explicit value of a term is displayed. When output abbreviation is on, explicit values are displayed in a way that does not require use of the ugly "***1***" prefix. When output abbreviation mode is off, explicit values are displayed in **QUOTE** notation. For example,

```
    (R-LOOP)
    Trace Mode: Off   Abbreviated Output Mode: Off
    Type ? for help.

    *(PAIRLIST '(A B C) (LIST 1 2 3))
```

```
 ' ((A . 1) (B . 2) (C . 3))
*(PAIRLIST ' (A B C) (LIST 0 T F))
 ' ((A . 0)
    (B . *1*TRUE)
    (C . *1*FALSE))


*ABBREV
Abbreviated Output Mode:  On
*(PAIRLIST ' (A B C) (LIST 1 2 3))
 ' ((A . 1) (B . 2) (C . 3))
*(PAIRLIST ' (A B C) (LIST 0 T F))
 (LIST ' (A . 0)
         (CONS 'B T)
         (CONS 'C F))


*OK
Exiting R-LOOP.
NIL
```

In the session above we start with abbreviated output mode off. We evaluate two **PAIRLIST**s. The values of both are printed in **QUOTE** notation. But the value of the second one requires the use of ***1*TRUE** and ***1*FALSE**.

Then we enter abbreviated output mode and re-evaluate both **PAIRLIST**s. The value of the first one is printed just as before. But the value of the second one is not printed in **QUOTE** notation. Instead, **LIST** and **CONS** are used to "unquote" enough of the value to expose those parts that would otherwise require use of the "***1***" prefix.

Below we list the special forms recognized by **R-LOOP**. The special forms are, in general, well-formed terms that are simply not treated as terms when read at the top level by **R-LOOP**.

OK   Exit **R-LOOP** and return to its caller. If you invoked **(R-LOOP)** from the Lisp command interpreter (as opposed to from within some other Lisp program), **OK** returns you to the Lisp command interpreter. No harm results from exiting **R-LOOP** via Lisp interrupt characters (see "Aborting Commands" page 251). Variable assignments in the **R-LOOP** assignment are maintained from one call of **R-LOOP** to the next.

(SETQ var term)   In any s-expression of this form, **var** should be a variable symbol and **term** should be a term. This special form causes **term** to be evaluated under the current **R-LOOP**

assignment and, if the evaluation succeeds and produces **val**, the current assignment is changed so that **var** has the value **val**. In addition, **val** is printed. If the evaluation of **term** fails, no change is made to the **R-LOOP** assignment.

TRACE	Set trace mode to "partial."
FULL-TRACE	Set trace mode to "full."
UNTRACE	Set trace mode to "off."
ABBREV	Turn on abbreviated output mode.
UNABBREV	Turn off abbreviated output mode.
?	Causes **R-LOOP** to print out a brief summary of the available special forms.

Special forms are given special treatment only when they are the top-level s-expression read by **R-LOOP**. If, for example, the **SETQ** special form is used as a proper subterm in an s-expression, it is evaluated in the usual sense of the logic. For example, suppose **X** is **7** in the **R-LOOP** assignment, and the user types the s-expression **(PLUS (SETQ X 3) X)** to **R-LOOP**. Unless the user has defined the dyadic function **SETQ** in the logic, this s-expression is ill-formed. If **SETQ** has been defined, the value of this s-expression is the value of **(PLUS (SETQ 7 3) 7)**.

The **R-LOOP** assignment is maintained from one call of **R-LOOP** to the next within a given session with the theorem prover. A typical use of **R-LOOP** in a session is to enter it periodically after function definitions to test the suitability of the definitions or the validity of a conjecture being formulated. The variable assignment feature is often used to store test data, e.g., the state argument of an interpreter for a programming language being formalized.

The variable assignment is not written to the library files created by **MAKE-LIB**. Unless otherwise saved, **R-LOOP** assignments are lost when the Lisp session terminates. The assignment is stored in an internal form as the value of the Lisp variable **R-ALIST**. This value may be printed and read back in via the usual Lisp print and read programs.

The Lisp routine **R** is the heart of **R-LOOP**. **R** takes a single s-expression as its input, translates it, reduces it with respect to **R-ALIST**, and returns either the special value **' (NOT REDUCIBLE)** or the result of introducing abbreviations back into the reduced value. The Lisp routine **S** takes two arguments. The first must be a Lisp symbol representing a variable in the logic and the second must be an s-expression whose translation is an explicit value. **S** modifies **R-ALIST** so that the value of the variable is the given explicit value.

12.38. REDUCE-TERM-CLOCK

General Form:
REDUCE-TERM-CLOCK

This Lisp variable may be set to any integer value. Its initial value is 100. The variable is used to prevent "infinite loops" in the executable counterparts of partial functions. In particular, the variable specifies the number of times such a function is permitted to recur before the execution is aborted.

For example, suppose that we introduce the function **APP** with

```
(DEFN APP (X Y)
   (EVAL$ T '(IF (EQUAL X (QUOTE NIL))
                 Y
                 (CONS (CAR X) (APP (CDR X) Y)))
          (LIST (CONS 'X X) (CONS 'Y Y))))
```

Then suppose we enter **R-LOOP** and try to evaluate **(APP '(A B C) '(1 2 3))**. The answer, **'(A B C 1 2 3)**, is quickly computed. However, if we try to evaluate **(APP 0 1))** we get the message: **APP aborted** and **R-LOOP** reports that the term is **(NOT REDUCIBLE)**.

Because **APP** was introduced without a proof of termination, its executable counterpart, ***1*APP**, is coded so that no more that **REDUCE-TERM-CLOCK** recursions are permitted. Because **(APP 0 1)** is undefined by the above recursion, the limit on the number of recursions is exceeded. Whenever the limit is exceeded the message **APP aborted** is printed by ***1*APP** and the term involving that computation is considered irreducible. While this seems perfectly sensible in the case of an infinite loop, like **(APP 0 1)**, it is less attractive in cases where **APP** is defined but the resource limitation imposed by **REDUCE-TERM-CLOCK** is insufficient to permit the computation to conclude. For example, **(APP '(1 2 3 ... 100) NIL)** cannot be computed if the **REDUCE-TERM-CLOCK** is set to 100.

Because the executable counterparts of defined functions are also called during proof attempts, the message that a computation has been **aborted** may appear in the middle of a proof attempt—even a successful proof attempt. This message is extremely annoying because it is not coordinated with the rest of the theorem prover's output and hence destroys the organization of that output. Furthermore, when the limit is set very high and a term involving an infinite loop occurs in the theorem, much time is spent in the needless attempt to evaluate the executable counterpart. In this case, time can be saved by setting **REDUCE-TERM-CLOCK** to some small positive integer—ideally to the depth of the maximum computation required in the proof. But we eschew such hackery because we don't like finding proofs only because of resource limitations.

When we are tempted to play with the setting of **REDUCE-TERM-CLOCK**, we more often disable the executable counterpart of the function involved, after proving **REWRITE** rules that exhibit the values of the necessary computations.

If **REDUCE-TERM-CLOCK** is set to -1 then no attempt is made to limit the recursion. This may result in Lisp stack overflows during the proofs of theorems.

12.39. REWRITE

REWRITE is one of the rule class tokens that may be given to **ADD-AXIOM** or **PROVE-LEMMA** to indicate what kinds of rules should be generated from a formula. **REWRITE** rules actually come in four different forms: type prescription rules, compound recognizer rules, replacement rules, and linear arithmetic rules. All four forms are used in the simplification process, which is the first process tried. In addition, type prescription rules are used throughout the system to help determine the type of a term.

It is perhaps a mistake for us to lump together into the class "**REWRITE**" all four kinds of rules. Only replacement rules cause terms to be rewritten in the way traditionally associated with term rewrite systems. If a theorem built in as a **REWRITE** rule fails to cause rewriting, it may be that the rules generated from the theorem were not replacement rules.

We describe the simplification process starting on page 222. Starting on page 233 we describe how the four types of **REWRITE** rules are generated and how they are used. Starting on page 317 we give some hints regarding the use of **REWRITE** rules.

12.40. Root Names

See the discussion of File Names on page 285.

12.41. Rule Classes

A *rule class* is one of the symbols **REWRITE, ELIM,** or **GENERALIZE** or else a list of the form (**META** fn_1 ... fn_n) where each fn_i is the name of a function in the logic. Rule classes are used to specify how a given axiom or theorem is to be stored as a rule in the data base. In Chapter 11 we describe in detail how rules are generated from formulas.

12.42. Time Triple

A *time triple* is a triple of numbers printed at the end of event commands and indicating the amount of time used. The printed form of the triple is

```
[ pre-post prove output ]
```

where **pre-post** is the number of seconds spent verifying the syntactic preconditions of the command and generating and adding the appropriate rules to the data base, **prove** is the number of seconds spent in formal proof, and **output** is the number of seconds spent printing information to the user.

For example, in a **DEFN** command, **pre-post** includes the time taken to check that the body of the definition involves no free variables, etc., as well as the time to preprocess the definition to compute such information as the the induction schemes suggested; **prove** is the time taken to prove the admissibility formulas; and **output** is the time taken to print the message associated with acceptance of a definition.

12.43. THM Mode

THM mode refers to the set of axioms added by **BOOT-STRAP**. The system can be brought up so that it supports a constructive variant of the logic described here. This is in fact the logic supported by our system before we introduced the nonconstructive function **V&C$** and the quantifier **FOR**. See the discussion of **BOOT-STRAP** on page 256.

12.44. TOGGLE

General Form:
(TOGGLE new-name old-name flg)

Example Forms:
(TOGGLE TIMES-2-REWRITE-OFF TIMES-2-REWRITE T)
and
(TOGGLE REVERSE-ON REVERSE NIL)

TOGGLE is an event command for setting the status of a citizen in the data base. **new-name** must be a new event name, **old-name** must be a citizen, and **flg** should be **T** or **NIL**. The name of the new event created is **new-name**. The effect of the event is to set the status of **old-name** to **DISABLED** if **flg** is **T** and to **ENABLED** if **flg** is **NIL**. **TOGGLE** then prints a time triple and returns **new-name**.

The event commands **DISABLE** and **ENABLE** are both abbreviations for **TOGGLE** events. For details on the effect of disabling and enabling names, see the discussion of **DISABLE**.

12.45. TOGGLE-DEFINED-FUNCTIONS

General Form:
`(TOGGLE-DEFINED-FUNCTIONS new-name flg)`

Example Form:
`(TOGGLE-DEFINED-FUNCTIONS DISABLE-ALL-COUNTERPARTS T)`

TOGGLE-DEFINED-FUNCTIONS is an event command. Its arguments are not evaluated. Roughly speaking, this command allows you to disable, globally, all executable counterparts, i.e., prevent all functions from automatically evaluating on explicit values.

The first argument, **new-name**, must be a new event name. The second argument, **flg**, must be either **T** or **NIL**. The command sets the "executable counterparts disabled" flag of the data base to **flg**, creates a new event named **new-name**, prints a time triple, and returns **new-name**. The effect of the "executable counterparts disabled" flag is that, when non-**NIL**, no executable counterpart, other than shell constructors and base functions, are used during proofs. Thus, if the executable counterparts disabled flag is **T**, the expression **(PLUS 3 4)**, for example, would not simplify to **7**, except by repeated expansion of the definitional axiom or by **REWRITE** rules.

Technically speaking, the flag is not stored explicitly in the data base. Instead, the node for **new-name** is stored, and the most recently executed **TOGGLE-DEFINED-FUNCTIONS** event in the graph determines the value of the flag.

12.46. TRANSLATE

General Form:
`(TRANSLATE x)`

Example Form:
`(TRANSLATE ' (TIMES X Y (CADDR U)))`

TRANSLATE is the Lisp procedure that maps user type-in into a well-formed term, or causes an error. The argument is evaluated. The value is then explored, abbreviations are expanded, and the result is checked for well-formedness.

TRANSLATE returns the internal representation of the given term. We include **TRANSLATE** in this documentation simply so that you can experiment with the features of the Lisp reader to which you are typing.

12.47. UBT

General Forms:
(UBT)
and
(UBT x)

Example Forms:
(UBT REVERSE)
and
(UBT 3)

    UBT is an abbreviated form of **UNDO-BACK-THROUGH**. The argument, **x**, is not evaluated and must be either an event name or a nonnegative integer. If **x** is an integer it defaults to the **x**[th] element of **CHRONOLOGY** (0-based counting, starting with the most recent event name). If no argument is provided, **x** defaults to the most recent event name. **UBT** removes from the data base every event from the most recent through **x**. The list of events forms removed, in chronological order, is stored in the global Lisp variable **UNDONE-EVENTS**. The list of events is suitable as the **events** argument to **PROVEALL** or **DO-EVENTS**; re-evaluating those events will reconstruct the data base. **UBT** returns the name of the oldest event removed, i.e., **x** or the name to which **x** defaulted.

    UBT is guaranteed to restore the data base to the state it was in immediately before event **x** was created. Using **UBT** thus preserves the integrity of the data base. **UNDO-NAME** may not. See page 271.

12.48. UNBREAK-LEMMA

General Forms:
(UNBREAK-LEMMA x)
or
(UNBREAK-LEMMA)

Example Form:
(UNBREAK-LEMMA ' REVERSE-REVERSE)

    The argument, **x**, is optional. If supplied, it is evaluated. If **x** is the name of a rule that is being monitored, it is removed from the list of monitored rules. See **BREAK-LEMMA**. If **x** is **NIL** or not supplied, all rules are removed from the list of monitored rules.

12.49. UNDO-BACK-THROUGH

General Form:
(UNDO-BACK-THROUGH x)

Example Form:
(UNDO-BACK-THROUGH 'REVERSE)

The argument, **x**, is evaluated and must be an event name. **UNDO-BACK-THROUGH** removes from the data base every event from the most recent through **x**. **UNDO-BACK-THROUGH** returns the list of event forms removed from the data base, in chronological order. The list returned is suitable as the **events** argument to **PROVEALL** or **DO-EVENTS**; re-evaluating those events will recreate the data base.

UNDO-BACK-THROUGH is guaranteed to restore the data base to the state it was in immediately before event **x** was created. Using **UNDO-BACK-THROUGH** thus preserves the integrity of the data base. **UNDO-NAME** may not. See page 271.

12.50. UNDO-NAME

General Form:
(UNDO-NAME name)

Example Form:
(UNDO-NAME 'REVERSE)

The argument, **x**, is evaluated and must be an event name. **UNDO-NAME** removes from the data base **x** and **ALL-DEPENDENTS** of **x** (see the discussion of **DATA-BASE** on page 269). **UNDO-NAME** returns the list of event forms removed from the data base, in chronological order. The list returned is suitable as the **events** argument of **DO-EVENTS**.

Wishfully speaking, **UNDO-NAME** removes from the data base **x** and all of its logical dependents. This is in fact often the case, but we do not guarantee that it is always the case. The problem, as noted on page 271, is that the theorem prover cannot track every use of certain kinds of rules and hence **ALL-DEPENDENTS** may not actually include all dependents. For this reason, **UNDO-NAME** prints a rather tiresome **WARNING** message every time it is called upon to remove any but the most recent event. **UNDO-NAME** is in fact correct when it removes only the most recent event and, more generally, when the events removed are those erased by **UNDO-BACK-THROUGH**.

Warning: Because **UNDO-NAME** may not maintain the integrity of the data base, we do not endorse any proof constructed in a session in which **UNDO-NAME** has been used. In particular, we say a data base is *endorsed* only if it was constructed by (a) **BOOT-STRAP**, (b) a **NOTE-LIB** of a file created by **MAKE-LIB** from an endorsed data base, or (c) an uninterrupted sequence of event commands from an endorsed data base. We endorse as theorems only those formulas proved in an endorsed data base.

Notwithstanding the foregoing caveat, it should be said that in day-to-day interaction with the theorem prover we make heavy use of **UNDO-NAME**. A common situation is to have defined a function, **fn**, differently than intended but not discover it until several dependent events (e.g., functions using **fn**) have been created. When we discover the discrepancy our usual response is to execute

        (SETQ XXX (UNDO-NAME 'fn))

which undoes the introduction of **fn** and all of its dependents but leaves in place any events not dependent on **fn**. The Lisp variable **XXX** above is set to the list of events undone, starting with **fn**. Then we define **fn** "properly." Finally, we execute

        (DO-EVENTS (CDR XXX))

which attempts to reconstruct the dependents of the old **fn** on top of the new definition of **fn**. The **CDR** above is necessary to skip past the first event of **XXX**, which is the old definition of **fn**. Of course, the **DO-EVENTS** may not succeed: the new definition of **fn** may not have the right properties. More often when the **DO-EVENTS** fails it is because proofs constructed the first time those events were processed cannot be found now because of additions to the data base that were not undone. The most common situation is that names that were enabled when the original events were processed are now disabled, or vice versa. It sometimes happens that rules added to the data base since the original definition of **fn** now lead the theorem prover astray.

In general, we make free use of **UNDO-NAME**, behaving exactly as though it satisfied its wishful specification. However, after several days of such interactive work, and always upon reaching our final goal, we replay the entire list of events created since the last event in some endorsed data base. One way to "replay" an appropriate event sequence is to use **UNDO-BACK-THROUGH** to roll back to some endorsed event and simultaneously collect the event forms since then. Then **PROVEALL** or **DO-EVENTS** may be used to re-evaluate the events. **PROVEALL** has the advantage that it creates a coherent file containing all the proofs. The method we more often use, given our use of a text editor to maintain our context as described on page 213, is to replay the events in the command file, starting from an endorsed library. This also certifies the correspondence between the events recorded in the file and those actually executed. We have never been burned by our use of **UNDO-NAME** and recommend its use provided its shortcomings are fully understood.

To illustrate how badly **UNDO-NAME** can burn you we offer the following command sequence which concludes with a proof that $T = F$.

```
(DEFN FN () 23)

(PROVE-LEMMA FN-ARITY-IS-0 NIL (NLISTP (FORMALS 'FN)))

(UNDO-NAME 'FN)

(DEFN FN (X) 45)

(PROVE-LEMMA FN-ARITY-IS-NON-0 NIL
             (LISTP (FORMALS 'FN)))

(PROVE-LEMMA SURPRISE NIL (EQUAL T F)
             ((USE (FN-ARITY-IS-0)
                   (FN-ARITY-IS-NON-0))))
```

The problem, of course, is that the **UNDO-NAME** above does not remove from the data base the theorem **FN-ARITY-IS-0** because its dependence on **FN** is not recorded since neither the statement of the theorem nor the proof involve the function symbol **FN**.

13   Hints on Using the Theorem Prover

This chapter is a loose collection of suggestions about how to use the theorem prover. Most of what is said here is not precise and there are exceptions to virtually every rule. This is unavoidable: if we could precisely describe successful techniques for using the system we would mechanize them.

The section headings of this chapter summarize the organization:

- How To Write "Good" Definitions

- How To Use REWRITE Rules

- How to Use ELIM Rules

13.1. How to Write "Good" Definitions

The theorem prover generally performs better on primitive recursive functions than on more complicated recursions. For example,

Definition.
```
(REVERSE X)
   =
(IF (LISTP X)
    (APPEND (REVERSE (CDR X)) (LIST (CAR X)))
    NIL)
```

is generally more manageable than the smaller and computationally more efficient

Definition.
```
(REV1 X A)
   =
(IF (LISTP X)
    (REV1 (CDR X) (CONS (CAR X) A))
    A).
```

Of course, the theorem prover can prove **(REV1 X A)** = **(APPEND (REVERSE X) A)** and hence **(REV1 X NIL)** = **(REVERSE X)**, but it is prudent to arrange things so that **REVERSE** is the preferred form.

It is generally easier to state inductively proved properties of primitive recursive functions than properties of equivalent functions that accumulate intermediate results. The reason is that properties about functions of the latter type require consideration of arbitrary initial values of the accumulating arguments. For example, one must consider **(REV1 X A)**, not **(REV1 X NIL)**. Users frequently forget to be sufficiently general. Furthermore, sufficiently general lemmas very rarely get produced by the system's own heuristics.

The system also has a performance bias towards definitions written as compositions of two or more recursive functions rather than those written as single complicated recursions. For example, in defining the optimizing expression compiler in [4], we optimized the expression in one pass and then generated compiled code for the optimized expression. To prove that the semantics of the expression was preserved by the composite compiler we had to prove two theorems, one for the optimizer and one for the code generator. We could have defined the compiler as a single function which did the optimization on the fly. Such functions may feel more efficient computationally, but intellectually they burden the proof process because one must address many different issues within the context of a single proof. If, for some reason, you want the top-level function to entangle several different issues, you should at least consider breaking the proof into pieces by defining the more elegant composite function and using it as a stepping stone to several isolated lemmas.

When a problem requires many different functions that recurse upon the same data structure, try to write each function so that it recurses in the same way. Put another way, adopt a given style and stick with it. This will pay off when the system does inductions on the data structure to unwind your functions.

Finally, the system is biased against large nonrecursive definitions. Nonrecursive definitions are always expanded by the rewriter. Hence, no abstraction is gained by making such a definition, and conjectures using the concept are immediately transformed into large case analyses. The recommended procedure for dealing with such definitions follows. Define the concept. Prove the necessary lemmas about it (usually as **REWRITE** rules). During this phase of the project, the definition buys you nothing because the concept is always replaced by its definition. When all the necessary lemmas are proved, **DISABLE** the concept. This prevents future use of the definition.

13.2. How To Use REWRITE Rules

Successful use of the theorem prover in even moderately interesting applications requires great care in the use of **REWRITE** rules. Experienced users of the system develop a "sense" of how to use **REWRITE** rules that is difficult to codify just yet. However, in this section we simply list a variety of hints one should keep in mind.

Almost all **REWRITE** rules are in fact replacement rules. Those that are not rarely seem to cause trouble. We therefore focus here entirely on the use of replacement rules. It is sometimes necessary to force a formula to generate a replacement rule even though it would otherwise generate a type prescription or linear arithmetic rule. To accomplish this, replace the conclusion, `concl`, by `(EQUAL concl T)`, thus removing the formula from the other two syntactic classes.

13.2.1. The Fundamental Fact: REWRITE Rules Rewrite

The most basic thing to keep in mind when you declare a formula to be a **REWRITE** rule is that it is (usually) a directive to replace some term by another when certain hypotheses rewrite to **T** (or, actually, to non-**F**). The directive generated is determined entirely by the syntax of the formula, in particular, the conditions you put in the hypothesis of the implication, the equality you put in the conclusion, and the orientation of that equality. (Without loss of generality here we assume all **REWRITE** lemmas conclude with an equality.)

Here is a simple mathematical truth: the last **CONS**-pair in the **REVERSE** of a nonempty list is the singleton list containing the first element of the list. Below are three equivalent ways of stating this fact:

```
1.    (IMPLIES (LISTP X)
              (EQUAL (LAST (REVERSE X))
                     (CONS (CAR X) NIL)))

2.    (IMPLIES (LISTP X)
              (EQUAL (CONS (CAR X) NIL)
                     (LAST (REVERSE X))))
```

3.   (IMPLIES (NOT (EQUAL (LAST (REVERSE X))
                              (CONS (CAR X) NIL)))
         (NOT (LISTP X)))

Note that the third formulation could be thought of as concluding with the equality **(EQUAL (LISTP X) F)**.

Consider the **REWRITE** rules generated by these three alternatives:

- **LAST-REVERSE-1**: replace every instance of **(LAST (REVERSE X))** by **(CONS (CAR X) NIL)** when **(LISTP X)** rewrites to **T**.

- **LAST-REVERSE-2**: replace every instance of **(CONS (CAR X) NIL)** by **(LAST (REVERSE X))** when **(LISTP X)** rewrites to **T**.

- **LAST-REVERSE-3**: replace every instance of **(LISTP X)** by **F** when **(EQUAL (LAST (REVERSE X)) (CONS (CAR X) NIL))** rewrites to **F**.

Note how different the three induced behaviors are. When the relationship between **LAST** and **REVERSE** is formulated it is necessary that you contemplate how you want the information used.

Never declare a formula a **REWRITE** rule unless you have contemplated its interpretation as a directive.

13.2.2. Decide Upon a Rewrite Strategy

Replacement rules do two things: they can be used to put terms into normal form and they can be used to chain truths together. Selection of the hypothesis and conclusion literals determines what backward chaining is done. Orientation of the concluding equality determines the normal form.

It is generally advised to back chain from complex truths to simple ones. That is, one generally makes the hypotheses of a **REWRITE** rule simpler than the conclusion. For example, **LAST-REVERSE-3** above is an unusual rule because it means that every time the system encounters a **LISTP** expression it will back chain to a question about **LAST** and **REVERSE**. Since **LISTP** is more primitive, it is used in contexts in which **REVERSE**, say, is most likely an irrelevant concept. Theorems about sorting, about searching, about permutations, about 1:1 correspondences, about s-expressions representing terms or parse trees, etc., are unlikely to require reasoning about **REVERSE**.

As for orienting the concluding equalities, *it is generally advised to replace complex terms by simpler ones.* That is, the more complex expression should generally be on the left-hand side of the concluding equality. For example, **LAST-REVERSE-2** is an unusual rule because it causes the system to replace every singleton list of the form **(CONS (CAR X) NIL)** by an expression involving **LAST** and **REVERSE**. In many contexts this would reformulate goal conjectures in terms of concepts that are only tenuously connected to the other concepts.

The above advice assumes an ordering on terms, under which some are "simpler" than others. Determining this ordering is exactly the problem faced by the **REWRITE** rule designer. However, whatever the order, it should be consistent with the ordering imposed by the subroutine hierarchy of function definitions in the data base. For example, since **LISTP** is used in the definition of **APPEND**, **LISTP** should be considered simpler than **APPEND**. Similarly, **APPEND** should be considered simpler than the definition of **REVERSE** which uses **APPEND**. The reason for this is that function definitions are used as replacement rules. Sometimes **REVERSE** expressions are replaced by expressions involving **APPEND**; sometimes **APPEND** expressions are replaced by expressions involving **LISTP**. If the user's sense of "simplicity" runs counter to this he is likely to generate circular sets of rules (see below).

However, this advice does not give any hint for how to compare independent functions. For example

Definition.
```
(REV1 X A)
   =
(IF (LISTP X)
    (REV1 (CDR X) (CONS (CAR X) A))
   A)
```

is an alternative definition of the "list reverse" function. In particular, **(REV1 X NIL)** is equal to **(REVERSE X)**. How do **APPEND** and **REVERSE** compare to **REV1** in simplicity? Several things can be said: **REV1** is simpler than **REVERSE** because it uses nothing but primitives while **REVERSE** uses the auxiliary concept **APPEND**. **REV1** is simpler than both **APPEND** and **REVERSE** because it is tail recursive and neither of the others are. **REV1** is more complicated than both because they are syntactically primitive recursive but **REV1** is not (it builds one of its arguments up as it recurses down the other).

Now, how should the equality

(REV1 X NIL) = (REVERSE X)

be oriented? It boils down to the following question: would you prefer to see **REV1** or **REVERSE** in the intermediate goals generated by the system? The important fact to keep in mind is that you should adopt one of the two as the *preferred* expression of the concept of list reversal and use the preferred one in all other rules.

Thus, another rule in determining which of two functions is simplest is *consider* **f** *simpler than* **g** *if* **g** *is a newly introduced function and there is a large body of* **REWRITE** *rules about* **f** *in the data base*.

As the title of this subsection suggests, the real problem here is adopting a strategy for controlling the rewriter and applying it uniformly. Furthermore, the strategy must be consistent with the built-in tendency of the system to expand function calls by replacing them with their definitions. It is often difficult to decide upon a strategy early in the game. It is thus probably a mistake for the new user to spend a great deal of time making up general rules to follow. A more pragmatic approach is the one we use when embarking on new territory. First, as always, keep in mind how replacement rules are used. Second, as each new truth comes to light, decide how to orient it based on the previous decisions made and how it is needed in the proof at hand. Third, be prepared occasionally to stop and reorganize the rules entirely based on your newly gained familiarity with the concepts. Often the first two parts of this plan are sufficient to construct interesting proofs. The third part comes into play because occasionally in the exploration of a clique of concepts you will recognize the central role of a "new" or previously unappreciated concept. This most often happens because the new concept is strong enough to permit inductive proofs of theorems that then specialize to the cases you initially thought were important. When that happens you find yourself wanting your previously proved "main" theorems to be stated in terms of the new concept so everything is done with the same set of concepts.

Much of the following advice about **REWRITE** rules can be inferred from what has now been said. However, since we see many mistakes made repeatedly by virtually all new users, we will spell out additional advice.

13.2.3. Use Preferred Left-Hand Sides

Consider a rule like **LAST-REVERSE-1**, above, which rewrites instances of **(LAST (REVERSE X))**. Suppose that after **REV1** is introduced, it is adopted as the "preferred" concept, and **REVERSE** expressions are replaced henceforth by **REV1** expressions. Observe then that **LAST-REVERSE-1** would never again be used. Suppose the rewriter encountered the term **(LAST (REVERSE A))**, where **A** is a **LISTP**. At first sight, **LAST-REVERSE-1** applies. But recall that it is applied only after the interior terms have been rewritten. When **(REVERSE A)** is rewritten it will become **(REV1 A NIL)**. Thus, by the time **LAST-REVERSE-1** is tried, the term being considered will be **(LAST (REV1 A NIL))**, which does not match.

When formulating the left-hand side of a **REWRITE** rule you must make sure that all the proper subterms of the left-hand side are in preferred form. For example, suppose you have decided to distribute **TIMES** over **PLUS**. Then it is useless to have a **REWRITE** rule whose left-hand side is **(REMAINDER (TIMES A (PLUS X Y)) A)** because no instance of that left-hand side will ever appear in a rewritten term. Put bluntly, if you have decided to distribute **TIMES** over **PLUS** you should write it that way in all your rules. That blunt advice is a little too strong: it is not necessary to use the preferred forms in the *right*-hand sides of replacement rules or in hypotheses that are free of free variables, because the rewriter doesn't look for those terms, it rewrites them. But rather than keep such caveats in mind it is easier simply to write everything in the preferred form.

Users seem frequently to forget that definitions are replacement rules and thus help determine the preferred form. For example, a left-hand side containing the term **(FIX X)**, as in the rule generated by

```
(EQUAL (NEXT-CLOCK (FIX X) Y)
       (FIX X))
```

is useless: any target term, **(NEXT-CLOCK (FIX a) b)**, matching the left-hand side of the rule, will have first been rewritten to

```
(NEXT-CLOCK (IF (NUMBERP a) a 0) b)
```

before the rule is tried. Thus, the rule will never apply because a match cannot be found.

In addition, the theorem prover contains many built-in rules about **IF**. Whenever **IF**'s appear in a formula they cause case splits at the top level of the clause containing the **IF**.

The general problem discussed here—of rewrite rules that apply to the left-hand sides of other rewrite rules—is a well-studied phenomenon in rewrite systems, called the *Knuth-Bendix* problem. The problem is first discussed in [21] where an algorithm for "completing" some sets of rewrite rules is presented. Since that seminal paper, many researchers have studied the ideas of term rewrite systems, extended senses of matching and unification, and improved or extended completion algorithms. For an excellent survey, see [19].

13.2.4. Avoid Circularities

The rewriter will "loop forever" on some sets of replacement rules when it is possible to rewrite some term **a** to **b** and **b** to **a**. This manifests itself as a stack overflow. Indeed, it is almost always the case that when a stack overflow occurs during a proof it is because of a circularity in the replacement rules.

Consider for example the rule generated from the formula

```
(EQUAL (CARDINALITY S) (CARDINALITY (NORM S))).
```

The intuition behind this rule is that the user wants all occurrences of his **CARDINALITY** function to have "normalized" arguments. But the effect is that whenever the system encounters **(CARDINALITY x)** it rewrites it to **(CARDINALITY (NORM x))**, which it then rewrites to **(CARDINALITY (NORM (NORM x)))**, etc. Thus, even a single rule can cause infinite looping.

In a misguided attempt to "break" the loop, the user might prove as a **REWRITE** rule the formula

```
(EQUAL (NORM (NORM X)) (NORM X)).
```

The idea is to "show the theorem prover that it is pointless to normalize more than once." This attitude presumes a great deal on the theorem prover's heuristics! With this rule in effect the loop becomes

```
  (CARDINALITY x)
= (CARDINALITY (NORM x))
= (CARDINALITY (NORM (NORM x)))
= (CARDINALITY (NORM x))
= (CARDINALITY (NORM (NORM x)))
= ...
```

In general, loops can involve an arbitrary number of rules, including recursive definitions. Consider, for example, the rule generated from

```
(EQUAL (ADD1 (PLUS X Y)) (PLUS (ADD1 X) Y)).
```

This rule "pushes **ADD1** into **PLUS**." But the definition of **PLUS** is used in the other direction. In particular, the system's use of the definition of **PLUS** (together with the rules for handling **IF**, **NUMBERP**, **EQUAL**, and **SUB1**) cause **(PLUS (ADD1 X) Y)** to split into two cases, according to **(NUMBERP X)**, and in one case to become **(ADD1 (PLUS X Y))**. If the rule for pushing **ADD1** into **PLUS** is available, the system then can loop.

It is difficult to characterize exactly when the system will loop because it has such an *ad hoc* collection of heuristics for controlling and sequencing the application of rules. But when a stack overflow occurs, it is most probable that a circularity has been hit. The only tool we have to help you track down circularities is **BREAK-REWRITE**, which allows you to inspect the rewrite path. Most often some hint of the circularity will appear there, but there are other recursive programs in our system (!) and it is possible the stack overflow—even one caused by replacement rules—will not show up on the rewrite path. See page 265.

13.2.5. *Remember the Restrictions on Permutative Rules*

Recall that the rule generated from

Theorem.
```
(EQUAL (PLUS I J)
       (PLUS J I))
```

has the special restriction that, when applied, it does not produce a term that is lexicographically larger than the target term to which it was applied. Thus, **(PLUS B A)** will rewrite under the rule to **(PLUS A B)** but not *vice versa*.

The restriction applies more generally to any rule which permutes the variables in its left- and right-hand sides. The restriction is obviously intended to prevent circular rewriting while permitting some use to be made of commutativity. This can be used to normalize certain kinds of expressions, but care must be taken to arrange an appropriate set of rules.

It is a very common situation to have a function symbol that is both associative and commutative. Suppose, in addition to the commutativity of **PLUS** above we had the associativity, expressed as the rule generated from

Theorem.
```
(EQUAL (PLUS (PLUS I J) K)
       (PLUS I (PLUS J K))).
```

Thus, any **PLUS** nest is right associated, and arguments are commuted within each **PLUS** to put them into lexicographically ascending order.

To what, then, does **(PLUS B (PLUS A C))** rewrite under these two rules? The obvious and desirable answer, namely **(PLUS A (PLUS B C))**, is incorrect! Neither of the two rules can be applied, either at the top level or to the inner **PLUS** expression. The left-hand side of the associativity rule matches neither **PLUS** expression in the target. The left-hand side of the commutativity rule matches both, but neither application is permitted under the permutative restriction. In particular, either would move a lexicographically heavy term forward over a light term. That is, both **(PLUS (PLUS A C) B)** (the result of commuting the outermost **PLUS**) and **(PLUS B (PLUS C A))** (the result of commuting the innermost one) are lexicographically larger than the target. Thus, **(PLUS B (PLUS A C))** is not rewritten by the two rules.

Of course, **(PLUS B (PLUS A C))** is equal to **(PLUS A (PLUS B C))** given associativity and commutativity; it is just that to derive the latter from the former it is necessary to "go against the grain" of the two rules and temporarily form **(PLUS (PLUS A C) B)**. Given our restrictions, though, how can such normalization be arranged?

The trick is to prove a third rule, derivable from the first two, namely

Theorem.
```
(EQUAL (PLUS I (PLUS J K))
       (PLUS J (PLUS I K))).
```

This is exactly what is needed above. More generally, any **PLUS** expression will be appropriately normalized now: the associativity rule will flatten the nest to the right, the new rule will sort all the addends but the last two into lexicographic order, and commutativity will take care of the last two.

13.2.6. Eliminate Unnecessary Hypotheses

It is often the case that new users encumber their **REWRITE** rules with logically unnecessary hypotheses. For example, while it is the case that

Theorem.
```
(IMPLIES (PROPERP B)
         (PROPERP (APPEND A B)))
```

a more powerful truth is

Theorem.
```
(EQUAL (PROPERP (APPEND A B))
       (PROPERP B)).
```

The latter theorem has as advantages that it is easier to prove because less case analysis is done in the inductive proof, the generated rule is unconditionally applied, the rule eliminates the occurrence of **APPEND** altogether, and the rule introduces explicitly the question of whether **B** is proper whenever the question is raised about **(APPEND A B)**.

The latter advantage is particularly noteworthy. Suppose **(PROPERP (APPEND A (REVERSE B)))** is involved in a conjecture. Suppose you expect it to simplify to **T**, using the first rule above, but that the system fails to apply it. Then you must realize that the hypothesis of the rule failed to simplify to **T**. To make the rule apply you must figure out why the hypothesis failed and what rules should be added to make it simplify to **T**. All of this must be done without ever seeing the hypothesis in anything the system prints. In the case where the hypothesis undergoes elaborate simplification—but does not reduce to **T**—this is a very awkward problem (see **BREAK-LEMMA**). If, on the other hand, the system knows the second rule above, it is unconditionally applied, whether **(PROPERP (REVERSE B))** can be established or not. Regardless of what happens to **(PROPERP (REVERSE B))**, the result will be visible because it is part of the goal formula. It is thus much easier to see what rules are needed. Once the necessary rules have been found and **(PROPERP (REVERSE B))** rewrites to **T**, it hardly matters whether the relation between

PROPERP and **APPEND** is phrased as a conditional or unconditional rule. But it is much easier to debug unsuccessful proof attempts when unconditional rewrite rules are used.

Sometimes the formulation of an unconditional replacement rule requires the introduction of an **IF** into the right-hand side of the rule. For example,

Theorem.
```
(IMPLIES  (NUMBERP N)
          (EQUAL (PLUS N 0) N))
```
is less useful than

```
          (EQUAL (PLUS N 0)
                 (IF (NUMBERP N) N 0))
```
for all the reasons noted above.

To eliminate a hypothesis, consider what happens in the left-hand side when the hypothesis is violated and try to accommodate that in the right-hand side. This may require the introduction of an **IF** or some other function symbol into the right-hand side. Because our functions usually "behave" on "unexpected" inputs, it is frequently possible to remove mere type constraints on the arguments by substituting the coercion functions on the right-hand side (**FIX** could have been used above instead of the **IF**). We generally eliminate any hypothesis we can, provided it is not necessary to define a new recursive function to do it.

13.2.7. Use Free Variables Wisely

Recall that a free variable in a hypothesis is a variable that does not occur in the left-hand side nor in any previous hypothesis. To use such a rule, the rewriter must "guess" a suitable instantiation of the variable to relieve all the hypotheses containing it. Accidentally creating a rule with a free variable in it almost always causes trouble. Such rules are seldom applied successfully. However, our handling of free variables can be exploited by the informed user to make the rewriter more efficient.

One easy way to exploit free variables is to use them to prevent the rewriter from duplicating the work associated with simplifying common subexpressions. Recall that if the hypothesis containing the free variable, **v**, is of the form **(EQUAL v term)**, where **term** does not contain **v**, then the instantiation of **v** is chosen by rewriting **term** and binding **v** to the result.

Consider the rule generated from

```
(EQUAL (EXEC (APPEND A B) R M)
       (EXEC B
             (REG (EXEC A R M))
             (MEM (EXEC A R M)))) .
```

Note that **(EXEC A R M)** occurs twice in the right-hand side. When the rewriter replaces **(EXEC (APPEND a b) r m)** by its counterpart, the expression **(EXEC a r m)** will be rewritten twice.

Consider now the rule generated from

```
(IMPLIES (EQUAL TEMP (EXEC A R M))
         (EQUAL (EXEC (APPEND A B) R M)
                (EXEC B (REG TEMP) (MEM TEMP)))) .
```

This rule contains the free variable **TEMP**. Upon applying the rule to **(EXEC (APPEND a b) r m)**, the system rewrites **(EXEC a r m)**, binds the result to **TEMP**, and then rewrites **(EXEC B (REG TEMP) (MEM TEMP))** under the extended substitution. In this case, **TEMP** is rewritten twice, but each time it is simply a variable lookup.

If the hypothesis introducing the free variable is not of the form **(EQUAL v term)**, as above, then the situation is more complicated. Consider the rule generated by

```
(IMPLIES (MEMBER X (DELETE U V))
         (MEMBER X V))
```

The variable **U** is free in the hypothesis. Consider the attempted application of this rule to the term **(MEMBER e s)**, occurring in the test of an **IF**. The left-hand side of the rule is **(MEMBER X V)**, and the right-hand side is **T**. Observe that when the left-hand side is matched against **(MEMBER e s)**, **X** is bound to **e** and **V** is bound to **s**. If the hypothesis can be established, the rule will replace **(MEMBER e s)** by **T**. Logically speaking, the formula permits such a replacement if there is a **U** such that **(MEMBER e (DELETE U s))**. Practically speaking, the rewriter must find some **U** with the hypothesized property.

It does this by searching through the known assumptions, looking for one of the form **(MEMBER e (DELETE d s))**. If such an assumption can be found, **U** is bound to **d** and the rule is applicable. If no such assumption is found, the rule is inapplicable. The important point to observe is that a hypothesis containing a free variable is not rewritten but is searched for among the assumptions. When a rule with free variables is generated, the system prints a warning message. Do not ignore these messages.

This state of affairs has its advantages and disadvantages. On the negative side, such hypotheses must be very carefully written if matches are to be found, since the assumptions, generally, are in rewritten form. A hypothesis containing both a free variable and an application of a nonrecursive function is likely never to be relieved, since the system will never find a call of a nonrecursive function in a rewritten assumption. This renders the entire rule useless. Given this restriction, it is perhaps surprising that rules containing free variables are ever used. Replacement rules with free variables in the hypotheses are often generated in response to a previously attempted proof that failed for want of that very rule. That is, in proving one's "main" result, a goal of the form **(IMPLIES (AND h_1 ... h_n) concl)** is adopted but not proved. Upon inspection at a check point the user notices that **(IMPLIES h_j concl)** is a theorem the system can prove. In this case it does not matter if the hypothesis contains free variables or not. The generated rule is applicable because the problematic hypothesis (in stable form) is literally among the hypotheses of the adopted goal.

On the positive side, the cavalier treatment of free variables severely limits the applicability of rules that otherwise would cause inefficiency. The previously mentioned rule

```
(IMPLIES (MEMBER X (DELETE U L))
         (MEMBER X L))
```

can be used to establish a completely arbitrary **MEMBER**ship relation. If great resources were used to establish the hypothesis, the rule would represent a terrible inefficiency since every single **MEMBER** expression triggers the attempt to relieve the hypotheses.

13.2.8. Bridge Lemmas—Hacking Around Knuth-Bendix

We have previously mentioned the "Knuth-Bendix" problem, which may be summarized as the situation in which a replacement rule fails to match a target term because some other rule has rewritten some interior subterm of the target.

Consider the function **TRUNC** that truncates a given bit-vector at a given position. It is a theorem that

Theorem. TRUNC-SIZE:
```
(IMPLIES (BITVP A)
         (EQUAL (TRUNC A (SIZE A)) A)).
```

That is, truncating a bit-vector at its **SIZE** is a no-op. The rule generated from **TRUNC-SIZE** replaces any target of the form **(TRUNC a (SIZE a))** by **a** provided **(BITVP a)** can be established.

Now consider the target term

```
(TRUNC (APPEND B1 B2) (SIZE (APPEND B1 B2)))
```

to which we wish to apply **TRUNC-SIZE**. But suppose we have the rule

Theorem. SIZE-APPEND:
```
(EQUAL (SIZE (APPEND X Y))
       (PLUS (SIZE X) (SIZE Y)))
```

which distributes **SIZE** over **APPEND**.

Since **SIZE-APPEND** is applied first (to the interior of the target term) the target becomes

```
(TRUNC (APPEND B1 B2)
       (PLUS (SIZE B1) (SIZE B2)))
```

and **TRUNC-SIZE** no longer applies.

One way to avoid this problem is to **DISABLE SIZE-APPEND** or, in general, the rules that are causing the subterms of the target to rewrite. This may not be convenient if those same rules are used to advantage elsewhere in the main proof.

Another way is to provide a **USE** hint to the theorem prover when the main conjecture is submitted, instructing it to use the instance of **TRUNC-SIZE** obtained by replacing **A** by **(APPEND B1 B2)**. This is, perhaps, the preferred solution because it makes explicit in the record the fact that user intervention was required.

However, another way is to prove alternative forms of the lemmas in question, causing new replacement rules to be generated. These alternative forms have come to be called "bridge" lemmas because they bridge the gap between the terms that arise in applications and the more elegant terms used in the statements of previously proved theorems. Unlike disabling and explicit **USE** hints, bridge lemmas have the advantage that they create general rules which can be used automatically in many proofs. But they look obscure and complicated, even though they are trivial consequences of other results. When we use bridge lemmas we generally tack the word **-BRIDGE** onto the name so that the geneology of the lemma is understood.

Consider the **TRUNC-SIZE** rule above. A bridge lemma suitable for handling the case described is

Lemma. TRUNC-SIZE-APPEND-BRIDGE:
```
(IMPLIES (BITVP (APPEND X Y))
         (EQUAL (TRUNC (APPEND X Y)
                       (PLUS (SIZE X)
                             (SIZE Y)))
                (APPEND X Y))).
```

This is just the lemma obtained by instantiating **A** in **TRUNC-SIZE** with **(APPEND X Y)** and then applying **SIZE-APPEND**—i.e., it is one of the lemmas generated by applying the Knuth-Bendix superpositioning process to **TRUNC-SIZE** and **SIZE-APPEND**. To *prove* this theorem with the theorem prover it may be necessary to give the appropriate **USE** hint, but once proved the bridge lemma will be available without explicit hints.

A more powerful version of the bridge lemma is

Lemma. TRUNC-SIZE-BRIDGE:
```
(IMPLIES (AND (BITVP A)
              (EQUAL N (SIZE A)))
         (EQUAL (TRUNC A N) A)).
```

This lemma is equivalent to **TRUNC-SIZE**, but it has the variable **N** where the **SIZE** expression was in the left-hand side and an equality hypothesis that **N** is that expression. But the rule generated from this lemma is much more powerful (more often applied) than that for **TRUNC-SIZE**. The left-hand side matches any **TRUNC** expression, causing the rewriter to backward chain to establish that the first argument is a bit-vector and that the second is provably equivalent to the **SIZE** of the first. If successful, the rewriter replaces the target with the first argument.

This rule will apply to the previously discussed rewritten target

```
(TRUNC (APPEND B1 B2)
       (PLUS (SIZE B1) (SIZE B2))).
```

In particular, **A** is **(APPEND B1 B2)**, which we will call **a**, **N** is **(PLUS (SIZE B1) (SIZE B2))**, which we will call **n**, and when the rewriter tries to establish **(EQUAL n (SIZE a))**, **SIZE-APPEND** or *whatever rules* transformed **(SIZE a)** into **n**, will apply to establish the hypothesis.

While **TRUNC-SIZE** requires the second argument to be of the form **(SIZE a)** syntactically, the bridge version requires only that it be provably equal to **(SIZE a)**. It should be noted that the bridge lemma is inefficient: every **TRUNC** expression **(TRUNC a n)** establishes the temporary subgoal of showing that **(EQUAL n (SIZE a))**.

Bridges can be built, in general, by replacing some non-variable proper subterm of the left-hand side by a new variable and adding the hypothesis that the new variable is equal to the subterm. This produces a more general, less efficient rule.

A problem with this rote construction of bridges is that it may introduce free variables. Consider

Theorem. PRIMES-DONT-DIVIDE-FACTS:
```
(IMPLIES (AND (PRIME P)
              (LESSP N P))
         (NOT (EQUAL (REMAINDER (FACT N) P)
                     0)))
```

and its bridged version in which the interior **(FACT N)** is replaced by **X**:

Theorem. PRIMES-DONT-DIVIDE-FACTS-BRIDGE:
(IMPLIES (AND (PRIME P)
              (LESSP N P)
              (EQUAL X (FACT N)))
         (NOT (EQUAL (REMAINDER X P)
                     0)))

Note that the bridge targets any term of the form **(EQUAL (REMAINDER x P) 0)** but has the free variable **N** which is chosen by instantiating **(LESSP N P)**. This bridge is thus not as generally applicable as it might appear at first sight.

13.2.9. Avoid Case Splits and Large Formulas

The theorem prover tends to do many proofs by cases. The reason is that every time an **IF**-expression is introduced into the conjecture, the conjecture is split into two parts according to whether the test of the **IF** is assumed true or false. The system is good at handling a large number of cases and so you should not give up a proof attempt simply because it has led to 20 or 30 cases. On the other hand, when a proof attempt has led to hundreds of cases, or cases are being spawned inside of cases inside of cases, etc., or the theorem prover simply is not printing anything (because the case explosion is so large that it is spending its time computing all the branches through the **IF**-tree), it is time to consider a new approach to your problem.

Most case explosions are caused by nonrecursive functions expanding. Therefore, it is generally advised to keep such functions disabled except when properties of their definitions are necessary. See the discussion of **DISABLE** in Chapter 12 and the discussion of preferred left-hand sides on page 320.

When the problem involves a hypothesis **(pred x)**, where the definition of **pred** is of the form

Definition.
(pred x)
     =
(AND (p1 x)
     (p2 x)
     . . .
     (pn x))

it is frequently convenient to disable **pred** after proving a sequence of lemmas of the form **(IMPLIES (pred x) (pi x))**. Thus, the **(pred x)** in the hypothesis of the main theorem is kept closed (thus saving the work associated with simplifying all of its conjuncts), but whenever one of its conjuncts is needed it is established by backchaining.

It is sometimes necessary to open a large function but desirable to wait until its arguments have been normalized. For example, **P** might be a function which takes a list as an argument and case splits on the **CAR** of the list, considering each of a finite set of possibilities. This frequently happens when **P** is an interpreter for some formal system. Suppose **P** is defined as

Definition.
```
(P X)
    =
(IF  (EQUAL  (CAR X)  'A)  (A-STEP X)
(IF  (EQUAL  (CAR X)  'B)  (B-STEP X)
(IF  (EQUAL  (CAR X)  'C)  (C-STEP X)
...
(IF  (EQUAL  (CAR X)  'Z)  (Z-STEP X)
    (NO-STEP X))...))).
```

It frequently happens in these situations that in any particular theorem the **CAR** of **X** is equal to one of the known cases, but that it takes a bit of simplification to reduce it to the particular one. In such situations it is an excellent idea to disable **P** after proving a lemma of the form

```
(P  (CONS  (PACK U)  V))
    =
(IF  (EQUAL  (PACK U)  'A)  (A-STEP  (CONS  (PACK U)  V))
(IF  (EQUAL  (PACK U)  'B)  (B-STEP  (CONS  (PACK U)  V))
(IF  (EQUAL  (PACK U)  'C)  (C-STEP  (CONS  (PACK U)  V))
...
(IF  (EQUAL  (PACK U)  'Z)  (Z-STEP  (CONS  (PACK U)  V))
    (NO-STEP  (CONS  (PACK U)  V)))...)))
```

Observe that this is just the definition of **P** with the formal replaced by **(CONS (PACK U) V)**. The advantage of this rule is that **P** will stay closed until the argument expression is canonicalized to a list with some literal atom in its **CAR**. Only then will **P** expand with the above rule. If the canonical form chosen makes the **CAR** explicit, then exactly one case will come out of the nest of **IF**'s above.

We make one final recommendation for dealing with large nests of **IF**'s: rewrite rules can be fashioned for manipulating **IF**-trees *before* they reach the top of the formula and cause case splits.

For example, suppose that for each of the **-STEP** functions used in **P** we have proved that the predicate **INVP** holds. That is, suppose we have the sequence of lemmas

```
(INVP (A-STEP X))
(INVP (B-STEP X))
(INVP (C-STEP X))
...
(INVP (NO-STEP X))
```

and we wish to prove `(INVP (P X))`. The naive approach is to let **P** expand to a nest of **IF**'s,

```
(INVP (IF (EQUAL (CAR X) 'A)
          (A-STEP X)
          (IF (EQUAL (CAR X) 'B)
              (B-STEP X)
              ...)))
```

then let the theorem prover explore the **IF**-tree and produce a set of 27 cases

```
(IMPLIES (EQUAL (CAR X) 'A)
         (INVP (A-STEP X)))
(IMPLIES (AND (NOT (EQUAL (CAR X) 'A))
              (EQUAL (CAR X) 'B))
         (INVP (B-STEP X)))
...
```

each of which will be proved by one of our lemmas.

A better approach is to prove the rewrite rule

```
(EQUAL (INVP (IF TEST X Y))
       (IF TEST
           (INVP X)
           (INVP Y))).
```

Using this rule the proof is much faster. During the initial rewrite, **P** is opened to the **IF**-nest, then the rule is applied 27 times in a linear pass to drive **INVP** down to the tips of the **IF**-nest, and then each tip is reduced to **T** by one of our lemmas. Thus, the formula rewrites to **T** in a single pass.

Using similar rules for manipulating the **IF**-nests that arise in your conjectures, it is frequently possible to eliminate case splits altogether.

Here is a slightly more complicated example. Suppose we have another function, **R**, that is like **P** except that it uses **RA-STEP** for **A-STEP**, **RB-STEP** for **B-STEP**, etc. Suppose we have proved that `(P->R (A-STEP X))` is `(RA-STEP X)`, `(P->R (B-STEP X))` is `(RB-STEP X)`, etc. We wish to prove

```
(EQUAL (P->R (P X)) (R X)).
```

The naive approach would be to let **P** and **R** each expand and let the system then handle the 27^2 paths generated. If the system does not exhaust its resources or the user's patience, it will eventually prove the theorem.

A better way is to prove the lemma that **P->R** can be driven through an **IF**, analogous to the lemma about **INVP** above. Then, after **(P X)** expands into an **IF**-nest, the **P->R** walks through it and returns an **IF**-nest with **(P->R (A-STEP X))**, etc., at the tips. Then let the **(R X)** expand. It produces an isomorphic **IF**-nest in the second argument of the **EQUAL**.

It is at this point that we do something subtle. Instead of letting the system compute the 27^2 cases, consider the lemma

```
(EQUAL (EQUAL (IF TEST P1 P2)
              (IF TEST R1 R2))
       (IF TEST
           (EQUAL P1 R1)
           (EQUAL P2 R2))).
```

After the two arguments to the **EQUAL** have been rewritten to isomorphic **IF**-nests, the above rule drives the **EQUAL** down to the corresponding tips. It does not produce the cross-product of the cases because we anticipated that the same test arises from each **IF**-nest. Furthermore, once the **EQUAL** settles in at the tips, our previous lemmas relating **(P->R (A-STEP X))** and **(RA-STEP X)**, etc., apply and reduce each tip to **T**. Thus, in a single pass of the rewriter the entire theorem is reduced to **T**.

Note that this approach completely eliminated the case split in a situation where we might have otherwise had 27^2 cases. The key is the thoughtful definition of concepts (the parallel **IF** structure of **P** and **R**) and the considered use of rules to manipulate **IF**'s.

13.3. How to Use ELIM Rules

Destructor elimination is important in domains where it is possible. Ask yourself "Can every object in this domain be uniquely represented as some combination of the outputs of the functions I'm using?" If so, it is likely you need an **ELIM** rule expressing that representability. If not, it is likely that you don't need to think about **ELIM** at all.

Below is the most sophisticated **ELIM** theorem in common use in our data bases, the lemma that says that every natural **X** can be represented in terms of its remainder and quotient by a nonzero natural **Y**:

Theorem. REMAINDER-QUOTIENT-ELIM:
```
(IMPLIES (AND (NUMBERP X)
              (NOT (ZEROP Y)))
```

```
(EQUAL (PLUS (REMAINDER X Y)
             (TIMES Y (QUOTIENT X Y)))
       X))
```

Typical eliminations we arrange in our own data bases are as follows: eliminate **SUB1** in favor of **ADD1**, eliminate **DIFFERENCE** in favor of **PLUS**, eliminate **QUOTIENT** and **REMAINDER** in favor of **PLUS** and **TIMES**, eliminate **CAR** and **CDR** in favor of **CONS**, and eliminate **INITIAL-SEGMENT** and **FINAL-SEGMENT** in favor of **APPEND**. Destructor elimination is nice because by so representing the objects in your domain you can convert theorems about one set of function names into theorems about another and consequently focus on what otherwise seems like just half the problem.

Occasionally it is necessary to prove **GENERALIZE** rules in tandem with **ELIM** rules. For example, **REMAINDER-QUOTIENT-ELIM** causes **X** to be replaced by **R+Y*Q** in theorems involving **(REMAINDER X Y)** or **(QUOTIENT X Y)**. However, that replacement preserves the provability of the formula only if **R** is known to be less than **Y**. That constraint on **R** is provided by a **GENERALIZE** lemma such as

Theorem. REMAINDER-LESSP:
```
(EQUAL (LESSP (REMAINDER X Y) Y)
       (NOT (ZEROP Y))).
```

Note that if **REMAINDER-QUOTIENT-ELIM** has been proved and stored as an **ELIM** rule before **REMAINDER-LESSP** is proved, an over-general elimination is performed during the proof attempt for **REMAINDER-LESSP**. The moral is simple:

When setting up the rules to arrange a destructor elimination that requires additional constraints on the new variables, prove the **GENERALIZE** theorems *before* you prove the **ELIM** theorem.

14   Installation Guide

14.1. The Source Files

In order to construct an executable version of the theorem prover, first obtain the source files. Inquiries may be sent to the authors at the Computer Sciences Department, University of Texas, Austin, Texas or at Computational Logic, Inc., 1717 West 6th Street, Austin, Texas. Currently, it is possible to obtain the sources on a tar tape (from Computational Logic, Inc.) or by using FTP, the File Transfer Protocol for the Arpanet/Internet. The sources are free. There is no charge to you if you obtain them via FTP, but there is a fee for the tape.

The theorem prover is written in Common Lisp in accordance with *Common Lisp The Language* [34].[44]

The sources come with the following warning, which limits our financial liability to $0.00.

> This program is a tool for computer science research. It is provided without license, copyright, or fee in a spirit of scientific cooperation. We have tried our very best to make this system logically sound, but we cannot accept financial responsibility for problems that arise with its use. Therefore, we make the

---

[44]In the past, our system has been written in Pop-2, Interlisp-10, Zetalisp, Maclisp, Franz Lisp, and Portable Standard Lisp. However, we now only support and distribute the Common Lisp version. Currently, the theorem prover runs in Kyoto Common Lisp, Sun/Lucid Common Lisp, and Symbolics Common Lisp. We personally use a variant of Kyoto Common Lisp developed by Bill Schelter which is called Austin Kyoto Common Lisp (AKCL). AKCL has many performance improvements that make our system run about twice as fast on a Sun 3/280 as it does under Sun/Lucid or Kyoto Common Lisp or under Symbolics Common Lisp on a Symbolics 3640.

335

following disclaimer: Robert S. Boyer, J Strother Moore, Computational Logic, Inc., the University of Texas, and other parties provide this program on an "as is" basis without warranty of any kind, either expressed or implied, including, but not limited to, the implied warranties of merchantability and fitness for a particular purpose.

Although we impose no copyright or license restrictions on the use and distribution of this program, we adamantly insist that it be changed only under the condition that all changes be prominently described and accurately attributed. A notice of any change should be included at the beginning of the file basis.lisp and announced to the user by terminal output when **BOOT-STRAP** or **NOTE-LIB** are called.

We also insist, as a matter of scientific accuracy, that any announcement of the proof of a theorem by any modification of this program clearly include in the announcement the fact that changes were made to the program.

Let us assume that by some means (e.g., reading a tape or electronically transferring files) you now possess a directory containing the following source files, which take up altogether approximately one megabyte:

```
basis.lisp
code-1-a.lisp
code-b-d.lisp
code-e-m.lisp
code-n-r.lisp
code-s-z.lisp
events.lisp
genfact.lisp
io.lisp
nqthm.lisp
ppr.lisp
sloop.lisp
```

Given these source files, there are two steps to building an executable version of the theorem prover: compilation and loading. Compilation must be done once (assuming changes are not made to the underlying Lisp or to our sources). Thereafter, loading the previously compiled source files is all that is necessary to build an executable version of the system.

14.2. Compiling

Before compiling the source files, check that you have enough space to hold the compiled files. How much space will be required depends upon your compiler, but a safe bet is to have an additional 1.2 megabytes of space on the same directory as the source files.

To compile the theorem prover

- Get connected to the directory with the sources. If you are running under a conventional operating system, use the **connect**, **cd**, or an equivalent command. If you are running on a Lisp machine, **(SETQ *DEFAULT-NQTHM-PATH*** "...") where "..." is a pathname for the directory with the sources.

- Get into Common Lisp. If you are running on a conventional operating system, this will involve using a command such as **lisp** or **kcl**. If you are running on a Lisp machine get into a "Common Lisp Listener" or a "window" which accepts Common Lisp input.

- Execute the Common Lisp form

      (LOAD "nqthm.lisp")

  which may be done by typing the form to the top-level Common Lisp read-eval-print loop, possibly followed by a carriage return. If you are on a Lisp machine, you may need to specify the directory explicitly, e.g. **(LOAD "doe:>nqthm>nqthm.lisp")**.

- Execute the Common Lisp form

      (COMPILE-NQTHM)

The compilation takes about 40 minutes on a Sun 3/280, much less on a Symbolics 3640. The result should be that for each of the source files (excepting **nqthm.lisp**) there should now appear on the same directory a corresponding compiled object file. The name of the compiled object file differs according to the system you are running. For example, if you are running on a Sun under Kyoto Common Lisp, the object file corresponding to our **basis.lisp** is named **basis.o**. If you are running on a Symbolics Lisp machine, the file is named **basis.bin**.

14.2.1. Example of Compilation - Sun

Suppose that you are running a Sun with Kyoto Common Lisp, and suppose that the source files for the theorem prover have been placed on the directory **/usr/smith/nqthm/**. The following commands result in the theorem prover's compilation:

```
cd /usr/smith/nqthm
kcl
(LOAD "nqthm.lisp")
(COMPILE-NQTHM)
```

Of course, the first two lines are intended to be read by the C-shell, and the last two lines are for Lisp.

14.2.2. *Example of Compilation - Symbolics*

Suppose that you are running a Symbolics Lisp machine, and suppose that the source files for the theorem prover have been placed on the directory **doe:>nqthm>**. The following commands result in the theorem prover's compilation:

```
(IN-PACKAGE "USER")
(LOAD "doe:>nqthm>nqthm.lisp")
(SETQ *DEFAULT-NQTHM-PATH* "doe:>nqthm>")
(COMPILE-NQTHM)
```

14.3. Loading

Once the theorem prover has been compiled, an executable version of it can be obtained whenever desired by "loading" the compiled files into Lisp. To do this, execute the first three of the four steps required for compilation, as described in the previous section. Then, execute the Common Lisp form **(LOAD-NQTHM)** instead of the form **(COMPILE-NQTHM)**. When this command is complete, you may begin using the theorem prover event commands, e.g. **(BOOT-STRAP NQTHM)**.

14.3.1. *Example of Loading - Sun*

Suppose that you are running a Sun with Kyoto Common Lisp and that the compiled files are located on directory **/usr/smith/nqthm/**. The following commands will load the theorem prover:

```
cd /usr/smith/nqthm
kcl
(LOAD "nqthm.lisp")
(LOAD-NQTHM)
```

14.3.2. Example of Loading - Symbolics

Suppose that you are running a Symbolics Lisp machine and suppose that the compiled files for the theorem prover are located on the directory **doe:>nqthm>**. The following commands will load the theorem prover:

```
(IN-PACKAGE "USER")
(LOAD "doe:>nqthm>nqthm.lisp")
(SETQ *DEFAULT-NQTHM-PATH* "doe:>nqthm>")
(LOAD-NQTHM)
```

14.4. Executable Images

At some sites, it may be economical to make an executable image of the theorem prover rather that to load it each time before using it. Such a process is not defined in Common Lisp but is entirely implementation dependent.

14.4.1. Kyoto Common Lisp

If you are using Kyoto Common Lisp on a Sun, an executable image of the theorem prover can be made with the command **(SAVE "nqthm")**. However, we instead recommend the following procedure. Invoke **(SAVE "saved_nqthm")**, which creates an executable image of about four to six megabytes under the name **saved_nqthm**. Suppose that the resulting file, **saved_nqthm**, now resides in the directory **/usr/smith/nqthm**. Create a two line text file:

```
#
/usr/smith/nqthm/saved_nqthm /usr/smith/nqthm
```

Call this text file **nqthm** and set the protection on the file so that it is executable, e.g. with the C-shell command

```
chmod a+x nqthm
```

Put this file in some convenient place on your search path, and type **nqthm** to the C-shell to invoke the theorem prover. This rather elaborate procedure is necessary to insure that the compiler in Kyoto Common Lisp will work correctly: the loader needs to know the location of the executable image in the file system to work correctly.

14.4.2. Symbolics

Because the theorem prover can be loaded in only a couple of minutes, because a Symbolics world save can be very large, and because booting such a machine takes a few minutes, we do not advise building an executable image containing the theorem prover on a Symbolics.

14.5. Example Installation

Here is an example session that compiles, loads, and runs the theorem prover. It was run on a Sun 3/280. We have deleted from this transcript some lines containing compiler commentary, the long warning message at the beginning of this chapter, and most of the output of the proof of the associativity of **APP**.

```
% cd /usr/local/src/nqthm-distrib
% ls -l
total 987
-rwxrwxr-x  1 smith    94133 Jan 30 10:49 basis.lisp
-rwxrwxr-x  1 smith   125887 Jan 30 10:49 code-1-a.lisp
-rwxrwxr-x  1 smith   158468 Jan 30 10:49 code-b-d.lisp
-rwxrwxr-x  1 smith   133180 Jan 30 10:49 code-e-m.lisp
-rwxrwxr-x  1 smith   184237 Jan 30 10:49 code-n-r.lisp
-rwxrwxr-x  1 smith   103355 Jan 30 10:49 code-s-z.lisp
-rwxrwxr-x  1 smith    12710 Jan 30 10:49 events.lisp
-rwxrwxr-x  1 smith    11184 Jan 30 10:49 genfact.lisp
-rwxrwxr-x  1 smith    60791 Jan 30 10:49 io.lisp
-rwxrwxr-x  1 smith     9397 Jan 30 10:49 nqthm.lisp
-rwxrwxr-x  1 smith     8293 Jan 30 10:49 ppr.lisp
-rwxrwxr-x  1 smith    39997 Jan 30 10:49 sloop.lisp


% kcl
KCl (Kyoto Common Lisp)   June 3, 1987

>(LOAD "nqthm.lisp")
Loading nqthm.lisp
T


>(COMPILE-NQTHM)
Compiling sloop.lisp.
Loading sloop.o
```

```
Compiling basis.lisp.
Loading basis.o
Compiling genfact.lisp.
Loading genfact.o
Compiling events.lisp.
Loading events.o
Compiling code-1-a.lisp.
Compiling code-b-d.lisp.
Compiling code-e-m.lisp.
Compiling code-n-r.lisp.
Compiling code-s-z.lisp.
Compiling io.lisp.
Compiling ppr.lisp.


>(BYE)
Bye.
% ls -l
total 2454
-rwxrwxr-x  1 smith     94133 Jan 30 10:49 basis.lisp
-rw-rw-r--  1 smith    100532 Jan 30 10:59 basis.o

-rwxrwxr-x  1 smith    125887 Jan 30 10:49 code-1-a.lisp
-rw-rw-r--  1 smith    166445 Jan 30 11:09 code-1-a.o
-rwxrwxr-x  1 smith    158468 Jan 30 10:49 code-b-d.lisp
-rw-rw-r--  1 smith    237176 Jan 30 11:18 code-b-d.o
-rwxrwxr-x  1 smith    133180 Jan 30 10:49 code-e-m.lisp
-rw-rw-r--  1 smith    206203 Jan 30 11:28 code-e-m.o
-rwxrwxr-x  1 smith    184237 Jan 30 10:49 code-n-r.lisp
-rw-rw-r--  1 smith    270420 Jan 30 11:41 code-n-r.o
-rwxrwxr-x  1 smith    103355 Jan 30 10:49 code-s-z.lisp
-rw-rw-r--  1 smith    171812 Jan 30 11:49 code-s-z.o
-rwxrwxr-x  1 smith     12710 Jan 30 10:49 events.lisp
-rw-rw-r--  1 smith     35493 Jan 30 11:01 events.o
-rwxrwxr-x  1 smith     11184 Jan 30 10:49 genfact.lisp
-rw-rw-r--  1 smith     15778 Jan 30 11:00 genfact.o
-rwxrwxr-x  1 smith     60791 Jan 30 10:49 io.lisp
-rw-rw-r--  1 smith     87394 Jan 30 11:52 io.o
-rwxrwxr-x  1 smith      9397 Jan 30 10:49 nqthm.lisp
-rwxrwxr-x  1 smith      8293 Jan 30 10:49 ppr.lisp
-rw-rw-r--  1 smith     18053 Jan 30 11:52 ppr.o
-rwxrwxr-x  1 smith     39997 Jan 30 10:49 sloop.lisp
-rw-rw-r--  1 smith    100971 Jan 30 10:57 sloop.o
% kcl
```

KCl (Kyoto Common Lisp)   June 3, 1987

>(LOAD "nqthm.lisp")
Loading nqthm.lisp
T

>(LOAD-NQTHM)
Loading sloop.o
Loading basis.o
Loading genfact.o
Loading events.o
Loading code-1-a.o
Loading code-b-d.o
Loading code-e-m.o
Loading code-n-r.o
Loading code-s-z.o
Loading io.o
Loading ppr.o
9700

>(BOOT-STRAP NQTHM)

[6.7 6.3 0.0]
GROUND-ZERO

>(ASSOC-OF-APP)

^L

(DEFN APP
      (X Y)
      (IF (LISTP X)
          (CONS (CAR X) (APP (CDR X) Y))
          Y))

        Linear arithmetic and the lemma CDR-LESSP inform
us that the measure (COUNT X) decreases according to
the well-founded relation LESSP in each recursive
call. Hence, APP is accepted under the definitional
principle. From the definition we can conclude that:

```
    (OR (LISTP (APP X Y))
        (EQUAL (APP X Y) Y))
is a theorem.
```

```
[ 0.2 0.1 0.2 ]
```

APP

^L

```
(PROVE-LEMMA ASSOC-OF-APP
             (REWRITE)
             (EQUAL (APP (APP A B) C)
                    (APP A (APP B C)))))
```

```
    Call the conjecture *1.
```

```
    Perhaps we can prove it by induction.
```

(Proof deleted)

```
    That finishes the proof of *1.  Q.E.D.
```

```
[ 0.1 0.5 0.3 ]
```

ASSOC-OF-APP
T

>

14.6. Installation Problems

We know of the following reasons that the theorem prover may fail to run in some perfectly good implementations of Common Lisp:

    1. Conflicts between our symbols and symbols added to package

USER by the Lisp system implementors but not mentioned in *Common Lisp The Language*. Any decent Common Lisp should report such a collision during the compilation or loading processes. If such a collision is reported, do not rely upon the theorem prover. Probably such a collision will just make some other program fail to work properly, not the theorem prover, but such a collision could corrupt the entire Lisp. See page 347.

2. Failure of the Lisp to use the standard ASCII character codes for the printing ASCII characters. For example, we require that **(CHAR-CODE #\A)** be 65. We check for this and cause an error during compilation if your Lisp does not use the ASCII codes. We do not make such a requirement about the white space characters, e.g. space and newline.

3. Too small a range of fixnums. We use the **SLOOP** iteration macro by Bill Schelter, which uses fixnum arithmetic by default but checks for violations. This problem may be overcome by setting **SLOOP::*AUTOMATIC-DECLARATIONS*** to **NIL**.

4. Resource limits. While proving theorems, you may run out of room on the control stack or exceed the limits of space for conses and symbols. Dealing with such problems is exceedingly operating system and Lisp implementation specific. During the execution of some of our benchmarks, notably Shankar's checking of Gödel's theorem, 20 megabytes of swap space may be required; to run this benchmark on a machine with insufficient swap space may require completely restructuring the disks to increase swap space. Random physical events, too, are a problem. Such is life today that the probability of something external going wrong during the day long execution of all our test files seems to be greater than .5. What can one do about such problems as freak memory errors, children accidentally hanging up phone lines, and the never ending joys of network reconfiguration? Certainly, you cannot blame the theorem prover or the Common Lisp implementation.

We now mention a few more problems that you may encounter and some solutions to them. We give special attention to installations using Kyoto Common Lisp because that is the Lisp we are now mainly using.[45]

It is crucial that some of the source files be compiled and loaded before others. The function **COMPILE-NQTHM** (in the file **nqthm.lisp**) does the compilation in the right order. If you try to start compiling the files one at a time by hand, you can expect utterly random results; use **(COMPILE-NQTHM)**.

---

[45]We use KCL because it is excellent, efficient, and comes without fee but with sources.

If you are an exceptionally talented programmer, you may want to build a "system" to do the compilation in a way that is more congenial for your Lisp implementation. Resist this urge.

A compilation problem may arise in some Common Lisps because of our use of proclamations.[46] If your Common Lisp does not correctly support function proclamations, you may wish to **(SETQ *NQTHM-MAKE-PROCLAMATIONS* NIL)** before invoking **(COMPILE-NQTHM)**. We declare almost all of our functions to take a fixed number of arguments and to return a single result. This results in a major speed up for us when running under Austin Kyoto Common Lisp because essentially every Lisp function call is translated into a single C function call. However, none of the proclamations are necessary for the correct operation of the theorem prover.

If you encounter problems compiling under KCL, it is more than likely that the problem is that the file **/usr/include/cmpinclude.h** is missing or that you do not have the right version of it. It usually requires super-user privileges to install this file. KCL runs perfectly well with nothing but the executable image provided you do not use the compiler. But if you want to use the compiler, **/usr/include/cmpinclude.h** must reside in the correct place. Furthermore, KCL must know its own location in the file system; see the section on making a save file in KCL (page 339).

Another problem that can arise when compiling under KCL is not having enough space in **/tmp**. The KCL compiler calls the C compiler, which in turn calls the assembler; temporary files are the medium of communication between these systems. During the compilation of the theorem prover, as much as two megabytes of space can be temporarily used on the directory **/tmp**. So make sure there is a lot of space on **/tmp**. This may require super-user privileges.

Under both Sun/Lucid and Symbolics compilation, there is likely to arise a very large number of warnings about functions that are called but not defined. These warnings may be ignored. The functions in questions are defined in later files. You might have thought that proclaiming a symbol to be a function would be sufficient advance notice for these Lisps not to issue a warning.

As noted in the Reference Guide in the discussion of File Names, the theorem prover assumes that Lisp source file names all share a common extension and that the extension is the value of the Lisp variable **FILE-EXTENSION-LISP**. In normal use of the theorem prover, this variable is only used by **MAKE-LIB** and **NOTE-LIB** to generate the name of the Lisp source file containing the executable counterparts to functions in the logic. But our function **COMPILE-NQTHM** also uses this variable in generating the names of the Lisp source files to compile. The initial value of the variable is **"lisp"**. Thus, for

---

[46]We do not yet know of any such Common Lisp.

example, **COMPILE-NQTHM** looks for the file **basis.lisp** to compile. If your Lisp requires a different extension, feel free to change the value of the variable **FILE-EXTENSION-LISP** to something other than **"lisp"**. But if you do, you will of course need to rename all of the theorem prover's ***.lisp** source files, too.

A similar problem exists with respect to the names for compiled object files. We have not found a mechanism that works across all Common Lisps for both specifying the name for a compiled object file and for loading that file. In most Common Lisps we have tried, **(LOAD "foo")** will load the compiled form of **foo** if it is available and up to date, even if it is really named something like **foo.o** or **foo.bin**. This works for KCL, Symbolics Common Lisp, and Sun/Lucid Common Lisp; *Common Lisp The Language* says it should work, but it doesn't seem to work in some Common Lisps. Therefore, it is necessary for both **COMPILE-NQTHM** (which loads some compiled files after generating them) and **LOAD-NQTHM** to know the names of the object files generated by the local compiler. What file names do we use? We generate them by tacking on, as an extension, the value of the variable **FILE-EXTENSION-BIN**, provided that value is non-**NIL**. So to get **COMPILE-NQTHM** and **LOAD-NQTHM** to work, you may need to specify a value for **FILE-EXTENSION-BIN** in some Common Lisps, e.g. **(SETQ FILE-EXTENSION-BIN "fasl")**. If your attempts at compiling the system result in an error such as "**File sloop not found**," then look at the directory and see if there is, in addition to **sloop.lisp**, a file named something like **sloop.lap**. If there is, **"lap"** is probably the extension name for compiled files for your Lisp, and so you want to **(SETQ FILE-EXTENSION-BIN "lap")** before invoking **COMPILE-NQTH** or **LOAD-NQTHM**.

14.7. Shakedown

As a very simple-minded test that the compilation and loading are successful, we recommend that you invoke **(BOOT-STRAP NQTHM)** and **(ASSOC-OF-APP)**. The result should be a couple of pages of readable output, printed to the terminal, defining the function **APP** analogously to **APPEND** and proving its associativity. This only takes a few cpu seconds.

As a more thorough check that the theorem prover is running as we expect it to, we recommend that you evaluate the first three forms of the example file **basic.events**. Each of the forms is a call of our function **PROVEALL** as described in the Reference Guide. Each form should execute without error, will print some information to the terminal, create several files, and return T. The first two forms are trivial and will execute within a minute or so each. The last will take about an hour; it will read some of the files produced by the earlier forms and produce about two megabytes of disk files, the largest of which will be called **proveall.proofs** and will be about 1.5 megabytes. The files created by these three forms can be deleted after the third form has successfully completed.

When running under Austin Kyoto Common Lisp on a Sun 3/280, the output produced by the third form is:

```
boot-strap-nqthm,basic-tmp,FROM-TO,
PLUS-RIGHT-ID2,...,
APPLY2,EVAL2,SUBST2,SUBST2-OK,

Total Statistics:
[ 68.1 2129.1 245.3 ]

(MAKE-LIB proveall)
```

and the value is **T**.

In the output above we have deleted some messages printed by the KCL loader and compiler. We have also deleted several hundred function and lemma names printed by the theorem prover as it processes the submitted events.

For much larger set of tests, see the section concerning the **events** files below.

14.8. Packages

The theorem prover's symbols (including those for functions, variables, and data structures) are all placed in the Common Lisp package **USER**.[47] Because we put our symbols into package **USER**, there is a potential for collision between our names and those of your implementation of Common Lisp. We have been careful to avoid collisions with existing symbols in the **USER** package of Kyoto Common Lisp, Sun/Lucid Common Lisp, and Symbolics Common Lisp. If you detect that our symbols collide with symbols in your **USER** package, *do not trust the theorem prover in such an environment*. It is possible that a suitable wizard can solve such a conflict problem for you by shadowing out the previously existing symbol, knowing that the use of that particular symbol is somehow irrelevant for your application. Evidence of such a collision is likely to arise during the invocation of **COMPILE-NQTHM** or **LOAD-NQTHM**.

We would have put our symbols into a package of our own if we had found a

---

[47]The symbols for **SLOOP** are in package **SLOOP**.

clear and consistent implementation of the "Put in seven extremely random user interface commands" of Common Lisp such as use-package, export, and import. However, we regard the package/module situation to be currently so confusing (and therefore unstable and likely to change) that we have opted for the simple albeit impolite position of putting our symbols in the **USER** package, a package known to exist in all Common Lisp implementations. Although it is a relatively minor exercise to make the theorem prover use a different package on any given Common Lisp, we strongly advise against making such a change because the soundness of the theorem prover may been undermined: the theorem prover depends upon the fact that if two symbols **s1** and **s2** that it encounters have the same symbol-name, then **(EQ s1 s2)**.

14.9. Example Event Files

Included with the standard distribution of the theorem prover are three files of example definitions and proofs. These files are

```
basic.events
fm8501.events
goedel.events
```

Together these files occupy approximately 1.6 megabytes and include about 1400 definitions and 2400 theorems. These files are completely unnecessary for the correct operation of the theorem prover. These example files may be used to produce over 30 megabytes of `.lib`, `.lisp`, and `.proof` files, an exercise that may require one to three days of cpu time but which produces a year of reading material.

The first file, **basic.events**, contains

- Most of Appendix A of *A Computational Logic* [4], which includes the major examples of that book.

- Fermat's theorem and the invertibility of the RSA public key encryption algorithm.

- Wilson's theorem.

- Gauss's law of quadratic reciprocity.

- The correctness of a simple controller.

- The existence a function that is not primitive recursive.

- The unsolvability of the halting problem.

- The Turing completeness of Lisp.

- The termination of Takeuchi's function.

- Newton's binomial theorem.

- The theorem that every tautology can be proved in Schoenfield's version of first order predicate calculus.

- The Church-Rosser theorem.

- The relationship between Ackermann's function and Peter's version of Ackermann's function.

- A large collection of theorems about quantifiers and **V&C$**, including all those mentioned in [11].

The file **fm8501.events** provides a proof of the correctness of a microprocessor of approximately 2,000 gates. This is the basis of Warren Hunt's PhD dissertation.

The file **goedel.events** contains a proof of Rosser's improvement upon Gödel's theorem: every consistent but sufficiently strong proof system contains propositions that are true but not provable. This and the proof of the Church-Rosser theorem, in the file **basic.events**, are the basis of N. Shankar's PhD dissertation.

To reproduce the various **.proof**, **.lib**, and **.lisp** files from the file **basic.events**, it is sufficient merely to **(LOAD "basic.events")**. To reproduce the various files for **fm8501.events**, do **(PROGN (LOAD "fm8501.events") (PROVEALL "fm8501" XXX))**. To reproduce the various files for **goedel.events**, do **(PROGN (LOAD "goedel.events") (PROVEALL "goedel" XXX))**.

Appendix I

A Parser for the Syntax

In this appendix we use the logic as a programming language and write a parser in it. We ultimately define the function **EXSYN** which takes as input a list of numeric character codes and delivers either **F** or the quotation of a formal term. Suppose **stream** is the **CONS** nest around **NIL** of the ASCII character codes of the characters in the sequence s. If **(EXSYN stream)** is **F**, then s is either not the display of any s-expression or else is the display of an ill-formed expression in the extended syntax. Otherwise **(EXSYN stream)** is the "primitive quotation" of a formal term **t**, and s is a display of a well-formed s-expression in the extended syntax and denotes (i.e., translates to) the term **t**.

The primitive quotation of a term is the quotation that uses no occurrence of **QUOTE** to represent explicit values. That is, the *primitive quotation* of term **t** is defined as follows. If **t** is a variable symbol, the primitive quotation is the **LITATOM** corresponding to **t**. Otherwise, **t** is (**fn** t_1 ... t_n), and the primitive quotation is the **CONS** nest around **NIL** of the **LITATOM** corresponding to **fn** and the primitive quotations of the successive t_i's.

For example, as previously noted, there are three quotations of **(PLUS 1 X)**

```
'(PLUS (ADD1 (ZERO)) X)

'(PLUS (ADD1 (QUOTE 0)) X)

'(PLUS (QUOTE 1) X)
```

351

The first is the "primitive quotation." The last is what we called the "preferred quotation."

To make our examples more succinct, we adopt the following notational convention in this section only. If s is a string of ASCII characters, then "s" is the **CONS** nest around **NIL** of the ASCII character codes in s.

For example, " **(PLUS 2 (CADR X))** " is

```
' (40 80 76 85 83 32 50 32 40
   67 65 68 82 32 88 41 41)
```

since **40** is the ASCII code for open parenthesis, **80** is the code for uppercase **P**, etc. The ASCII code for control-J is 10. We assume for the purposes of these examples that 10 is the code for the newline character, sometimes also called "linefeed."

The following theorem illustrates **EXSYN**:

Theorem.
```
(EXSYN "(PLUS 2 (CADR X))")
  =
' (PLUS (ADD1 (ADD1 (ZERO)))
        (CAR (CDR X))))
```

That is, its input is a list of ASCII character codes and its output, when not **F**, is the primitive quotation of a term in the formal syntax.

EXSYN is defined as the composition of two functions, **READ** and **TRANSLATE**. The first parses a string of ASCII character codes into an s-expression, represented in the logic by **CONS**-trees of **LITATOM**s and numbers. For example, given " **(FOO X B)** " **READ** produces the object ' **(FOO X B)**. **TRANSLATE** then computes the term, if any, thus abbreviated.

This decomposition of the problem is similar to that given in the precise presentation of the extended syntax starting on page 112. There we defined the notion of "s-expression," defined how they are "displayed," and then defined the "well-formed" s-expressions and their "translations." Our formal notion of **READ** is the inverse of the notion of "display" presented earlier. Both our formal **READ** and our formal **TRANSLATE** have analogues in the actual implementation of the theorem prover. User commands—and thus all terms submitted as part of user commands—are usually typed to the Lisp reader, a routine very similar to our **READ**. The s-expressions delivered by the Lisp reader are then translated into formal terms by a routine exactly analogous to the formal **TRANSLATE** developed here.

In order that this section might also serve to clarify the extended syntax itself, we limit ourselves almost entirely to the formal syntax in the definitions below. The exceptions are that we write integers instead of the corresponding **ADD1** nests and we use the **QUOTE** convention to write down **LITATOM**s. That is, we permit ourselves to write **2** for **(ADD1 (ADD1 (ZERO)))**, and we permit **'ABC** for **(PACK (CONS 65 (CONS 66 (CONS 67 0))))**. Otherwise we eschew completely the **QUOTE** notation and the other features of the extended syntax. This renders some of the constants below unnecessarily large, but it offers the reader who does not know how to read **QUOTE** notation the opportunity to learn.

I.1. Some Preliminary Conventions

Recall that the extended syntax permits the abbreviation of explicit values with the **QUOTE** notation. To determine if a given object denotes an explicit value in the current history, it is necessary to know the current constructors, base objects, and type restrictions. Since we wish to express the entire concept in the logic itself, we must imagine answering these questions in the logic, e.g., we need functions in the logic to answer such questions as "is this the (**QUOTE**d) name of a shell constructor?" or "what is the 2nd type restriction of **CONS**?"

The necessary functions are not in the logic but could be defined for any given extension of the logic. For the current purposes we simply imagine that the following three functions have been defined:

(SHELL-BASE-TYPE X)

> If **X** is the quotation of the base function symbol of the shell class with recognizer function symbol **r**, return the quotation of **r**; otherwise return **F**.

(SHELL-CONS-TYPE X)

> If **X** is the quotation of the constructor function symbol of the shell class with recognizer function symbol **r**, return the quotation of **r**; otherwise return **F**.

(SHELL-CONS-TYPES X)

> If **X** is not the quotation of the constructor function symbol of some shell class, return **F**. Otherwise, **X** is the quotation of some constructor function with type restrictions $(flg_1$ $s_{1,1} \cdots s_{1,k_1})$, ..., $(flg_n \ s_{n,1} \cdots s_{n,k_n})$. Let tr_i be the **CONS** nest around **NIL** of the **LITATOM**s corresponding to flg_i and each of the symbols $s_{i,1}$, ..., s_{i,k_i}. Return the **CONS** list around **NIL** of tr_1, ..., tr_n.

Each of these functions could be defined for a given history. For example, at Ground Zero

Definitions.
```
(SHELL-BASE-TYPE X)
   =
(IF (EQUAL X 'TRUE) 'TRUEP
(IF (EQUAL X 'FALSE) 'FALSEP
(IF (EQUAL X 'ZERO) 'NUMBERP
    F)))

(SHELL-CONS-TYPE X)
   =
(IF (EQUAL X 'ADD1) 'NUMBERP
(IF (EQUAL X 'CONS) 'LISTP
(IF (EQUAL X 'PACK) 'LITATOM
(IF (EQUAL X 'MINUS) 'NEGATIVEP
    F))))

(SHELL-CONS-TYPES X)
   =
(IF (OR (EQUAL X 'ADD1)
        (EQUAL X 'MINUS))
    (CONS (CONS 'ONE-OF (CONS 'NUMBERP NIL))
          NIL)
(IF (EQUAL X 'CONS)
    (CONS (CONS 'NONE-OF NIL)
          (CONS (CONS 'NONE-OF NIL)
                NIL))
(IF (EQUAL X 'PACK)
    (CONS (CONS 'NONE-OF NIL)
          NIL)
    F))).
```

In addition, we need to know how many arguments each function symbol expects. This function is also not in the logic but could be defined for any given history:

(ARITY FN)   If **FN** is a function symbol of arity **n**, return **n**; otherwise, return **F**.

I.2. The Formal Definition of READ

READ is the composition of two functions, **LEXEMES**, which parses a list of ASCII codes into a list of atoms, including the atoms for open and close parentheses, and **PARSE**, which constructs a tree.

I.2.1. The Formal Definition of LEXEMES

In this subsection we define a function that takes as its argument a list of numbers and returns a list of "lexemes." Each lexeme is either a positive or negative integer or is a literal atom obtained by **PACK**ing the sequence of character codes denoting the lexeme.

We start by naming and grouping certain ASCII character codes.

Definitions.

```
(ASCII-OPEN-PAREN) = 40          ; code for (
(ASCII-CLOSE-PAREN) = 41         ; code for )
(ASCII-SINGLE-QUOTE) = 39        ; code for '
(ASCII-SPACE) = 32               ; code for <space>
(ASCII-TAB) = 9                  ; code for <tab>
(ASCII-NEWLINE) = 10             ; code for <lf>
(ASCII-PLUS-SIGN) = 43           ; code for +
(ASCII-MINUS-SIGN) = 45          ; code for -
(ASCII-DOT) = 46                 ; code for .
(ASCII-SEMI-COLON) = 59          ; code for ;
```

Definition.

```
(PARENP N)
  =
(OR (EQUAL N (ASCII-OPEN-PAREN))
    (EQUAL N (ASCII-CLOSE-PAREN)))
```

Definition.

```
(WHITEP N)
  =
(OR (EQUAL N (ASCII-SPACE))
 (OR (EQUAL N (ASCII-TAB))
    (EQUAL N (ASCII-NEWLINE))))
```

Definition.

```
(ALPHABETICP N) = (AND (LESSP 64 N) (LESSP N 91))
```

Definition.

```
(DIGITP N) = (AND (LESSP 47 N) (LESSP N 58))
```

Definition.
```
(SIGNP N)                    ; Is N the ASCII code for one of
    =                        ; $ ^ & * _ - + = ~ { } ? < >?
(OR (EQUAL N 36)
(OR (EQUAL N 94)
(OR (EQUAL N 38)
(OR (EQUAL N 42)
(OR (EQUAL N 95)
(OR (EQUAL N 45)
(OR (EQUAL N 43)
(OR (EQUAL N 61)
(OR (EQUAL N 126)
(OR (EQUAL N 123)
(OR (EQUAL N 125)
(OR (EQUAL N 63)
(OR (EQUAL N 60)
    (EQUAL N 62)))))))))))))))
```

The lexical analyzer uses white space, parentheses, certain occurrences of the single quote mark, and semicolons to break the input stream into lexemes. The analyzer accumulates into a list the character codes of each lexeme, in reverse order. Those lists having the syntax of an optionally signed nonempty sequence of digits optionally followed by a decimal point are parsed into positive or negative integers. The function **NUMERALP** recognizes such lists, using **NUMERALP1** to recognize optionally signed nonempty sequences of digits.

Definition.
```
(NUMERALP1 A)
    =
(IF (NLISTP A)
    F
    (AND (DIGITP (CAR A))
         (OR (NLISTP (CDR A))
             (OR (AND (OR (EQUAL (CAR (CDR A))
                                 (ASCII-PLUS-SIGN))
                          (EQUAL (CAR (CDR A))
                                 (ASCII-MINUS-SIGN)))
                      (NLISTP (CDR (CDR A))))
                 (NUMERALP1 (CDR A))))))
```

Definition.
```
(NUMERALP A)
    =
(AND (LISTP A)
     (IF (EQUAL (CAR A) (ASCII-DOT))
```

```
          (NUMERALP1 (CDR A))
          (NUMERALP1 A)))
```

(GEN-INTEGER A 1 0) returns the positive or negative integer denoted by **A**, provided **A** is a **NUMERALP**.

Definition.
```
(GEN-INTEGER A SHIFT N)
    =
(IF  (NLISTP A)
     N
(IF  (EQUAL (CAR A) (ASCII-DOT))
     (GEN-INTEGER (CDR A) SHIFT N)
(IF  (EQUAL (CAR A) (ASCII-PLUS-SIGN))
     N
(IF  (EQUAL (CAR A) (ASCII-MINUS-SIGN))
     (IF (ZEROP N) N (MINUS N))
     (GEN-INTEGER
         (CDR A)
         (TIMES 10 SHIFT)
         (PLUS N
               (TIMES SHIFT
                      (DIFFERENCE (CAR A) 48)))))))))
```

Those lexemes not parsed as numbers are treated as literal atoms obtained by **PACK**ing up the list of characters typed (using **0** as the final **CDR**). Since the characters are accumulated in reverse order, they must be reversed before being **PACK**ed.

Definition.
```
(REVPNAME A PNAME)
    =
(IF  (NLISTP A)
     PNAME
     (REVPNAME (CDR A) (CONS (CAR A) PNAME)))
```

GEN-LEXEME generates each lexeme, given the list of character codes accumulated.

Definition.
```
(GEN-LEXEME A)
    =
(IF  (NUMERALP A)
     (GEN-INTEGER A 1 0)
     (PACK (REVPNAME A 0)))
```

Certain lexemes cannot be written down using our **QUOTE** convention because they are not the quotations of variable or function symbols. We therefore define functions to permit us to refer to these lexemes more conveniently.

Definitions.
```
(OPEN-PAREN) = (PACK (CONS (ASCII-OPEN-PAREN) 0))
(CLOSE-PAREN) = (PACK (CONS (ASCII-CLOSE-PAREN) 0))
(SINGLE-QUOTE) = (PACK (CONS (ASCII-SINGLE-QUOTE) 0))
(DOT) = (PACK (CONS (ASCII-DOT) 0))
```

EMIT is used to add a new lexeme to the emerging stream of lexemes. The first argument is the accumulated list of character codes, and the second is the rest of the lexemes. If the first argument is **0** it means no character codes were accumulated since the last lexeme was emitted.

Definition.
```
(EMIT PNAME LST)
 =
(IF (EQUAL PNAME 0)
    LST
    (CONS (GEN-LEXEME PNAME) LST))
```

IGNORE-COMMENT scans the input stream until it has passed a newline.

Definition.
```
(IGNORE-COMMENT STREAM)
 =
(IF (NLISTP STREAM)
    STREAM
    (IF (EQUAL (CAR STREAM) (ASCII-NEWLINE))
        (CDR STREAM)
        (IGNORE-COMMENT (CDR STREAM))))
```

LEXEMES is the lexical analyzer. The first argument is the list of input character codes. The second argument is the list of character codes accumulated for the current lexeme thus far. **(LEXEMES STREAM 0)** is the list of lexemes.

Definition.
```
(LEXEMES STREAM PNAME)
 =
(IF (NLISTP STREAM)
    (EMIT PNAME NIL)
(IF (EQUAL (CAR STREAM) (ASCII-SEMI-COLON))
    (EMIT PNAME
            (LEXEMES (IGNORE-COMMENT (CDR STREAM))
                0))
```

```
(IF  (AND  (EQUAL  (CAR STREAM)  (ASCII-SINGLE-QUOTE))
          (EQUAL PNAME 0))
    (EMIT  (CONS  (CAR STREAM)  0)
          (LEXEMES  (CDR STREAM)  0))
(IF  (PARENP  (CAR STREAM))
    (EMIT PNAME
          (EMIT  (CONS  (CAR STREAM)  0)
                (LEXEMES  (CDR STREAM)  0)))
(IF  (WHITEP  (CAR STREAM))
    (EMIT PNAME  (LEXEMES  (CDR STREAM)  0))
    (LEXEMES  (CDR STREAM)
              (CONS  (CAR STREAM)  PNAME))))))))
```

We illustrate **LEXEMES** by exhibiting a few theorems about it.

Theorems.
```
(LEXEMES  "(ABC DEF)"  0)
    =
(CONS  (OPEN-PAREN)
 (CONS  'ABC
  (CONS  'DEF
   (CONS  (CLOSE-PAREN)  NIL))))
```

```
(LEXEMES  "X(A-B)Z"  0)
    =
(CONS  'X
 (CONS  (OPEN-PAREN)
  (CONS  'A-B
   (CONS  (CLOSE-PAREN)
    (CONS  'Z NIL)))))
```

```
(LEXEMES  "'A ''B C'D"  0)
    =
(CONS  (SINGLE-QUOTE)
 (CONS  'A
  (CONS  (SINGLE-QUOTE)
   (CONS  (SINGLE-QUOTE)
    (CONS  'B
     (CONS  (PACK  (CONS 67
                        (CONS 39
                              (CONS 68 0))))
            NIL))))))
```

```
(LEXEMES "A; COMMENT
   B"                    0)
   =
(CONS 'A (CONS 'B NIL))


(LEXEMES "A.B . C" 0)
   =
(CONS (PACK (CONS 65
                 (CONS 46
                   (CONS 66 0))))
      (CONS (DOT)
            (CONS 'C NIL)))


(LEXEMES "-12 3. 4-5 6.7" 0)
   =
(CONS -12
  (CONS 3
   (CONS (PACK (CONS 52 (CONS 45 (CONS 53 0))))
    (CONS (PACK (CONS 54 (CONS 46 (CONS 55 0))))
          NIL))))
```

I.2.2. The Formal Definition of PARSE

We now define the function that attempts to parse a list of lexemes into an
"S-expression." An **S**-expression is just a data structure in the logic that
represents the s-expressions of Chapter 4. We say **x** is an **S**-*expression* if and
only if either **x** is a **NUMBERP**, a **NEGATIVEP**, a **LITATOM** whose **UNPACK** is a
CONS nest around **0** of a sequence of ASCII codes, or a **LISTP** whose **CAR** and
CDR are both recursively S-expressions.

    Our parser takes two arguments. The first is a list of lexemes. The second is
a list used as a pushdown stack on which lists are accumulated. Each element of
the stack is called a "frame" and is itself a list of three items. Whenever the
parser encounters an open parenthesis, a new frame is pushed on the stack and
parsing continues with the lexeme after the open parenthesis. One of the items
in the frame collects the **S**-expressions that are the elements of the list. When
the **S**-expression is completely assembled, that stack frame is popped, and the
S-expression is added to the end of the list being assembled in the newly exposed frame. When a single quote mark is read, a count in the frame, initially **0**
for each element, is incremented by **1**. When the next element of the list is
added it is first embedded in as many **QUOTE** expressions as single quotes

preceded it. When the dot lexeme is read, a flag in the frame is set, and the next
time an S-expression is added to the list being assembled it is put into the final
CDR instead of added as the last element.

Here is the function that adds a new frame to the stack:

Definition.
```
(PUSH-FRAME STACK)
   =
(CONS (CONS NIL (CONS 0 (CONS F NIL)))
      STACK)
```

The following three functions return the three items in the topmost frame of
the stack:

Definition.
```
(LIST-BEING-ASSEMBLED STACK) = (CAR (CAR STACK))
```

Definition.
```
(QUOTE-CNT STACK) = (CAR (CDR (CAR STACK)))
```

Definition.
```
(DOT-FLG STACK) = (CAR (CDR (CDR (CAR STACK))))
```

The following function increments the count of single quote marks read:

Definition.
```
(BUMP-QUOTE-CNT STACK)
   =
(CONS (CONS (LIST-BEING-ASSEMBLED STACK)
            (CONS (ADD1 (QUOTE-CNT STACK))
                  (CONS (DOT-FLG STACK) NIL)))
      (CDR STACK))
```

The next two functions turn on and off the flag signalling that a dot has been
read.

Definition.
```
(SET-DOT-FLG STACK)
   =
(CONS (CONS (LIST-BEING-ASSEMBLED STACK)
            (CONS (QUOTE-CNT STACK)
                  (CONS T NIL)))
      (CDR STACK))
```

Definition.
```
(UNSET-DOT-FLG STACK)
   =
```

```
(CONS (CONS (LIST-BEING-ASSEMBLED STACK)
            (CONS (QUOTE-CNT STACK)
                  (CONS F NIL)))
      (CDR STACK))
```

KWOTEN is the function used to embed each **S**-expression in **QUOTE**s.

Definition.
```
(KWOTEN N X)
  =
(IF (ZEROP N)
    X
    (CONS 'QUOTE
          (CONS (KWOTEN (SUB1 N) X) NIL)))
```

The next function adds its first argument to the list being assembled in the top frame of the stack, taking account of the number of quote marks that preceded it and whether the dot flag is set. Note that the function resets the quote mark count to **0** in anticipation of the processing of the next element of the list.

Definition.
```
(ADD-ELEMENT X STACK)
  =
(CONS (CONS (IF (DOT-FLG STACK)
                (APPEND (LIST-BEING-ASSEMBLED STACK)
                        (KWOTEN (QUOTE-CNT STACK) X))
                (APPEND (LIST-BEING-ASSEMBLED STACK)
                        (CONS
                          (KWOTEN (QUOTE-CNT STACK)
                                  X)
                          NIL)))
            (CONS 0
                  (CONS (DOT-FLG STACK) NIL)))
      (CDR STACK))
```

Here, finally, is the parser. The top-level call of the parser should have a stack with one empty frame on it. The deepest stack frame is treated specially by **PARSE**: as soon as an element has been added to it, parsing stops and the element is returned.

If the parser encounters ill-formed syntax—e.g., unmatched parentheses, illegal uses of the dot notation, or unnecessary terminal lexemes after the completion of the parsing—it returns **F**.

Definition.
```
(PARSE L STACK)
  =
```

```
(IF (NLISTP L)
    F
(IF (EQUAL (CAR L) (OPEN-PAREN))
    (PARSE (CDR L) (PUSH-FRAME STACK))

(IF (EQUAL (CAR L) (CLOSE-PAREN))
    (IF (OR (NLISTP STACK)
            (NLISTP (CDR STACK)))
        F
        (IF (AND (DOT-FLG (CDR STACK))
                 (OR (NLISTP (CDR L))
                     (NOT (EQUAL (CAR (CDR L))
                                 (CLOSE-PAREN)))))
            F
            (IF (NLISTP (CDR (CDR STACK)))
                (IF (LISTP (IF (DOT-FLG (CDR STACK))
                               (CDR (CDR L))
                               (CDR L)))
                    F
                    (CAR (LIST-BEING-ASSEMBLED
                          (ADD-ELEMENT
                            (LIST-BEING-ASSEMBLED
                             STACK)
                            (CDR STACK)))))
                (PARSE (CDR L)
                       (ADD-ELEMENT
                         (LIST-BEING-ASSEMBLED STACK)
                         (CDR STACK))))))

(IF (EQUAL (CAR L) (SINGLE-QUOTE))
    (PARSE (CDR L) (BUMP-QUOTE-CNT STACK))
(IF (EQUAL (CAR L) (DOT))
    (IF (OR (NLISTP STACK)
            (NLISTP (LIST-BEING-ASSEMBLED STACK)))
        F
        (IF (DOT-FLG STACK)
            F
            (IF (NOT (ZEROP (QUOTE-CNT STACK)))
                F
                (PARSE (CDR L) (SET-DOT-FLG STACK)))))

    (IF (NLISTP STACK)
        F
        (IF (AND (DOT-FLG STACK)
```

```
              (OR (NLISTP (CDR L))
                  (NOT (EQUAL (CAR (CDR L))
                             (CLOSE-PAREN))))))
      F
      (IF (NLISTP (CDR STACK))
          (IF (LISTP (CDR L))
              F
              (CAR (LIST-BEING-ASSEMBLED
                       (ADD-ELEMENT (CAR L)
                                   STACK))))
          (PARSE (CDR L)
                 (UNSET-DOT-FLG
                  (ADD-ELEMENT (CAR L)
                              STACK))))))))))))
```

I.2.3. READ

The reader is the composition of the parser and the lexical analyzer.

Definition.
```
(READ STREAM)
  =
(PARSE (LEXEMES STREAM 0)
       (PUSH-FRAME NIL))
```

We now illustrate **READ** by exhibiting some theorems about it:

Theorems.
```
(READ "(A (B C) D)")
  =
(CONS 'A
 (CONS (CONS 'B
        (CONS 'C NIL))
  (CONS 'D NIL)))


(READ "(A 'B C)")
  =
(CONS 'A
      (CONS (CONS 'QUOTE
                  (CONS 'B NIL))
            (CONS 'C NIL)))
```

```
(READ  " (A  B  .  C) ")  =  (CONS  'A  (CONS  'B  'C))


(READ  " (A  .  (B  .  (C  .  ())))")
   =
(CONS  'A  (CONS  'B  (CONS  'C  NIL)))


(READ  "' ((A  .  1) (B  .  -2)  ; COMMENT
          (C  .  +3.))")
   =
(CONS  'QUOTE
       (CONS  (CONS  (CONS  'A  1)
                     (CONS  (CONS  'B  (MINUS  2))
                     (CONS  (CONS  'C  3)
                            NIL)))
              NIL))


(READ  " (PLUS  I  (TIMES  33  J)  (LOOKUP  'X  ALIST))")
   =
(CONS  'PLUS
       (CONS  'I
              (CONS  (CONS  'TIMES
                            (CONS  33  (CONS  'J  NIL)))
                     (CONS  (CONS  'LOOKUP
                                   (CONS
                                    (CONS  'QUOTE
                                           (CONS  'X  NIL))
                                    (CONS  'ALIST  NIL)))
                            NIL))))
```

I.3. The Formal Definition of TRANSLATE

TRANSLATE takes as input an S-expression and produces either **F** or the primitive quotation of a formal term.

Roughly speaking, **TRANSLATE** transforms **LITATOM**s into themselves, provided they have the syntax of our variable symbols, and transforms S-expressions of the form (CONS **fn** (CONS **arg$_1$** ... (CONS **arg$_n$** NIL))) into (CONS **fn** (CONS **arg'$_1$** ... (CONS **arg'$_n$** NIL))), where **arg'$_i$** is the translation of **arg$_i$**, provided **fn** is the quotation of a function symbol of arity **n**. However, there are many special cases in which more elaborate transformations are performed. The most complicated involve the extended **QUOTE** notation for denoting explicit values and the handling of **FOR** expressions.

We first define the function **SYMBOLP** which recognizes when a **LITATOM** has the syntax of the symbols in our logic, i.e., is a sequence of alphanumeric characters or signs, beginning with an alphabetic character.

Definition.
```
(LEGAL-CHAR-CODE-SEQ1 L)
  =
(IF (NLISTP L)
    T
    (AND (OR (ALPHABETICP (CAR L))
             (OR (DIGITP (CAR L))
                 (SIGNP (CAR L))))
         (LEGAL-CHAR-CODE-SEQ1 (CDR L)))))
```

Definition.
```
(LAST X)
  =
(IF (NLISTP X)
    X
    (IF (NLISTP (CDR X))
        X
        (LAST (CDR X)))))
```

Definition.
```
(LEGAL-CHAR-CODE-SEQ L)
  =
(AND (LISTP L)
     (AND (EQUAL (CDR (LAST L)) 0)
          (AND (ALPHABETICP (CAR L))
               (LEGAL-CHAR-CODE-SEQ1 (CDR L)))))
```

Definition.
```
(SYMBOLP X)
  =
(AND (LITATOM X)
     (LEGAL-CHAR-CODE-SEQ (UNPACK X)))
```

TRANSLATE processes the submitted **S**-expression top-down, checking that each subexpression is legal in the context in which it occurs. As it processes each legal subexpression it **CONS**es together the primitive quotation of the formal term represented. However, if it encounters an illegal subexpression it must return **F** as the top-level answer. Thus, instead of using **CONS** to construct the quotation, **TRANSLATE** uses **FCONS** below:

Definition.
```
(FCONS X Y) = (IF (AND X Y) (CONS X Y) F)
```

Perhaps the most complicated part of **TRANSLATE** is the transformation of **QUOTE**d expressions. **TRANSLATE** transforms an input of the form **(CONS 'QUOTE (CONS evg NIL))** into the primitive quotation of an explicit value, provided **evg** is an "evg" ("explicit value guts"). An evg is analogous to the notion of an "explicit value descriptor" defined in the section on **QUOTE** notation, page 118.

For example, if **evg** is an integer, the **QUOTE**-expression is translated into the primitive quotation of a nest of **ADD1**'s around **(ZERO)**, possibly with a top-level **MINUS**.

If evg is a **LITATOM** satisfying the restrictions on symbols, the **QUOTE**-expression denotes a **PACK** expression. For example, the result of **READ**ing " (QUOTE ABC) " is **TRANSLATE**d into the primitive quotation of the **PACK** expression we abbreviate as 'ABC in the formal syntax: **(PACK (CONS 65 (CONS 66 (CONS 67 0))))**.

However, not all **LITATOM** evgs denote **PACK** expressions; we use two of the non-symbol **LITATOM**s to stand for **T** and **F**. The two **LITATOM**s are those produced by **READ**ing "*1*TRUE" and "*1*FALSE" and are returned by the functions **EVG-TRUE** and **EVG-FALSE** below.

If **evg** is a **LISTP**, e.g., the result of **READ**ing " (ABC . DEF) ", it represents a **CONS**, e.g., **(CONS 'ABC 'DEF)**, provided both the **CAR** and the **CDR** are evgs.

If **evg** is a **LISTP** whose **CAR** is a certain mark called the **EVG-QUOTE-MARK**, it represents a nonprimitive shell object or an "unusual" primitive one, such as a non-symbol **LITATOM**. The mark is the non-symbol **LITATOM** produced by **READ**ing "*1*QUOTE".

We now begin defining the functions to manipulate evgs.

LENGTH returns the length of a list:

Definition.
```
(LENGTH L)
  =
(IF (LISTP L)
    (ADD1 (LENGTH (CDR L)))
    (ZERO))
```

ADD1-NEST returns the primitive quotation of the formal term denoted by a nonnegative integer:

Definition.
```
(ADD1-NEST N)
  =
(IF (ZEROP N)
    (CONS 'ZERO NIL)
    (CONS 'ADD1
          (CONS (ADD1-NEST (SUB1 N)) NIL)))
```

Here are the non-symbol **LITATOM**s we use in evgs:

Definition.
```
(EVG-TRUE)
  =
(PACK (CONS 42
      (CONS 49
       (CONS 42
        (CONS 84 (CONS 82 (CONS 85 (CONS 69 0)))))))))
```

Definition.
```
(EVG-FALSE)
  =
(PACK (CONS 42
      (CONS 49
       (CONS 42
        (CONS 70
         (CONS 65
          (CONS 76 (CONS 83 (CONS 69 0))))))))))
```

Definition.
```
(EVG-QUOTE-MARK)
  =
(PACK (CONS 42
      (CONS 49
       (CONS 42
        (CONS 81
         (CONS 85
          (CONS 79 (CONS 84 (CONS 69 0)))))))))))
```

In order for an evg to represent an explicit value it is necessary that its components represent explicit values of the appropriate type. The following functions are used to check type agreement:

Definition.
```
(SHELL-TYPE FN)
  =
(IF (SHELL-BASE-TYPE FN)
    (SHELL-BASE-TYPE FN)
    (IF (SHELL-CONS-TYPE FN)
        (SHELL-CONS-TYPE FN)
        F))
```

Definition.
```
(SHELL-TYPE-OKP FN RESTRICTION)
  =
(IF (EQUAL (CAR RESTRICTION) 'ONE-OF)
    (MEMBER (SHELL-TYPE FN)
            (CDR RESTRICTION))
    (NOT (MEMBER (SHELL-TYPE FN)
                 (CDR RESTRICTION))))
```

SHELL-TYPES-OKP takes as its first argument the quotations of n explicit value terms and as its second argument a list of n type restrictions. The function checks that each explicit value term satisfies the corresponding type restriction.

Definition.
```
(SHELL-TYPES-OKP TERMS RESTRICTIONS)
  =
(IF (NLISTP TERMS)
    T
    (AND (LISTP (CAR TERMS))
         (AND (SHELL-TYPE-OKP (CAR (CAR TERMS))
                              (CAR RESTRICTIONS))
              (SHELL-TYPES-OKP (CDR TERMS)
                               (CDR RESTRICTIONS)))))
```

Here is the function that transforms **X** into the primitive quotation of an explicit value or else returns **F** signifying that **X** is not an evg. If **FLG** is **'LIST**, **X** is considered as a list of evgs instead of as a single evg.

Definition.
```
(EVG FLG X)
  =
(IF (EQUAL FLG 'LIST)
    (IF (NLISTP X)
        NIL
        (FCONS (EVG T (CAR X))
```

```
                    (EVG 'LIST (CDR X))))

(IF (NLISTP X)
    (IF (NUMBERP X) (ADD1-NEST X)
    (IF (NEGATIVEP X)
        (CONS 'MINUS
              (CONS (ADD1-NEST (NEGATIVE-GUTS X))
                    NIL))
    (IF (EQUAL X (EVG-TRUE)) (CONS 'TRUE NIL)
    (IF (EQUAL X (EVG-FALSE)) (CONS 'FALSE NIL)
    (IF (SYMBOLP X)
        (CONS 'PACK
              (CONS (EVG T (UNPACK X))
                    NIL))
        F)))))

(IF (EQUAL (CAR X) (EVG-QUOTE-MARK))
    (IF (AND (LISTP (CDR X))
        (AND (EQUAL (CDR (LAST X)) NIL)
        (AND (EQUAL (LENGTH (CDR (CDR X)))
                    (ARITY (CAR (CDR X))))
          (AND (EVG 'LIST (CDR (CDR X)))
            (AND
              (OR (SHELL-BASE-TYPE (CAR (CDR X)))
                  (AND
                    (SHELL-CONS-TYPES (CAR (CDR X)))
                    (SHELL-TYPES-OKP
                      (EVG 'LIST (CDR (CDR X)))
                      (SHELL-CONS-TYPES (CAR (CDR X))))))
              (IF (EQUAL (CAR (CDR X)) 'PACK)
                  (NOT (LEGAL-CHAR-CODE-SEQ
                         (CAR (CDR (CDR X)))))
                  (IF (EQUAL (CAR (CDR X)) 'MINUS)
                      (EQUAL (CAR (CDR (CDR X))) 0)
                      (NOT
                        (OR (EQUAL (CAR (CDR X)) 'ADD1)
                            (OR (EQUAL (CAR (CDR X))
                                       'ZERO)
                                (EQUAL (CAR (CDR X))
                                       'CONS)))))))))))
        (CONS (CAR (CDR X))
              (EVG 'LIST (CDR (CDR X))))
        F)
```

```
(FCONS 'CONS
        (FCONS (EVG T (CAR X))
               (FCONS (EVG T (CDR X)) NIL))))))
```

This completes the development of the functions for processing evgs.

The next function is similar to our notion of the "fn nest around b for s." If **FN** is the **LITATOM** corresponding to **fn** and **L** is a list of the primitive quotations of the terms $t_1, ..., t_n$, then **(MAKE-TREE FN L)** is the primitive quotation of $(fn\ t_1\ ...\ (fn\ t_{n-1}\ t_n)...)$. If $n < 2$, the function returns **F**.

Definition.

```
(MAKE-TREE FN L)
  =
(IF (NLISTP L)
    F
    (IF (NLISTP (CDR L))
        F
        (IF (NLISTP (CDR (CDR L)))
            (FCONS FN
                   (FCONS (CAR L)
                          (FCONS (CAR (CDR L)) NIL)))
            (FCONS FN
                   (FCONS (CAR L)
                          (FCONS (MAKE-TREE FN
                                            (CDR L))
                                 NIL))))))
```

Our extended notation includes the Lisp convention for abbreviating nests of **CAR**s and **CDR**s with such function symbols as **CADR**, **CADDR**, etc. The functions explained next are used to implement this feature.

CAR-CDRP recognizes those literal atoms which are written down with **C** as the first character, **R** as the last, and **A**'s and **D**'s in between. The ASCII codes for **A, C, D,** and **R** are **65, 67, 68,** and **82**.

Definition.

```
(CAR-CDRP1 L)
  =
(IF (NLISTP L)
    F
    (IF (NLISTP (CDR L))
        (AND (EQUAL (CAR L) 82)
             (EQUAL (CDR L) 0))
        (AND (OR (EQUAL (CAR L) 65)
                 (EQUAL (CAR L) 68))
             (CAR-CDRP1 (CDR L)))))
```

Definition.
```
(CAR-CDRP X)
   =
(AND (LITATOM X)
     (AND (LISTP (UNPACK X))
          (AND (EQUAL (CAR (UNPACK X)) 67)
               (CAR-CDRP1 (CDR (UNPACK X)))))))
```

This function constructs the quotation of the term denoted by a term beginning with a **CAR-CDRP** symbol.

Definition.
```
(CAR-CDR-NEST L X)
   =
(IF (OR (NLISTP L) (NLISTP (CDR L)))
    X
    (IF (EQUAL (CAR L) 65)
        (CONS 'CAR
              (CONS (CAR-CDR-NEST (CDR L) X) NIL))
        (CONS 'CDR
              (CONS (CAR-CDR-NEST (CDR L) X) NIL))))
```

We now move on to the transformation of **FOR** expressions. We first define
convenient "accessors" for the components of the **FOR** term. Recall that we
permit five, six, and seven argument versions of **FOR**.

Definition.
```
(ABBREVIATED-FOR-VAR X) = (CAR (CDR X))
```

Definition.
```
(ABBREVIATED-FOR-RANGE X) = (CAR (CDR (CDR (CDR X))))
```

Definition.
```
(ABBREVIATED-FOR-WHEN X)
   =
(IF (EQUAL (LENGTH X) 8)
    (CAR (CDR (CDR (CDR (CDR (CDR X))))))
    'T)
```

Definition.
```
(ABBREVIATED-FOR-OP X)
   =
```

```
(IF (EQUAL (LENGTH X) 8)
    (CAR (CDR (CDR (CDR (CDR (CDR (CDR X)))))))
    (CAR (CDR (CDR (CDR (CDR X)))))))
```

Definition.
```
(ABBREVIATED-FOR-BODY X) = (CAR (LAST X))
```

The next function recognizes those **LITATOM**s that name the operations handled by **FOR**:

Definition.
```
(FOR-OPERATIONP X)
   =
(OR (EQUAL X 'ADD-TO-SET)
 (OR (EQUAL X 'ALWAYS)
  (OR (EQUAL X 'APPEND)
   (OR (EQUAL X 'COLLECT)
    (OR (EQUAL X 'COUNT)
     (OR (EQUAL X 'DO-RETURN)
      (OR (EQUAL X 'EXISTS)
       (OR (EQUAL X 'MAX)
        (OR (EQUAL X 'SUM)
         (OR (EQUAL X 'MULTIPLY)
          (EQUAL X 'UNION)))))))))))
```

We now define the function that recognizes those **FOR**s requiring fancy translation:

Definition.
```
(ABBREVIATED-FORP X)
   =
(AND (LISTP X)
 (AND (EQUAL (CAR X) 'FOR)
  (AND (OR (EQUAL (LENGTH X) 8)
           (EQUAL (LENGTH X) 6))
   (AND (SYMBOLP (ABBREVIATED-FOR-VAR X))
    (AND (NOT (EQUAL (ABBREVIATED-FOR-VAR X) NIL))
     (AND (NOT (EQUAL (ABBREVIATED-FOR-VAR X) 'T))
      (AND (NOT (EQUAL (ABBREVIATED-FOR-VAR X) 'F))
       (AND (EQUAL (CAR (CDR (CDR X))) 'IN)
        (AND (OR (EQUAL (LENGTH X) 6)
                 (EQUAL
                  (CAR (CDR (CDR (CDR (CDR X)))))
                  'WHEN))
              (FOR-OPERATIONP
```

```
                    (ABBREVIATED-FOR-OP X))))))))))))
```

One of the things we do with abbreviated **FOR**s is to compute the association list that binds the "free" variables in the conditional expression and body. We keep those alists in alphabetic order. **ALPHABETIC-LESSP** compares two **LITATOM**s and determines whether the first is alphabetically smaller than the second.

Definition.
```
(ALPHABETIC-LESSP1 L1 L2)
    =
(IF (NLISTP L1)
    T
    (IF (NLISTP L2)
        F
        (IF (LESSP (CAR L1) (CAR L2))
            T
            (IF (EQUAL (CAR L1) (CAR L2))
                (ALPHABETIC-LESSP1 (CDR L1) (CDR L2))
                F)))))
```


Definition.
```
(ALPHABETIC-LESSP X Y)
    =
(ALPHABETIC-LESSP1 (UNPACK X)
                   (UNPACK Y))
```

Below we define an insertion sort function that sorts lists of **LITATOM**s alphabetically:

Definition.
```
(ALPHABETIC-INSERT X L)
    =
(IF (NLISTP L)
    (CONS X NIL)
    (IF (ALPHABETIC-LESSP X (CAR L))
        (CONS X L)
        (CONS (CAR L)
              (ALPHABETIC-INSERT X (CDR L)))))
```


Definition.
```
(ALPHABETIZE L)
    =
(IF (NLISTP L)
```

```
      L
      (ALPHABETIC-INSERT (CAR L)
                         (ALPHABETIZE (CDR L))))
```

We next define the function that explores the quotation of a term **X** and collects the set of variable symbols used in it. If **FLG** is **'LIST**, **X** is considered as a list of quotations instead of a single quotation.

Definition.
```
(ALL-VARS FLG X)
   =
(IF (EQUAL FLG 'LIST)
    (IF (NLISTP X)
        NIL
        (UNION (ALL-VARS T (CAR X))
               (ALL-VARS 'LIST (CDR X))))
    (IF (NLISTP X)
        (CONS X NIL)
        (ALL-VARS 'LIST (CDR X))))
```

The function **MAKE-ALIST1** takes a list of **LITATOM**s and returns the quotation of the alist in which the quotation of each symbol is bound to the symbol. That is, if **vars** is the quotation list of, say, **A**, **B**, and **C**, then (**MAKE-ALIST1 VARS**) is the primitive quotation of (**CONS** (**CONS** **'A A**) (**CONS** (**CONS** **'B B**) (**CONS** (**CONS** **'C C**) **NIL**))).

Definition.
```
(MAKE-ALIST1 VARS)
   =
(IF (NLISTP VARS)
    (EVG T NIL)
    (CONS 'CONS
          (CONS (CONS 'CONS
                      (CONS (EVG T (CAR VARS))
                            (CONS (CAR VARS) NIL)))
                (CONS (MAKE-ALIST1 (CDR VARS))
                      NIL))))
```

DELETE deletes the first occurrence of its first argument from its second argument. It is used to remove the "indicial variable" of a **FOR** statement from the list of variables that occur in the conditional and body expressions.

Definition.
```
(DELETE X L)
   =
(IF (NLISTP L)
```

```
L
(IF  (EQUAL X (CAR L))
     (CDR L)
     (CONS (CAR L) (DELETE X (CDR L))))))
```

Here is the function that constructs the alist for abbreviated **FOR**s, given the indicial variable symbol, the conditional expression, and the body:

Definition.
```
(MAKE-ALIST VAR WHEN BODY)
   =
(MAKE-ALIST1
  (ALPHABETIZE (DELETE VAR
                       (UNION (ALL-VARS T WHEN)
                              (ALL-VARS T BODY))))))
```

We finally define **TRANSLATE**. If **FLG** is **'LIST**, **X** is considered to be a list of **S**-expressions to be translated.

Definition.
```
(TRANSLATE FLG X)
   =
(IF  (EQUAL FLG 'LIST)
     (IF  (NLISTP X)
          NIL
          (FCONS (TRANSLATE T (CAR X))
                 (TRANSLATE 'LIST (CDR X))))

(IF  (NLISTP X)
     (IF  (NUMBERP X) (EVG T X)
          (IF  (NEGATIVEP X) (EVG T X)
               (IF  (LITATOM X)
                    (IF  (EQUAL X 'T) (CONS 'TRUE NIL)
                         (IF  (EQUAL X 'F) (CONS 'FALSE NIL)
                              (IF  (EQUAL X NIL) (EVG T NIL)
                                   (IF  (LEGAL-CHAR-CODE-SEQ
                                        (UNPACK X))
                                        X
                                        F))))
                    F)))

(IF  (NOT (EQUAL (CDR (LAST X)) NIL))
     F

(IF  (EQUAL (CAR X) 'QUOTE)
     (IF  (AND (LISTP (CDR X))
```

```
                    (EQUAL (CDR (CDR X)) NIL))
              (EVG T (CAR (CDR X)))
              F)

(IF (OR (EQUAL (CAR X) NIL)
        (OR (EQUAL (CAR X) 'T)
            (EQUAL (CAR X) 'F)))
    F

(IF (EQUAL (CAR X) 'LIST)
    (IF (TRANSLATE 'LIST (CDR X))
        (IF (NLISTP (CDR X))
            (EVG T NIL)
            (MAKE-TREE 'CONS
                       (APPEND (TRANSLATE 'LIST
                                          (CDR X))
                               (CONS (EVG T NIL)
                                     NIL))))
        F)

(IF (CAR-CDRP (CAR X))
    (IF (AND (LISTP (CDR X))
             (AND (NLISTP (CDR (CDR X)))
                  (TRANSLATE T (CAR (CDR X)))))
        (CAR-CDR-NEST (CDR (UNPACK (CAR X)))
                      (TRANSLATE T (CAR (CDR X))))
        F)

(IF (EQUAL (LENGTH (CDR X)) (ARITY (CAR X)))
    (FCONS (CAR X) (TRANSLATE 'LIST (CDR X)))

(IF (EQUAL (CAR X) 'FOR)
    (IF (ABBREVIATED-FORP X)
        (FCONS 'FOR
          (FCONS (EVG T (ABBREVIATED-FOR-VAR X))
            (FCONS (TRANSLATE T
                        (ABBREVIATED-FOR-RANGE X))
              (FCONS (EVG T
                        (TRANSLATE T
                           (ABBREVIATED-FOR-WHEN X)))
                (FCONS (EVG T (ABBREVIATED-FOR-OP X))
                  (FCONS (EVG T
                            (TRANSLATE T
                               (ABBREVIATED-FOR-BODY X)))
```

```
            (FCONS (MAKE-ALIST
                    (ABBREVIATED-FOR-VAR X)
                    (TRANSLATE T
                     (ABBREVIATED-FOR-WHEN X))
                    (TRANSLATE T
                     (ABBREVIATED-FOR-BODY X)))
                   NIL)))))))
       F)

(IF (AND (LESSP 2 (LENGTH (CDR X)))
         (OR (EQUAL (CAR X) 'AND)
             (OR (EQUAL (CAR X) 'OR)
                 (OR (EQUAL (CAR X) 'PLUS)
                     (EQUAL (CAR X) 'TIMES)))))
    (MAKE-TREE (CAR X) (TRANSLATE 'LIST (CDR X)))
    F)))))))))
```

Let us reconsider the specification of **TRANSLATE**. It takes as input an (**S**-expression representing an) s-expression and returns either the primitive quotation of a formal term, or else it returns **F**. When **TRANSLATE** returns **F**, the input s-expression is not a well-formed term in the extended syntax. When **TRANSLATE** returns some non-**F** object, ′**t**, it is the primitive quotation of the term, **t**, denoted by the input s-expression.

For example,

Theorem.
```
(TRANSLATE T '3)
   =
'(ADD1 (ADD1 (ADD1 (ZERO))))
```

Since the answer is not **F**, we know that the s-expression **3** is well-formed. The result of **TRANSLATE** is the primitive quotation of the term (**ADD1** (**ADD1** (**ADD1** (**ZERO**)))) denoted by **3**.

Here are some other examples of **TRANSLATE**:

Theorems.
```
(TRANSLATE T 'ABC)
   =
'ABC

(TRANSLATE T '(IF R S T))
   =
'(IF R S (TRUE))

(TRANSLATE T '(QUOTE 3))
   =
```

```
' (ADD1 (ADD1 (ADD1 (ZERO))))

(TRANSLATE T ' (QUOTE (1 . 0)))
     =
' (CONS (ADD1 (ZERO)) (ZERO))

(TRANSLATE T ' (CADAR ABC))
     =
' (CAR (CDR (CAR ABC)))

(TRANSLATE T ' (PLUS I J K L))
     =
' (PLUS I (PLUS J (PLUS K L)))
```

All of the examples above illustrate well-formed s-expressions. Here are some examples of ill-formed s-expressions.

Theorems.
(TRANSLATE T ' (PLUS X Y . 3)) = F

(TRANSLATE T ' (QUOTE X Y)) = F

(TRANSLATE T ' (NIL T F)) = F

(TRANSLATE T ' (CADAR X Y)) = F

(TRANSLATE T ' (PLUS X)) = F

None of the examples so far have illustrated **NIL**, interesting **QUOTE**d objects such as **(QUOTE ABC)** or **(QUOTE (1 2 3))**, **LIST**, or abbreviated **FOR**s. The reason is that the primitive quotations of explicit values are extremely large. Here, simply for amusement, is **(TRANSLATE T ' (QUOTE ABC))**:

```
' (PACK
  (CONS

   (ADD1 (ADD1 (ADD1 (ADD1 (ADD1 (ADD1 (ADD1 (ADD1
   (ADD1 (ADD1 (ADD1 (ADD1 (ADD1 (ADD1 (ADD1 (ADD1
   (ADD1 (ADD1 (ADD1 (ADD1 (ADD1 (ADD1 (ADD1 (ADD1
   (ADD1 (ADD1 (ADD1 (ADD1 (ADD1 (ADD1 (ADD1 (ADD1
   (ADD1 (ADD1 (ADD1 (ADD1 (ADD1 (ADD1 (ADD1 (ADD1
   (ADD1 (ADD1 (ADD1 (ADD1 (ADD1 (ADD1 (ADD1 (ADD1
   (ADD1 (ADD1 (ADD1 (ADD1 (ADD1 (ADD1 (ADD1 (ADD1
   (ADD1 (ADD1 (ADD1 (ADD1 (ADD1 (ADD1 (ADD1 (ADD1
   (ADD1 (ZERO))))))))))))))))))))))))))))))))))))))
   ))))))))))))))))))))))))))))))))

  (CONS
```

```
(ADD1 (ADD1 (ADD1 (ADD1 (ADD1 (ADD1 (ADD1 (ADD1
(ADD1 (ADD1 (ADD1 (ADD1 (ADD1 (ADD1 (ADD1 (ADD1
(ADD1 (ADD1 (ADD1 (ADD1 (ADD1 (ADD1 (ADD1 (ADD1
(ADD1 (ADD1 (ADD1 (ADD1 (ADD1 (ADD1 (ADD1 (ADD1
(ADD1 (ADD1 (ADD1 (ADD1 (ADD1 (ADD1 (ADD1 (ADD1
(ADD1 (ADD1 (ADD1 (ADD1 (ADD1 (ADD1 (ADD1 (ADD1
(ADD1 (ADD1 (ADD1 (ADD1 (ADD1 (ADD1 (ADD1 (ADD1
(ADD1 (ADD1 (ADD1 (ADD1 (ADD1 (ADD1 (ADD1 (ADD1
(ADD1 (ADD1 (ZERO))))))))))))))))))))))))))))))))
))))))))))))))))))))))))))))))))))))))

(CONS

(ADD1 (ADD1 (ADD1 (ADD1 (ADD1 (ADD1 (ADD1 (ADD1
(ADD1 (ADD1 (ADD1 (ADD1 (ADD1 (ADD1 (ADD1 (ADD1
(ADD1 (ADD1 (ADD1 (ADD1 (ADD1 (ADD1 (ADD1 (ADD1
(ADD1 (ADD1 (ADD1 (ADD1 (ADD1 (ADD1 (ADD1 (ADD1
(ADD1 (ADD1 (ADD1 (ADD1 (ADD1 (ADD1 (ADD1 (ADD1
(ADD1 (ADD1 (ADD1 (ADD1 (ADD1 (ADD1 (ADD1 (ADD1
(ADD1 (ADD1 (ADD1 (ADD1 (ADD1 (ADD1 (ADD1 (ADD1
(ADD1 (ADD1 (ADD1 (ADD1 (ADD1 (ADD1 (ADD1 (ADD1
(ADD1 (ADD1 (ADD1 (ZERO)))))))))))))))))))))))))))
))))))))))))))))))))))))))))))))))))))))

(ZERO)))))
```

This is not an effective way to communicate what **(TRANSLATE T ' (QUOTE ABC))** is.

However, note that **(TRANSLATE T ' (QUOTE ABC))** is the same thing as **(TRANSLATE T ' (PACK (CONS 65 (CONS 66 (CONS 67 0)))))**. In this spirit we therefore offer, in Table I.1, some additional examples of **TRANSLATE**. The table shows two columns, one labelled **x** and the other **y**. In each case, **(TRANSLATE T x)** is equal to **(TRANSLATE T y)**.

Table I.1

x	y
' (QUOTE ABC)	' (PACK (CONS 65 (CONS 66 (CONS 67 0))))
NIL	' (PACK (CONS 78 (CONS 73 (CONS 76 0))))

```
'(QUOTE (A B C))          '(CONS (PACK (CONS 65 0))
                            (CONS (PACK (CONS 66 0))
                             (CONS (PACK (CONS 67 0))
                                  NIL)))


'(LIST A B C)             '(CONS A
                            (CONS B
                             (CONS C NIL)))


'(FOR X IN L              '(FOR 'X L '(TRUE)
    ALWAYS                   'ALWAYS
      (EQUAL X Y))            '(EQUAL X Y)
                             (LIST (CONS 'Y Y)))
```

I.4. EXSYN

Here finally is the definition of **EXSYN**:

Definition.
```
(EXSYN STREAM) = (TRANSLATE T (READ STREAM))
```

Here are some theorems about **EXSYN**:

Theorems.
```
(EQUAL (EXSYN ";here is a PLUS expression
               ;preceded by white space
                   (PLUS A ;first argument
                        B ;second
                        C ;third
                  )")
       '(PLUS A (PLUS B C)))


(EQUAL (EXSYN "(IF(CAR X)T -1)")
       '(IF (CAR X)
            (TRUE)
            (MINUS (ADD1 (ZERO)))))


(EQUAL (EXSYN "(QUOTE (1 *1*TRUE . 0))")
       '(CONS (ADD1 (ZERO))
              (CONS (TRUE)
```

                          (ZERO))))

   Table I.2 contains some other examples of **EXSYN**. For each **x** and **y** shown,
it is a theorem that **(EQUAL (EXSYN x) (EXSYN y))**.

Table I.2

x	y
`"(LIST A B C)"`	`"(CONS A (CONS B (CONS C NIL)))"`

`"'(A B C)"`	`"(LIST (PACK (CONS 65 0))`
	`       (PACK (CONS 66 0))`
	`       (PACK (CONS 67 0)))"`

`"'(A B C)"`	`"(LIST 'A 'B 'C)"`
`"(APPEND '(A B C) X)"`	`"(APPEND (LIST 'A 'B 'C) X)"`

`"'(A 'B ''C)"`	`"(LIST 'A`
	`       (LIST 'QUOTE 'B)`
	`       (LIST 'QUOTE`
	`             (LIST 'QUOTE 'C)))"`

`"'((A . 84)`
`  (B . *1*TRUE)`
`  (C . T))"`
	`"(LIST (CONS 'A 84)`
	`       (CONS 'B T)`
	`       (CONS 'C (PACK`
	`                (CONS 84 0))))"`

`"'(-1`
`  (*1*QUOTE MINUS 0)`
`  -0`
`  +1)"`
	`"(LIST (MINUS 1) (MINUS 0) 0 1)"`

`"(CADAR X)"`	`"(CAR (CDR (CAR X)))"`

`"(FOR I IN L`
`     MAX`
`     (PLUS X I A))"`
	`"(FOR 'I L '(TRUE)`
	`      'MAX`
	`      '(PLUS X (PLUS I A))`
	`      (LIST (CONS 'A A)`
	`            (CONS 'X X)))"`

Appendix II
The Primitive Shell Axioms

In this appendix we present the axioms defining the primitive shells, namely the natural numbers, the ordered pairs, the literal atoms, and the negative integers. In our treatment of the formal theory in Chapter 4, we used the shell principle to add these axioms. This appendix is provided both for those readers who wish to understand the shell principle by inspecting the axioms generated by its schemas and for those who wish to see the basic axioms of our logic. The reader who eschews use of the shell principle can eliminate it entirely from the logic by substituting the axioms shown below for the four invocations of the principle in Chapter 4.

The axioms shown below are mild simplifications of those generated by the invocations of the shell principle. For example, in the schema for axiom 11 of the Shell Principle the subterm

```
(PLUS (COUNT (ac₁ X))
      . . .
      (COUNT (acₙ X)))@(ZERO)
```

appears. When instantiated to generate the axioms for ordered pairs the subterm generated is

```
(PLUS (COUNT (CAR X))
      (PLUS (COUNT (CDR X))
            (ZERO)))
```

However, here we display the equivalent term:

```
(PLUS (COUNT (CAR X))
      (COUNT (CDR X))) .
```

Similarly, when no base object is supplied or the type restrictions are **(NONE-OF)**, the axioms generated can be greatly simplified by applying such propositional transformations as **(OR P F)** $\leftrightarrow$ P and **(IF F X Y)** = Y.

II.1. The Natural Numbers

The axioms added by

Shell Definition.
Add the shell **ADD1** of one argument
with base function **ZERO**,
recognizer function **NUMBERP**,
accessor function **SUB1**,
type restriction **(ONE-OF NUMBERP)**,
default function **ZERO**.

are

Axiom 12.1.
```
(OR (EQUAL (NUMBERP X) T)
    (EQUAL (NUMBERP X) F))
```

Axiom 12.2.
```
(NUMBERP (ADD1 X1))
```

Axiom 12.3.
```
(NUMBERP (ZERO))
```

Axiom 12.4.
```
(NOT (EQUAL (ADD1 X1) (ZERO)))
```

Axiom 12.5.
```
(IMPLIES (AND (NUMBERP X)
              (NOT (EQUAL X (ZERO))))
         (EQUAL (ADD1 (SUB1 X)) X))
```

Axiom 12.6.
```
(IMPLIES (NUMBERP X1)
         (EQUAL (SUB1 (ADD1 X1)) X1))
```

Axiom 12.7.
```
(IMPLIES (OR (NOT (NUMBERP X))
             (OR (EQUAL X (ZERO))
                 (AND (NOT (NUMBERP X1))
                      (EQUAL X (ADD1 X1)))))
         (EQUAL (SUB1 X) (ZERO)))
```

Axiom 12.8.
```
(NOT (NUMBERP T))
```

Axiom 12.9.
```
(NOT (NUMBERP F))
```

Axiom 12.11.
```
(IMPLIES (NUMBERP X)
         (EQUAL (COUNT X)
                (IF (EQUAL X (ZERO))
                    (ZERO)
                    (ADD1 (COUNT (SUB1 X))))))
```

Axiom 12.12.1.
```
(AND (EQUAL (SUBRP 'ADD1) T)
     (EQUAL (APPLY-SUBR 'ADD1 L)
            (ADD1 (CAR L))))
```

Axiom 12.12.2.
```
(AND (EQUAL (SUBRP 'ZERO) T)
     (EQUAL (APPLY-SUBR 'ZERO L)
            (ZERO)))
```

Axiom 12.12.3.
```
(AND (EQUAL (SUBRP 'NUMBERP) T)
     (EQUAL (APPLY-SUBR 'NUMBERP L)
            (NUMBERP (CAR L))))
```

Axiom 12.12.4.
```
(AND (EQUAL (SUBRP 'SUB1) T)
     (EQUAL (APPLY-SUBR 'SUB1 L)
            (SUB1 (CAR L))))
```

Shell axiom schema (10) does not generate any axioms here because there are no previously added shells.

II.2. The Ordered Pairs

The axioms added by

Shell Definition.
Add the shell **CONS** of two arguments
with recognizer function **LISTP**,
accessor functions **CAR** and **CDR**,
default functions **ZERO** and **ZERO**.

are

Axiom 19.1.
```
(OR (EQUAL (LISTP X) T)
    (EQUAL (LISTP X) F))
```

Axiom 19.2.
```
(LISTP (CONS X1 X2))
```

Axiom 19.5.
```
(IMPLIES (LISTP X)
         (EQUAL (CONS (CAR X) (CDR X)) X))
```

Axiom 19.6.1.
```
(EQUAL (CAR (CONS X1 X2)) X1)
```

Axiom 19.6.2.
```
(EQUAL (CDR (CONS X1 X2)) X2)
```

Axiom 19.7.1.
```
(IMPLIES (NOT (LISTP X))
         (EQUAL (CAR X) (ZERO)))
```

Axiom 19.7.2.
```
(IMPLIES (NOT (LISTP X))
         (EQUAL (CDR X) (ZERO)))
```

Axiom 19.8.
```
(NOT (LISTP T))
```

Axiom 19.9.
```
(NOT (LISTP F))
```

Axiom 19.10.
```
(IMPLIES (LISTP X) (NOT (NUMBERP X)))
```

Axiom 19.11.
```
(IMPLIES (LISTP X)
         (EQUAL (COUNT X)
                (ADD1 (PLUS (COUNT (CAR X))
                            (COUNT (CDR X)))))))
```

Axiom 19.12.1.
```
(AND (EQUAL (SUBRP 'CONS) T)
     (EQUAL (APPLY-SUBR 'CONS L)
            (CONS (CAR L) (CADR L))))
```

Axiom 19.12.2.
```
(AND (EQUAL (SUBRP 'LISTP) T)
     (EQUAL (APPLY-SUBR 'LISTP L)
            (LISTP (CAR L))))
```

Axiom 19.12.3.
```
(AND (EQUAL (SUBRP 'CAR) T)
     (EQUAL (APPLY-SUBR 'CAR L)
            (CAR (CAR L))))
```

Axiom 19.12.4.
```
(AND (EQUAL (SUBRP 'CDR) T)
     (EQUAL (APPLY-SUBR 'CDR L)
            (CDR (CAR L))))
```

Schemas (3) and (4) generate the trivial axiom **T** since there is no base object.

II.3. The Literal Atoms

The axioms added by

Shell Definition.
Add the shell **PACK** of one argument
with recognizer function **LITATOM**,
accessor function **UNPACK**,
default function **ZERO**.

are

Axiom 20.1.
```
(OR (EQUAL (LITATOM X) T)
    (EQUAL (LITATOM X) F))
```

Axiom 20.2.
```
(LITATOM (PACK X1))
```

Axiom 20.5.
```
(IMPLIES (LITATOM X)
         (EQUAL (PACK (UNPACK X)) X))
```

Axiom 20.6.
```
(EQUAL (UNPACK (PACK X1)) X1)
```

Axiom 20.7.
```
(IMPLIES (NOT (LITATOM X))
         (EQUAL (UNPACK X) (ZERO)))
```

Axiom 20.8.
```
(NOT (LITATOM T))
```

Axiom 20.9.
```
(NOT (LITATOM F))
```

Axiom 20.10.1.
```
(IMPLIES (LITATOM X) (NOT (LISTP X)))
```

Axiom 20.10.2.
```
(IMPLIES (LITATOM X) (NOT (NUMBERP X)))
```

Axiom 20.11.
```
(IMPLIES (LITATOM X)
         (EQUAL (COUNT X)
                (ADD1 (COUNT (UNPACK X)))))
```

Axiom 20.12.1.
```
(AND (EQUAL (SUBRP 'PACK) T)
     (EQUAL (APPLY-SUBR 'PACK L)
            (PACK (CAR L))))
```

Axiom 20.12.2.
```
(AND (EQUAL (SUBRP 'LITATOM) T)
     (EQUAL (APPLY-SUBR 'LITATOM L)
            (LITATOM (CAR L))))
```

Axiom 20.12.3.
```
(AND (EQUAL (SUBRP 'UNPACK) T)
     (EQUAL (APPLY-SUBR 'UNPACK L)
            (UNPACK (CAR L))))
```

Schemas (3) and (4) generate the trivial axiom **T** since there is no base object.

II.4. The Negative Integers

The axioms added by

Shell Definition.
Add the shell **MINUS** of one argument
with recognizer function **NEGATIVEP**,
accessor function **NEGATIVE-GUTS**,
type restriction **(ONE-OF NUMBERP)**,
default function **ZERO**.

are

Axiom 21.1.
```
(OR (EQUAL (NEGATIVEP X) T)
    (EQUAL (NEGATIVEP X) F))
```

Axiom 21.2.
```
(NEGATIVEP (MINUS X1))
```

Axiom 21.5.
```
(IMPLIES (NEGATIVEP X)
         (EQUAL (MINUS (NEGATIVE-GUTS X)) X))
```

Axiom 21.6.
```
(IMPLIES (NUMBERP X1)
         (EQUAL (NEGATIVE-GUTS (MINUS X1)) X1))
```

Axiom 21.7.
```
(IMPLIES (OR (NOT (NEGATIVEP X))
             (AND (NOT (NUMBERP X1))
                  (EQUAL X (MINUS X1))))
         (EQUAL (NEGATIVE-GUTS X) (ZERO)))
```

Axiom 21.8.
```
(NOT (NEGATIVEP T))
```

Axiom 21.9.
```
(NOT (NEGATIVEP F))
```

Axiom 21.10.1.
```
(IMPLIES (NEGATIVEP X) (NOT (LITATOM X)))
```

Axiom 21.10.2.
```
(IMPLIES (NEGATIVEP X) (NOT (LISTP X)))
```

Axiom 21.10.3.
```
(IMPLIES (NEGATIVEP X) (NOT (NUMBERP X)))
```

Axiom 21.11.
```
(IMPLIES (NEGATIVEP X)
         (EQUAL (COUNT X)
                (ADD1 (COUNT (NEGATIVE-GUTS X))))))
```

Axiom 21.12.1.
```
(AND (EQUAL (SUBRP 'MINUS) T)
     (EQUAL (APPLY-SUBR 'MINUS L)
            (MINUS (CAR L))))
```

Axiom 21.12.2.
```
(AND (EQUAL (SUBRP 'NEGATIVEP) T)
     (EQUAL (APPLY-SUBR 'NEGATIVEP L)
            (NEGATIVEP (CAR L))))
```

Axiom 21.12.3.
```
(AND (EQUAL (SUBRP 'NEGATIVE-GUTS) T)
     (EQUAL (APPLY-SUBR 'NEGATIVE-GUTS L)
            (NEGATIVE-GUTS (CAR L))))
```

Schemas (3) and (4) generate the trivial axiom **T** since there is no base object.

Appendix III

On the Difficulty of Proofs

In the Preface we note that the difficulty of the theorems proved by the theorem prover has grown substantially over the years. We recently quantified "complexity" and then compared some of the important landmarks over the years. While several of the complexity measures are completely artificial, we find that the numeric comparisons substantiate the claim that the proofs produced in the last few years are much deeper than those in *A Computational Logic*.

We defined six different measures of the complexity of a theorem.

- The number of lines of prettyprinted text in the "understandable statement" of the theorem. This is the number of lines of text you would have to read, starting at the Ground Zero logic, simply to understand what was being proved. We omit from consideration the definitions of "existential" functions—those functions used only to express existential quantification and whose definitions are irrelevant to the intended interpretation of the theorem.

- The "conceptual depth" of the understandable statement of the theorem. This is an entirely artificial concept attempting to measure how hard it is to understand a formula. It is defined as follows. The depth of a variable is 0; the depth of a term (**fn a$_1$ ... a$_n$**) is the depth of the function symbol **fn** plus the depth of the deepest **a$_i$**. The depth of a primitive function symbol is 0; the depth of a defined function is one greater than the depth of its body. Thus, **INSERT** has depth 1, **SORT** has depth 2, and **(SORT (SORT X))** has depth 4. Again, we omit from consideration the existential terms in a theorem.

- The maximum conceptual depth of any concept used in the proof. Some of our proofs involve concepts significantly deeper than those in the statement.

- The number of "supporters" in the proof. The supporters is the set of all function and lemma names involved in the dependency graph of the proof, except for those functions used in the understandable statement of the theorem. Thus, you would have to look at every supporter to understand the proof.

- The number of lines necessary to prettyprint all the supporters.

- The depth of the proof. This is the length of the longest branch in the dependency graph from the theorem to the axioms.

The theorems measured are all included in the standard release of the theorem prover (see the files described on page 348). The names of the theorems and brief descriptions are given below.

- **ORDERED-SORT**: **(ORDERED (SORT L))**. This was the most interesting theorem proved by the "Edinburgh version" of our system, the theorem prover first released in 1973 and described in [2]. The theorem is found in the **"proveall"** section of **basic.events**. We refer to the theorem below simply as the "**SORT**" theorem, for brevity.

- **CORRECTNESS-OF-OPTIMIZING-COMPILER**: the correctness of a simple expression compiler for a push-down stack machine. The theorem was first proved by our theorem prover in 1976. The proof was described in [3] and used as one of the examples in *A Computational Logic* [4] in 1979. The theorem is found in the **"proveall"** section of **basic.events**. We refer to the theorem below as the "**COMPILER**" theorem.

- **TAUTOLOGY-CHECKER-IS-COMPLETE**: the completeness of a tautology checker for **IF**-expressions, similar to the Wang algorithm. The theorem was proved by the theorem prover in 1978 and used as one of the examples in [4] in 1979. The theorem is found in the **"proveall"** section of **basic.events**. We call it "**TAUT**" below.

- **PRIME-FACTORIZATION-UNIQUENESS**: two lists of primes with equal products are permutations of one another. The theorem was first proved by the theorem prover in 1978 and used as an example in [4]. The theorem is found in the **"proveall"** section of **basic.events**. We call it "**PRIME**" below.

- **UNSOLVABILITY-OF-THE-HALTING-PROBLEM**: no Pure Lisp program can solve the halting problem for Pure Lisp. The theorem was proved by the theorem prover in 1982 and published in [10]. The theorem is found in the **"unsolv"** section of **basic.events**. We call it "**UNSOLV**" below.

- **CRYPT-INVERTS**: the RSA public key encryption algorithm is invertible. The proof, a formalization of that published in [28] by Rivest, Shamir, and Adleman, was carried out by the theorem prover in 1983 and described in [9]. The theorem is found in the **"rsa"** section of **basic.events**. We call it "**RSA**" below.

- **LAW-OF-QUADRATIC-RECIPROCITY**: Gauss's law, often referred to as the "jewel of elementary number theory." The mechanical proof was carried out under the direction of David Russinoff in 1984. The theorem is found in the **"gauss"** section of **basic.events**. We call it "**GAUSS**" below.

- **FINALLY-CHURCH-ROSSER**: the Church-Rosser theorem (in its final form rather than in the intermediate, variable-free form). The proof was carried out under the direction of Natarajan Shankar in 1985 and is described in [31]. The theorem is found in the **"church-rosser"** section of **basic.events**. We call it "**C-R**" below.

- **SOFT-RESET-WORKS**: the correctness of the FM8501 microprocessor. The mechanical proof was carried out under the direction of Warren Hunt in 1985 and is described in [20]. The theorem is found in **fm8501.events**. We call it "**FM8501**" below.

- **INCOMPLETENESS-THEOREM**: Gödel's incompleteness theorem. The mechanical proof was carried out under the direction of Natarajan Shankar in 1986 and is described in [32]. The theorem is found in **goedel.events**. We call it "**GOEDEL**" below.

Table III.1 contains the data. By all measures, the complexity of the theorems and their proofs have increased dramatically over the years.

A few comments are in order. The correctness of the FM8501 microprocessor is the most verbose theorem proved to date. Its 991 lines of text are primarily devoted to the gate level description of the machine. Gödel's theorem is a close second, with 864 lines, most of which are devoted to the definition of the object logic proved incomplete. The object logic is defined with a proof checker for it expressed as a function in our logic.

Until FM8501 and Gödel's theorem were proved, all of our theorems were

Table III.1

Number of Lines in Understandable Stmt
. Concept Depth of Stmt
   . . Max Concept Depth in Proof
   . . . Number of Supporters
   . . . . Lines of Supporters
   . . . . . Depth of Proof

73	SORT	24	3	2	0	0	3
76	COMPILER	88	6	5	7	39	5
78	TAUT	96	6	4	31	162	9
78	PRIME	49	4	8	108	696	17
82	UNSOLV	164	2	7	18	153	6
83	RSA	43	4	8	172	1134	24
84	GAUSS	48	3	8	348	2928	37
85	C-R	114	5	42	133	1196	16
85	FM8501	991	157	152	230	2171	18
86	GOEDEL	864	48	40414	1741	20002	58

pretty understandable, with statements of depth at most 6. The depth of the statement of Gödel's theorem, 48, reflects how deep the associated proof checker is. The record depth, that for FM8501, at 157, is due to the nesting of hardware modules representing the composition of circuits. If the concept of "depth" is to be believed, we conclude that it is harder to understand what is said about FM8501 than it is to understand what the incompleteness theorem says. We find that a plausible contention.

The comparison of the various proofs give much food for thought.

We find it pleasing that the uniqueness of prime factorizations, **PRIME**, the unsolvability of the halting problem, **UNSOLV**, and Gauss's law, **GAUSS**, have "shallow" statements (4, 2, and 3, respectively) but require relatively deep concepts in their proofs (8, 7, and 8). The Church-Rosser theorem, **C-R**, is even more pronounced, with 5 in the statement and 42 in the proof—reflecting the existential functions for constructing the lambda expression alleged to exist. FM8501 is satisfyingly straightforward—its proof involves only concepts of the same depth needed to state the theorem. And then there's Gödel's theorem! The existential functions, which construct proofs of inconsistencies from supposed proofs of the undecidable sentence, have depths in the 40,000's because they involve repeated nests of encoders, etc.

Until Gödel's theorem was proved, Gauss's law held the record for the largest number of lemmas in a proof development, with 348. That is dwarfed by Gödel's 1741.

The number of lines typed to prove FM8501 correct (2171) is comparable to that for Gauss's law (2928)—a reasonable state of affairs even though Gauss's law requires more lemmas since the FM8501 formulas are typically larger. But the number of lines for Gödel's theorem is an order of magnitude bigger at 20,002—there are many lemmas and they are large, because they involve large quoted constants representing functions and proofs in the object logic.

Finally, we find the depth of lemma development also satisfying. The prime theorem, Church-Rosser, and FM8501 are all about the same depth, 17 or so levels above the axioms. Gauss's law pushes that to 34, which isn't surprising since it builds on both the prime results and the RSA theorem. But then Gödel's theorem stands 58 levels above Ground Zero.

In closing we would like to reiterate a remark of the Preface: the theorem prover's achievements, as clearly indicated by the table above, is, more than anything, a tribute to the people who "led the expeditions" up these peaks.

References

1. W. Bevier. *A Verified Operating System Kernel.* Ph.D. Th., University of Texas at Austin, 1987.

2. R. S. Boyer and J S. Moore. "Proving Theorems about Pure LISP Functions." *JACM 22*, 1 (1975), 129-144.

3. R. S. Boyer and J S. Moore. A Lemma Driven Automatic Theorem Prover for Recursive Function Theory. Proceedings of the 5th Joint Conference on Artificial Intelligence, 1977, pp. 511-519.

4. R. S. Boyer and J S. Moore. *A Computational Logic.* Academic Press, New York, 1979.

5. R. S. Boyer and J S. Moore. Metafunctions: Proving Them Correct and Using Them Efficiently as New Proof Procedures. In *The Correctness Problem in Computer Science*, R. S. Boyer and J S. Moore, Eds., Academic Press, London, 1981.

6. R. S. Boyer and J S. Moore. A Verification Condition Generator for FORTRAN. In *The Correctness Problem in Computer Science*, R. S. Boyer and J S. Moore, Eds., Academic Press, London, 1981.

7. R. S. Boyer and J S. Moore. The Mechanical Verification of a FORTRAN Square Root Program. SRI International, 1981.

8. R. S. Boyer and J S. Moore. MJRTY - A Fast Majority Vote Algorithm. Technical Report ICSCA-CMP-32, Institute for Computing Science and Computer Applications, University of Texas at Austin, 1982.

9. R. S. Boyer and J S. Moore. "Proof Checking the RSA Public Key Encryption Algorithm." *American Mathematical Monthly 91*, 3 (1984), 181-189.

10. R. S. Boyer and J S. Moore. "A Mechanical Proof of the Unsolvability of the Halting Problem." *JACM 31*, 3 (1984), 441-458.

11. R. S. Boyer and J S. Moore. The Addition of Bounded Quantification and Partial Functions to A Computational Logic and Its Theorem Prover. Tech. Rept. ICSCA-CMP-52, Institute for Computer Science, University of Texas at Austin, January, 1988. To appear in the *Journal of Automated Reasoning*, 1988.

12. R. S. Boyer and J S. Moore. Integrating Decision Procedures into Heuristic Theorem Provers: A Case Study with Linear Arithmetic. In *Machine Intelligence 11*, Oxford University Press, 1988.

13. R. S. Boyer and J S. Moore. A Mechanical Proof of the Turing Completeness of Pure Lisp. In *Automated Theorem Proving: After 25 Years*, W.W. Bledsoe and D.W. Loveland, Eds., American Mathematical Society, Providence, R.I., 1984, pp. 133-167.

14. R. S. Boyer, M. W. Green and J S. Moore. The Use of a Formal Simulator to Verify a Simple Real Time Control Program. Technical Report ICSCA-CMP-29, University of Texas at Austin, 1982.

15. R. Burstall. "Proving Properties of Programs by Structural Induction." *The Computer Journal 12*, 1 (1969), 41-48.

16. Benedetto Lorenzo Di Vito. *Verification of Communications Protocols and Abstract Process Models*. Ph.D. Th., University of Texas at Austin, 1982.

17. G. Gentzen. New Version of the Consistency Proof for Elementary Number Theory. In *The Collected Papers of Gerhard Gentzen*, M.E. Szabo, Eds., North-Holland Publishing Company, Amsterdam, 1969, pp. 132-213.

18. C.-H. Huang and C. Lengauer. "The Automated Proof of a Trace Transformation for a Bitonic Sort." *Theoretical Computer Science 1*, 46 (1986), 261-284.

19. G. Huet and D. Oppen. Equations and Rewrite Rules: A Survey. In *Formal Languages: Perspectives and Open Problems*, R. Book, Ed., Academic Press, 1980.

20. Warren A. Hunt, Jr. *FM8501: A Verified Microprocessor*. Ph.D. Th., University of Texas at Austin, 1985.

21. D. E. Knuth and P. Bendix. Simple Word Problems in Universal Algebras. In *Computational Problems in Abstract Algebras*, J. Leech, Ed., Pergamon Press, Oxford, 1970, pp. 263-297.

22. C. Lengauer. "On the Role of Automated Theorem Proving in the Compile-Time Derivation of Concurrency." *Journal of Automated Reasoning 1*, 1 (1985), 75-101.

23. C. Lengauer and C.-H. Huang. A Mechanically Certified Theorem about Optimal Concurrency of Sorting Networks, and Its Proof. Tech. Rept. TR-85-23, Department of Computer Sciences, The University of Texas at Austin, Oct., 1985.

24. J. McCarthy. Towards a Mathematical Science of Computation. Proceedings of IFIP Congress, 1962, pp. 21-28.

25. J. McCarthy, et al.. *LISP 1.5 Programmer's Manual.* The MIT Press, Cambridge, Massachusetts, 1965.

26. J S. Moore. "A Mechanical Proof of the Termination of Takeuchi's Function." *Information Processing Letters 9*, 4 (1979), 176-181.

27. J S. Moore. Piton: A Verified Assembly-Level Language. Tech. Rept. CLI-22, Computational Logic, Inc., Austin, Tx, June, 1988.

28. R. Rivest, A. Shamir, and L. Adleman. "A Method for Obtaining Digital Signatures and Public-Key Cryptosystems." *Communications of the ACM 21*, 2 (1978), 120-126.

29. David M. Russinoff. A Mechanical Proof of Wilson's Theorem. Department of Computer Sciences, University of Texas at Austin, 1983.

30. N. Shankar. "Towards Mechanical Metamathematics." *Journal of Automated Reasoning 1*, 4 (1985), 407-434.

31. N. Shankar. A Mechanical Proof of the Church-Rosser Theorem. Tech. Rept. ICSCA-CMP-45, Institute for Computing Science, University of Texas at Austin, 1985.

32. N. Shankar. *Proof Checking Metamathematics.* Ph.D. Th., University of Texas at Austin, 1986.

33. J. R. Shoenfield. *Mathematical Logic.* Addison-Wesley, Reading, Ma., 1967.

34. G. L. Steele, Jr. *Common Lisp The Language.* Digital Press, 30 North Avenue, Burlington, MA 01803, 1984.

35. W. Teitelman. INTERLISP Reference Manual. Xerox Palo Alto Research Center, 3333 Coyote Hill Road, Palo Alto, Ca., 1978.

36. Hao Wang. "Toward Mechanical Mathematics." *IBM Journal 4* (1960), 2-22.

Index

Perspectives in Computing

Volumes 1–12 were published as **Notes and Reports in Computer Science and Applied Mathematics.**